www.thegoodwebguide.co.uk

Dedication

This book is dedicated to my mother, Bella, and others like her, for whom the Internet remains a complete mystery but who nevertheless manage their financial affairs perfectly well without it.

thegoodwebguide

Money

David Emery

The Good Web Guide Limited • London

First Published in Great Britain in 2000 by The Good Web Guide Limited
Broadwall House, 21 Broadwall, London, SE1 9PL

www.thegoodwebguide.co.uk

Email:feedback@thegoodwebguide.co.uk

© 2000 The Good Web Guide Ltd

Text © 2000 David Emery

Original series concept by Steve Bailey

Cover photo © Peter Zeray/Photonica

10 9 8 7 6 5 4 3 2 1

A catalogue record for this book is available from the British Library.

ISBN 1-903282-02-0

Project Editor Michelle Clare

Design by Myriad Creative Ltd

Typesetting and additional design by Karen Brain

Printed in Italy at LEGO S.p.A.

Acknowledgements

I am indebted to Professor Trevor Thomson of the School of Management, University of Cape Town for his assistance with the chapter on Internet Auctions, and his efforts to instruct me in the finer points of cryptography. My thanks, too, to Phil Flaxton of Interforum, for his patience in the face of some embarrassingly elementary questions about public and private keys.

I acknowledge the help of Andrew Chitty of VLP Ltd in supplying me with a never-ending catalogue of new sites to review, and thereby contributing to a growing sensation of swimming against the tide.

My thanks to Stephen Nicoll of A to Z Financial Intermediaries for his expertise and valuable feedback regarding online mortgages.

I would also like to thank Michael Drewett, Hemi Bajaj, Stephen Yeo, Maeve Heneke, Nita Hanmer and Shaun Viljoen for their encouragement and support. Credit is also due to Elaine Collins for flexibility with deadlines above and beyond the call of duty.

I am grateful to Henry Kuang (aged 14) for pointing out that the name of the new online pan-European Stock Exchange is pronounced Zhihui and not Jiway as suggested by the Daily Telegraph. Clearly, you can't believe everything that you read in the press.

Finally, my thanks to Sarah Hooper-Smith for identifying me as an 'authority' on the Internet, entirely mistaken but well intentioned.

All errors of fact, omissions and other shortcomings are the sole responsibility of the author.

Contents

The Good Web Guides

The World Wide Web is a vast resource, with millions of sites on every conceivable subject. There are people who have made it their mission to surf the net: cyber communities have grown, and people have formed relationships and even married on the net.

However, the reality for most people is that they don't have the time or inclination to surf the net for hours on end. Busy people want to use the internet for quick access to information. You don't have to spend hours on the internet looking for answers to your questions and you don't have to be an accomplished net surfer or cyber wizard to get the most out of the web. It can be a quick and useful resource if you are looking for specific information.

The Good Web Guides have been published with this in mind. To give you a head start in your search, our researchers have looked at hundreds of sites and what you will find in the Good Web Guides is a collection of reviews of the best we've found.

The Good Web Guide recommendation is impartial and all the sites have been visited several times. Reviews are focused on the website and what it sets out to do, rather than an endorsement of a company, or their product. A small but beautiful site run by a one-man band may be rated higher than an ambitious but flawed site run by a mighty organisation.

Relevance to the UK-based visitor is also given a high premium: tantalising as it is to read about purchases you can make in California, because of delivery charges, import duties and controls it may not be as useful as a local site.

Our reviewers considered a number of questions when reviewing the sites, such as: How quickly do the sites and individual pages download? Can you move around the site easily and get back to where you started, and do the links work? Is the information up to date and accurate? And is the site pleasing to the eye and easy to read? More importantly, we also asked whether the site has something distinctive to offer, whether it be entertainment, inspiration or pure information. On the basis of the answers to these questions sites are given ratings out of five. As we aim only to include sites that we feel are of serious interest there are very few low-rated sites.

Bear in mind that the collection of reviews you see here are just a snapshot of the sites at a particular time. The process of choosing and writing about sites is rather like painting the Forth Bridge: as each section appears complete, new sites are launched and others are modified. When you've registered at the Good Web Guide site (see p.127 for further details) you can check out the reviews of new sites and updates of existing ones, or even have them emailed to you. By using the disc at the back of the book or registering on our site, you'll find hot links to all the sites listed, so you can just click and go without needing to type the addresses accurately into your browser.

As this is the first edition of the Good Web Guide, all our sites have been reviewed by the author and research team, but we'd like to know what you think. Contact us via the website or email feedback@thegoodwebguide.co.uk. You are welcome to recommend sites, quibble about the ratings, point out changes and inaccuracies or suggest new features to assess.

You can find us at www.thegoodwebguide.co.uk

User Key text	
UK / US	Country of origin
£	Subscription required
R	Registration required
🔒	Secure online ordering.

Introduction

Students of Greek mythology will recall the trials of Sisyphus, a resident (and domicile) of Hades who was condemned to rolling a boulder to the top of a hill for eternity. Every time he approached the summit, the boulder would roll to the bottom of the hill and he would have to start again.

Compiling an anthology of financial Internet sites is something of a Sisyphean labour. In the first place, the number of new financial websites shows no sign of slackening. Find, the leading UK directory of financial websites adds about 100 new sites to its list every month. Secondly, established financial sites have the habit of remodelling themselves with frustrating regularity. A line has had to be drawn in the sand or else this anthology could never have seen the light of day.

Here are the parameters:

Reviews are confined to personal finance sites, namely those concerned with the management of personal disposable income and capital.

Sites selected are those considered to be of most interest to UK residents. Foreign-based sites are reviewed where they are deemed to be important indicators of future developments in the UK.

Sites are selected for their independence, thereby excluding direct providers of financial products with the exception of the online banking sector. Preference is given to free sites.

Any rigid classification of personal finance sites is fraught with difficulty, as they extend their scope and constantly adapt. Accordingly, sites reviewed in this book are classified according to their perceived dominant function at the time of writing:

Directory sites which catalogue and classify financial websites and act as pure portals by providing links to them from a central location.

Information sites ranging from general information to narrow specialised sites.

Advisory sites for generic and regulated advice, and investor education.

E-Commerce sites for transacting in financial services (banking, stockbroking, real estate and mortgages, life and general insurance) and consumer goods (shopping and auctioning).

The first objective of each review is to summarise the information and facilities that can be found on each site and which may not be apparent at first acquaintance. Few are well-enough organised to reveal all their treasures from the home page. I hope to save the reader some time and toil.

The second objective is to convey something of the site architecture and assist with navigation.

Site ratings are expressed by a star system (out of five). I confess that my ratings are partially subjective. While it is possible to make an objective assessment of hard data, the quality of advisory material is often a matter of personal opinion. The alert reader may also notice that the author's favourites at the end of the book are not necessarily consistent with the number of stars awarded previously.

The reader should allow for the fact that site content and architecture may have changed between compilation and publishing. In any event, the current list should be regarded as a starting point for a personal voyage of discovery. Updates are carried on the Good Web Guide's online money channel at www.thegoodwebguide.co.uk.

The reader should appreciate that familiarity with internet sites is as much the product of sweat and toil, persistence, curiosity, intuition and luck as it is of prior knowledge, and is urged to use the current listing as a vehicle for uncovering others by exploring on-site links.

David Emery, March 2000

Chapter 1

Directory Sites

If you come to the internet without any prior knowledge of financial sites, then your first port of call should be a net directory. A net directory is the purest form of portal site. In effect it functions as an address book or telephone directory and links you to any site listed without having to type out the URL each time.

Net directories can be all-rounders, like Find, or specialised like E-Trader UK, which concentrates on internet share dealing and related sites. Find's monthly press release is a microcosm of online personal finance as a whole. Share dealing and personal loans regularly head the Find popularity stakes, as measured by the number of click throughs (visits to sites which originate with Find). Motor insurance, market prices, savings rates and mortgage lenders regularly appear in the top 10 categories, but, surprisingly, online banking has recently fallen below 10th place, reflecting perhaps some cooling of interest just as the banks are launching new stand-alone internet operations (see Online Banking pp. 54-67).

www.find.co.uk			
Find			
Overall rating: ★ ★ ★ ★ ★			
Classification: Directory		**Readability:**	★ ★ ★
Updating: Weekly		**Reliability:**	★ ★ ★ ★
Navigation: ★ ★ ★ ★ ★		**Speed:**	★ ★ ★ ★
UK			

www.e-traderuk.com			
E-Trader UK			
Overall rating: ★ ★ ★ ★			
Classification: Directory		**Readability:**	★ ★ ★ ★
Updating: Irregular		**Reliability:**	n/a
Navigation: ★ ★ ★ ★ ★		**Speed:**	★ ★ ★ ★ ★
UK £ R			

Find has little or no content of its own but provides links to over 2,700 personal finance sites grouped under the headings: investments, insurance, information services, advice and dealing, banking and savings, mortgages and loans, business services and services for investors.

Each heading hosts five to seven site groupings with a common theme. For example, under Investments you will find fund management companies, equity ISAs, and investment trusts, to name a few. Each group is in turn a listing of Internet sites. Click on a name and you're in.

Alternatively, use the **Quicksearch** button to find any site by name. There is also a tiny navigation bar running along the top of the screen, which is just about visible from any page.

SPECIAL FEATURES

Use this site to find, say, an accountant, a general insurance broker or an execution-only IFA who will rebate your commission. Short-cut your search for specialist information like mortgage rates, personal loans and credit cards or investment data, without having to trawl through an omnibus information site.

You really have to log on to this site in order to appreciate its usefulness. Make this one your first port of call.

The growing demand for online sharedealing has spawned countless websites offering information to the would-be investor in one form or another. Finding out which they are and sorting the wheat from the chaff can be a major headache.

E-Trader UK was launched in October 1999 as a free specialist portal for online sharedealing and related sites. It does not carry its own data or tools. For now, it is devoted to online sharedealing but it would be nice if it could extend the service to managed fund sites. Don't hold your breath.

Despite a rather cluttered home page, E-Trader UK is very easy to get about. Sites can be accessed alphabetically or by site category using the navigation panel at the left-hand side of the homepage. Categories include:
• Online Stockbrokers
• Real-time and delayed-time price quotes
• New issues
• Online portfolio tracking
• Investment software
• Company information
• Finance/business news
• Market news
• Bulletin boards
• Tips/recommendations
• Government & miscellaneous bodies

- UK Exchanges (AIM, LIFFE, London Metal Exchange, LSE, Nasdaq UK, OFEX, Techmark, Tradepoint)
- Tutorials/glossary
- Finance/business books (Global Investor Bookshop)
- Business directories

Click on any one of these and you get through to an array of icons representing the relevant linked websites. For example, if you select Real-time quotes you get the icons for FTrade, Firstquote, Freequotes, Interactive Investor International and Market Eye, and UIC Invest.

SPECIAL FEATURES

E-Trader UK carries its own Guide to E-trading, E-Trader news, editorial, Broker Comparisons (services and charges for all online stockbrokers) and Trends and Forecasts. You can access these pages using a navigation bar running along the top of the home page.

The acid test for this site will be the number of listings that it can attract in the future. By its own admission, not all the listings are fully comprehensive at present, save for online stockbrokers. Nevertheless, despite its narrow focus, it is a fine directory site that makes lighter work of the sharebuying jungle.

www.investment-gateway.com
Investment Gateway

Overall rating: ★ ★ ★ ★ ☆			
Classification:	Directory	**Readability:**	★ ★ ★ ★
Updating:	Irregular	**Reliability:**	n/a
Navigation:	★ ★ ★ ★ ☆	**Speed:**	★ ★ ★ ★ ☆

UK

This is a directory of savers and investors. The home page is a catalogue of topics: Shares, Unit Trusts, Investment Trusts, ISAs and PEPs, Fixed Interest and Bonds, and Deposit Rates. Click on any of these and the list turns into the navigation panel.

Select any topic to reveal a list of subtopics, such as Free Charts, Your Portfolio, and Online Brokers. Click on any subheading for content details or data sites. Select a data site and transfer directly.

The links include heavyweights like Interactive Investor International, MoneyWorld, and Market Eye, plus news sources including Bloombergs and The Electronic Telegraph.

SPECIAL FEATURES

This site is particularly useful for dealing with 'repeated registration syndrome'. A multiregister facility enables you to register for a number of sites simultaneously under one password, but is confined to TrustNet, Interactive Investor International, Market Eye, Stockpoint The Motley Fool, UK-Invest and UK Shares. Freequotes, FT.com and E-Trade require individual registration.

This is a neat launch pad for getting to key investment sites easily and painlessly.

Chapter 2

Information Sites

The great strength of the internet can also be its greatest curse. Whereas a little knowledge (or learning) can be a dangerous thing, too much can give you indigestion.

The best information sites achieve a balance between content and presentation. Content is king, but logical layout and strong navigation are essential. There is nothing as frustrating as knowing that the data is present, but buried away out of sight.

Getting to grips even with a narrowly based information site can be like a voyage of discovery, and few omnibus information sites yield up their treasures without a struggle. One way to size up a site is to ignore all the distractions of the home page and to work your way systematically down the navigation panel - time consuming but the most thorough. Alternatively, if you want a quick fix, try to locate the site map. You can then jump to whatever section or subsection takes your fancy, and decide whether it meets your needs.

SITE LOYALTY

There is no need to tie your self to one financial infomediary site. Registration is normally free and usually only required if you want to enter and retain personal data. In theory, there is no reason why you can't browse several sites. However, you will probably want to reserve one site for tracking your investments, if only to spare yourself the trouble of duplicating data entry and updating. It makes sense therefore to choose a portfolio tracker that can display a wide range of assets. Two of the best are found on Interactive Investor International and MoneyWorld.

RELIABILITY

The acid test of all information sites is the reliability of the information. The sheer convenience of having all that data to hand may blind you to certain realities:

Share and fund performance data usually comes from unimpeachable sources like Reuters or S&P Micropal. Reputable information sites also maintain their data in the light of changing events, such as share splits.

Product illustrations may not be representative of the full range. With only a partial picture, and you could end up paying a competitive premium for the wrong product.

Mortgage and insurance quotations and best buys should not necessarily be taken at face value. They may be drawn from a narrow panel and may not be completely independent. Run the same scenario on several sites.

Product guides are inevitably of variable quality and should not be regarded as holy writs.

Financial information sites help you to do your financial homework in your own time and without sales pressure, but they are not substitutes for independent advice or sound judgement.

www.ft.com
FT.com

Overall rating: ★ ★ ★ ★			
Classification: Newspaper		Readability:	★ ★ ★ ★
Updating:	Daily	Reliability:	★ ★ ★ ★ ★
Navigation:	★ ★ ★ ★	Speed:	★ ★ ★ ★

UK R

The renowned newspaper site has recently given itself a facelift; a significant shot in the war with arch-rival The Wall Street Journal (WSJ) for domination of the worldwide dissemination of business and financial news. Recent FT initiatives include the launch of the (terrestrial) FT Deutschland and the acquisition of an interest in American news website CBS Marketwatch, with a view to launching FT Marketwatch later this year, which will eventually link up with FT.Com. In turn, the WSJ has tarted up its European edition with colour pics and other gimmicks. *C'est la guerre!*

Personal finance has been hived off to a specialist site, FT Your Money (www.ftyourmoney.co.uk), which is reviewed on p. 44. The new FT.com has ditched some other features of the old model. Gone is the familiar coral-pink wallpaper, as has the beloved trademark clutter and the two-tier navigation bar at the top of the screen. Instead we have an ingenious sliding navigation panel which glides into view when you hit the View Navigation button, and disappears to enlarge the working page when you have made a selection.

Unlike the WSJ Interactive Edition (www.wsje.com), FT.com is free. Registration is only necessary if you want to use the Personal Office, Personal Portfolio, discussion forums and news by e-mail. Content quality seems to have survived the cosmetic surgery. The sliding left-hand navigation panel takes you to the key features:

News and Analysis provides coverage of industries, market news, business in brief, world news, companies, special reports, and special surveys of countries and industries.

Markets and Portfolio provides a personal portfolio of equities, with interactive charting, and coverage of managed funds, capital (bond) markets, currencies and commodities, IPOs, Euro special report and economic indicators.

People has articles on newsworthy individuals and there is a power search tool to retrieve cuttings on people or companies.

Career Advisor provides resources for career development and business education (including ratings of executive educational providers).

Community takes you to discussion forums and a forums directory.

Time off covers sports, travel, going out, US shop and Euro shop.

Search and Archive You can browse the Business Directory by categories, or use an advanced search facility to access the Global Archive.

Personal Office This panel on the right-hand side takes you to your address book, email and files downloaded from your hard drive.

SPECIAL FEATURES

There are too many good things about this site to describe in the space available. The reader is urged to work systematically through the navigation panel. In the interim, here are three features that are particularly note-worthy:

Advanced Search Archive A power search tool for looking up news items. Enter the key words and search the archives for all articles published within the last three years. The search is not necessarily confined to the FT. FT.com claims that it holds five million articles from 3000 publications in its archives, most of which are accessible without charge.

The Managed Fund Pricing Service is found under Markets and Portfolio. You can power search for the latest prices by fund type (some 22,500 unit trusts/OEICs and life, pension and offshore funds) and by product provider. Prices are updated at midnight - a good excuse for staying up late.

Capital Markets News and Data International bond data is traditionally a bit thin on the net. The FT.com data is rather limited at present but this service is in the process of being expanded. It is currently confined to benchmark government bonds and 10-year annualised spreads (against Euros and T. Bonds) for 21 countries, a limited selection of Eurobonds and Emerging Markets bonds (Eastern Europe, Latin America, Asia-Pacific, Africa/Middle East and Brady Bonds).

COULD DO BETTER

The limited interactivity is the main disappointment. In competitor sites you can link directly from company names in the news coverage to the Markets and Portfolio section, and view the impact of current events on the share prices. Notwithstanding the encyclopaedic Managed Fund pricing service, the Personal Portfolio only displays share prices - a terrible waste.

The new (and old) FT.com has been criticised for being closer to a daily printed newspaper than an online publication. A true online news service updates content continuously throughout the day, rather than at set times for successive editions. News stories on FT.com are retained too long, and are not always displaced, as new events unfold during the day.

FT.com remains the number one electronic newspaper, archive and financial database. The data and research features are quite superb. The navigational and cosmetic changes may not be significant improvements, but the new model runs a bit faster than the old one.

www.iii.co.uk

Interactive Investor International Ltd

Overall rating: ★ ★ ★ ★ ☆

Classification:	Information	**Readability:**	★ ★ ★ ★
Updating:	Daily	**Reliability:**	★ ★ ★ ★
Navigation: ★ ★ ★ ☆		**Speed:**	★ ★ ★ ☆

UK R

The site was launched on 30 October 1995 and was floated on the London Stock Exchange in February 2000. As its name suggests, the initial aim was to display information pertinent to private investors. However, the site has since broadened its scope and is developing into an ambitious, innovative and well-rounded information site, regulated by the Securities and Future Association (SFA). The longer-term goal of the company is to turn the site from a passive information centre into a portal for active trading, or 'a one-stop shop for a community of private investors, financial advisors and offshore users'.

III also develops branded, independent websites for product providers and fund managers, and has built private client trading engines for online sharedealing services such as Stocktrade and James Brearley and Sons.

Registration is free, but is only strictly necessary if you want to track your personal investment portfolio or use the UK Equities Service.

The fulcrum of the site is a series of information centres. Current topics are UK and US equitites, mortgages, credit cards, investment trusts, ISAs, new share issues, savings rates, pensions, traded endowments, tax, online banking and general insurance (home, motor and travel). A life assurance centre is pending.

The data is imported from a number of accredited and independent sources:

Mortgage data is supplied by John Charcoal Online.
Savings and credit card data by MoneyFacts.
15-minute delayed share prices by S&P Comstock.
Unit trust, life assurance and pension fund performance data by S&P Micropal.
Offshore investment data by Lipper, a division of Reuters.
General insurance quotes via the Screentrade website.

An overhead navigation bar at the top of your screen directs you to delayed share price quotes, performance data for shares and domestic and offshore funds, news, discussion groups, products, library, advice and the personal portfolio tracker (delayed prices). The same share and funds data is also accessible from within the portfolio tracker and the ISA centre.

Alternatively, you can use the Take Me To button to reach the furthest corners of the site, or simply navigate via the information centre panel on the left-hand side of the screen.

SUBSCRIPTION SERVICES

For £5 per month you can subscribe to the UK Equities Snap Service, which gives you real-time share price quotes one at a time, company fundamentals (that is, turnover, profits, price to earnings ratios, and so on), real-time news and interactive analysis.

For £15 per month you can have the UK Equities Real-Time Service with all the benefits of the Snap service plus multiple share price quotes (that is, several share-price quotes displayed simultaneously).

SPECIAL FEATURES

Quotation Service is a very impressive feature. Click on Quotes on the overhead navigation bar and select the asset category from a list that includes UK equities, unit trusts, life assurance funds and pension funds. Enter the name of the share or the fund and hit the Search button for a display of the current bid/offer prices. Click on the adjacent Performance or Graph button for a performance history, or link to the bulletin board by hitting the Discussion icon.

Portfolio Tracker The free delayed-price portfolio tracker is easy to operate. To add an investment to your portfolio, you enter the name of the share or fund and tick its asset category from a list (such as UK equities, unit trusts, life assurance fund, pension fund, and so on). When you have found the share or fund, just click the Add button and enter the number of shares or units. The portfolio tracker will update the value of your shares every 15 minutes, and display the value of your funds at the previous day's closing prices. Editing or deleting a share or fund holding is just as easy, and you can access the share and fund performance history directly from the portfolio tracker.

Traded Endowment Policy (TEP) centre is a unique feature of III. You can get a quote from three market makers (Policy Plus, First Policy and Policy Portfolio) for your unwanted endowment, as an alternative to auctioning or tamely surrendering it to the life assurance company. With endowments under fire, this page attracts about 7,500 hits a week. Well spotted, III!

Online Sharedealing You get access to a panel of online stockbrokers for buying or selling shares. A power search tool identifies the panel member who will deal at lowest cost. At present you can apply for a dealing account and trade through Stocktrade and James Brearley and Sons directly from the III site, with another dozen or so online share-dealing services waiting to join the party. Having this facility means that you can act on the share data quickly and cheaply.

You can also apply for a mortgage via John Charcol Online. But this is just the beginning. 'We aim to transact everything that we display,' says Managing Director John Blowers.

Finally, if you fancy a flutter, have a go at the **Fantasy Spread Betting game**.

COULD DO BETTER

Keeping the knowledge banks up to date has been a bit of a problem. However, the appointment of Steve McDowell, former editor of Money Marketing, to the position of editor-in-chief will bring this area up to speed. The savings centre could do with a power search tool and inclusion of National Savings rates. We are still waiting for the life assurance centre.

This site is rapidly developing into a solid all-rounder, with greater appeal to dedicated investors than occasional cyber-shoppers.

www.thisismoney.co.uk
This Is Money

Overall rating: ★ ★ ★ ★ ☆			
Classification: Information		**Readability:**	★ ★ ★ ★
Updating: Daily		**Reliability:**	★ ★ ★ ★
Navigation: ★ ★ ★ ★		**Speed:**	★ ★ ★ ★ ☆

UK

This Is Money belongs to Associated Newspapers and is the joint personal finance Internet site of *The Daily Mail*, *Mail On Sunday* and *London Evening Standard*.

Registration is not required, even for the personal portfolio tracker. Site structure is immediately apparent from the home page. On the right-hand side is a panel divided into three broad headings: **Top Tools**, **Money Makers** and **Money Savers**. These are essentially data pages. You can power search for any particular share, unit trust or investment trust. Click on the share/fund name and you will generate a neat performance graph.

SPECIAL FEATURES

Top Tools includes the personal portfolio tracker, interactive calculators (mortgage, currency and interest), tourist rates and a directory of companies that appear on the site. Mortgage data is provided by London and Country Mortgages Ltd.

The Portfolio Tracker admits shares, investment trusts and unit trusts. You can add shares and investment trusts to your portfolio directly from the graphics area. For some strange reason you do not seem to be able to do the same for unit trusts.

Money Makers includes unit trusts, unit trust PEPs/ISAs,

top savings rates, an ISA centre and online banking and share dealing. Unit Trust prices come courtesy of Financial Express (a pricing service for IFAs). Unit trust performance data is imported from S&P Micropal. Share and Investment Trust data comes from Lipper. The top savings rates are a bit thin on the ground with only two or three deals in each category.

Money Savers covers best buys in mortgage rates, personal loans and credit cards, cheapest life cover and comparative overdrafts. Personal loan, credit card and overdraft data is sponsored by MoneyFacts.

A blue panel on the right-hand side of the home page draws material from Top Tools, Money Makers and Money Savers, and groups it together with related news reports under the following headings: News and Markets, Saving and Investing, Pensions, Insurance, Taxes, Small Business, Borrow and Spend.

Fact Files is effectively a series of guides to Saving and Investing, Mortgages and Homes, Small Business, Pensions, Consumer, Insurance and Taxes. They seem to be well written in the main, without being over-technical. Look out for the Complete Guides to Savings Investment/Pensions/Mortgages/Income Tax (although titles are occasionally more comprehensive than the content).

Ask the Experts is self explanatory and worth a look.

This site will probably appeal to those who find the likes of Times-Money too daunting and prefer their financial information served with a lighter touch. This Is Money is easy on the eye (in a fetching shade of light yellow!).

www.moneyextra.com
MoneyeXtra

Overall rating: ★ ★ ★ ★ ☆

Classification:	Information	Readability:	★ ★ ★ ☆
Updating:	Daily	Reliability:	★ ★ ★ ★
Navigation:	★ ★ ★ ☆	Speed:	★ ★ ★

(UK) (R)

MoneyeXtra is owned by The Exchange Holdings plc, which supplies policy information and product illustrations to some 90 per cent of all UK independent financial advisers. It is currently the default website for Microsoft Money, the financial management software site. The site was launched in April 1999 and is regulated by the Financial Services Authority (FSA).

In October 1999 MoneyeXtra acquired MoneyWorld. At present both sites are operating independently, although they dovetail in certain areas. It is likely that they will eventually merge into one site.

Registration is free and only really required for accessing confidential sections of the site, such as the personal portfolio tracker.

The core of the site is a series of financial product centres covering domestic and international investment, taxation, mortgages, homefinding, credit cards, deposit accounts, current accounts, ISAs, life assurance, general insurance, and personal loans. For some strange reason you can only access the MoneyeXtra Pensions Centre from the MoneyWorld site.

This is a very solid all-round site, and a first choice if you want to compare products or select them by personal criteria. The mortgage, credit card, deposit account, current account, personal loans, ISA and life assurance centres come with user-friendly power search tools to narrow down your quest for the right product.

Recent innovations include the development of dedicated mortgage site called Emfinance (www.emfinance.co.uk) and a home-finder service called Home Pages (www.homepages.co.uk). You can reach Emfinance independently or via the MoneyeXtra mortgage page, for online morgage and remortgage quotations by a panel of lenders currently made up of Bristol and West, Birmingham Midshires, Market Harborough, West Bromwich and the Woolwich. You can apply for a mortgage and track the progress of your application online (see Emfinance review on p. 102). Home Pages enables you to power search for a property by location, price range and number of bedrooms.

You navigate using a panel on the left-hand side of the screen, which lists all the product centres, a portfolio tracker, a tax centre and an international section that feeds you (nearly) real-time data from the American stock exchanges. Sensibly, this panel remains visible wherever you are on site.

A nice touch is the overview panel that opens up on the right-hand side of your screen when you enter the mortgages, credit cards, deposit accounts, current accounts and personal loans product centres. This effectively shows current 'best buys' at a glance.

The site has smartened itself up significantly, and is generally much tidier than before. However, the product guides tend to be slightly haphazardly scattered about the site. For example, the ISA and the Mortgage Guides are accessed from the home page, whereas you normally get to the remaining guides from within their respective product centres. It would be more intuitive to access all the guides from one central location, as with MoneyWorld.

SPECIAL FEATURES

Life Assurance If you are serious about life assurance, then this commendably detailed calculator computes the correct level of cover, based on your living costs and taking your existing policies into account.

Portfolio Tracker not only values your shares, unit trusts and life and pension funds, but uniquely allows you to list your deposit account and credit-card details, and balances and automatically updates the prevailing rates of interest.

Cut Your Bills is a particularly practical section. You enter your postcode, annual consumption (from your past bills), current tariff (for example, quarterly) and preferred new tariff (for example, monthly by direct debit) and a calculator identifies the cheapest supplier.

A nice touch is the Overview panel that opens up on the right-hand side of your screen when you enter the mortgages, credit cards, deposit accounts, current accounts and personal loans centres. This effectively shows current best buys at a glance by selected product category.

MoneyeXtra wears its heart on its sleeve. Each product centre contains the ubiquitous A-Z of independent financial advisers (IFA), and invites (nay, exhorts) you to power search by name or postcode. The clear message is that information needs to be tempered with advice. Although independent financial advice is clearly favoured, the longer-term plan is to offer site visitors the choice of dealing directly with the product providers or through IFAs.

www.moneynet.co.uk
MoneyNet

Overall rating: ★★★★☆			
Classification:	Information	**Readability:**	★★★★
Updating:	Regularly	**Reliability:**	★★★★
Navigation:	★★★★	**Speed:**	★★★★

UK

MoneyNet was launched in October 1997 and has acquired a reputation as an excellent data-only information site. It is distinguished by the absence of news, articles or guides of any description on site. It concentrates on providing hard data only, organised for easy access.

The site is unregulated, which means that you have to look elsewhere for advice. If you want guidance, you are directed to a specialist from a narrow circle of independent financial advisors.

The current panel of advisors comprises the Millfield Partnership, which handles conventional onshore enquiries; HIFAC PMI Ltd, which is a specialist in medical insurance: and Charlesworth International (Guernsey) for offshore financial planning.

An extensive navigation panel on the left-hand side of the screen directs you to the following information centres: mortgages, savings and deposits, life assurance, medical insurance, personal loans, credit cards, funds, the stock market, best buys, and MoneyNet offshore.

Most of the data displayed is obtained directly from the product providers. The exceptions are the funds and stock market data which is imported from MoneyWorld and includes the portfolio tracker, power search tool and power graphics.

The absence of on-site news, articles and guides gives a really streamlined feel to this site without loss of substance.

This site is distinguished by its excellent coverage of loans. The mortgage section is particularly good and covers conventional and impaired loans (applicants with history of arrears and County Court Judgements), non-status loans (great for the newly self-employed), buy-to-let finance and offshore mortgages. The ability to compare the terms and costs of your existing mortgage with some of the newer and better offerings in the market is a real eye-opener and a spur to action.

SPECIAL FEATURES

Medical Insurance These pages are produced in collaboration with HIFAC PMI Ltd and provide an impressive Private Medical Insurance (PMI) quotation service, which enables you to initiate an application online with any of nine major insurers.

MoneyNet Offshore is a sub-site for which Charlesworth International (Guernsey) advises on offshore financial planning. It is very comprehensive and a valuable source of financial advice for the growing band of British expatriates.

Although the site remains essentially data-only, there are moves afoot to enable you to transact online in the mortgage, life assurance and health insurance areas. In the meanwhile, the panel of advisers seems to be on the ball. HIFAC PMI Ltd will turn around a health insurance enquiry in 24 hours and Charlesworth International were on the telephone ten minutes after completion of their online questionnaire. Watch out for the online conveyancing service that allows you to monitor the progress of your mortgage application.

www.moneyworld.co.uk
MoneyWorld

Overall rating: ★ ★ ★ ★			
Classification: Information		**Readability:**	★ ★ ★ ★
Updating: Daily		**Reliability:**	★ ★ ★ ★
Navigation:	★ ★ ★	**Speed:**	★ ★ ★

UK R

MoneyWorld was launched in 1995 and is the creation of Danny Bowers, the former financial editor of Independent Radio News. It took the prize for best personal finance website at the 1999 Bradford & Bingley media awards ceremony.

In September 1999, MoneyWorld was bought by The eXchange Holdings plc, owner of the MoneyeXtra website. The rival sites continue to operate independently, but they share a great deal of data and a merging of the sites is inevitable.

Registration is free, and only necessary for entering the Investors' Club and accessing your personal portfolio. The site is built around the familiar list of product centres packaged with product guides and sundry words of wisdom.

Mortgage, savings, loans, and life-assurance data is shared with MoneyeXtra; unit trust, life assurance and pension-funds data is provided by Lipper, with power graphics supplied by QData.

Easy access to these pages is provided by a navigation panel on the left of the screen which holds all the product centres and gives you access to the Investors' Club. A second navigation bar runs across the top of the screen and directs the viewer towards sections on ISAs, online banking and online sharedealing (for looking and not yet for dealing).

Your personal portfolio tracker is also accessible through the Stockmarket Centre or the Investors Club.

SPECIAL FEATURES

Personal savings is a particular strength, covering a full range of fixed deposit accounts including National Savings. Savings and loan data is changed weekly.

Stockmarket is another strong area, with 'Powergraphics' by Q-Data enabling performance comparisons between shares, sectors and indices. You can call up funds (unit trust, life and pension) performance histories over 1, 3 and 5 years in numerical form, and power search for the top-performers. Share prices are updated every 15 minutes and funds data is updated daily.

Portfolio Tracker is unusual in that it allows you to include your possessions (such as jewellery, the antiques in the attic, the Picasso at the back of the store) in addition to your share, fund and cash holdings. Adding, deleting and editing is a doddle, provided that you can remember your user name and password. This area requires registration

Product Guides are available on homebuying, pensions, insurance (life, heath and medical and general), online banking and stockbroking, venture capital trusts, ISAs, and collective investments including ethicals. The guides are written in an agreeable question-and-answer format and are very practical.

Calculators The Tax Caculator is a boon to anyone on self-assessment. The Currency Converter allows you to compare 50 currencies (1225 possible pairs). A House Price Calculator puts a value on the ancestral pile.

Investors' Club enables you to exchange idea with your peers and to win fine wines and weekend breaks.

COULD DO BETTER

Despite an apparently encyclopaedic drop-down menu, the offshore funds data is incomplete to the detriment of the portfolio tracker. The power graphics are not available for investment funds (unit trusts, life and pensions), although you can still get the information in numerical form. It's perfectly adequate but not nearly as much fun. Some of the calculators are little more than advertising sites for product providers.

MoneyWorld packs a lot of information into a very compact site. Although it is clearly preparing to take the name of MoneyeXtra, it is the better site of the two in some ways. Once hopes that it can bring its influence to bear upon its partner.

www.thestreet.co.uk
The Street

Overall rating: ★ ★ ★ ☆			
Classification:	News	Readability:	★ ★ ★ ★
Updating:	Daily	Reliability:	★ ★ ★ ☆
Navigation:	★ ★ ★ ★	Speed:	★ ★ ★ ☆

UK R

The Street.co.uk is the local offspring of the troubled American financial news service, which is reportedly up for sale. This has placed something of a question mark against its future, although it has apparently some £11m of start-up capital to spend and has a number of institutional backers including Barclays Private Equity and 3i.

Although it is early days, the site shows some ambition. 'The Street.co.uk provides you with information at the heart of every successful investment strategy,' it claims for itself with reassuring modesty.

You have to register to use the service but there are no subscriptions, unlike the American parent, which charges $99.95 p.a. for access to premium services.

It is quite easy to find your way around. Everything you need is located on the left-side navigation panel. However, the best way to get to grips with the architecture at first may be through the Site Map button, located towards the top right hand corner of the home page.

SPECIAL FEATURES

Without saying so explicitly, the site seems to divide naturally into market news and data, personal finance and advice.

Archives Each news section contains a selection of current articles plus a limited archive of older news stories ('All' companies/technology/personal finance). Click on any subject heading to get through to the relevant mini-archive. Alternatively, you can power search by key words. This gives you access to the complete news archive.

Quick Quotes is a handy facility providing performance data for equities, unit trusts, investment trusts and pension and life assurance funds. Share price quotes are accompanied by interactive charts. There is some neat additional interactivity along the lines of The Wall Street Journal. You can hotlink directly from LSE-listed company names in the text to the Quotes section.

The Market delivers five daily news bulletins: Dawn Trader, Mid Morning, Afternoon Call, Market Hour and After Hours. You can arrange to have Mid Morning and Afternoon Call reports e-mailed to you, and their jaunty style makes this a welcome addition to your in-box.

The City brings the Streetwise columns and City analysis of Banking, Hedge Funds, Financial Services and the Indexation Market (spread betting).

Companies delivers analysis of Media, Consumer Industries, Healthcare, Oils and Energy, and IPOs.

Technology brings you the UK Silicon column and keeps you up to date with Internet and Telecoms companies.

Funds deals with onshore and offshore investment, focuses on funds and performs limited fund rankings within chosen fund sectors.

Personal Finance deals with the usual array of retail products: ISAs, pensions, mortgages, life assurance, general insurance, loans, credit cards, savings and share dealing.

Investor Basics is a major feature, delivering generic

financial advice: Your Money and Your Life, Investment Essentials, a Financial Wealthcheck and a Glossary. This section is comprehensive and level headed. Lorna Bourke gets off to a great start in my book by advising folk to use up their full ISA allowances before getting into personal pensions.

Portfolio Tracker admits shares, funds and cash. You can display up to four separate portfolios. Share prices are displayed 15 minutes in arrears.

Catch The Word delivers some off-the-wall news ('irreverent, informed, incisive' are the terms used).

COULD DO BETTER

Site content is currently rather thin compared with the US parent, and there is always the suspicion that coverage is not updated as the news breaks.

There is a general lack of hard company information to accompany the share performance data (such as company background and key financial information, access to annual reports and analysts' estimates). This kind of information is displayed on The Street.com, so there is no reason to believe that it won't eventually appear on the UK site.

Strong on news and personal finance but short on hard corporate data at present. Easy on the eye although the colour scheme will probably appeal most to Norwich City FC supporters. It is still early days, though, and this site may well earn some more stars once it's into its stride.

www.times-money.co.uk
Times-Money

Overall rating: ★ ★ ★ ☆			
Classification:	Information	**Readability:**	★ ★ ★ ★ ★
Updating:	Regular	**Reliability:**	★ ★ ★ ★
Navigation:	★ ★ ★ ☆	**Speed:**	★ ★ ★ ☆

UK

This is the personal finance site for *The Times* newspaper, and a good one, too, full of really original angles that you won't find on others.

The site is organised around the familiar set of activities and categories: Mortgage, Save, Borrow, Invest, Travel, Tax, Insure, Pensions, Family, Students and Young Investors. These are displayed on a navigation bar at the top and bottom of the home page.

The hard data is drawn from a number of sources: mortgage, savings and loan data best buys are provided by MoneyFacts, and interactive power searches by MoneyNet; funds data is imported from S&P Micropal and 15-minute delayed share prices and charts from E*Trade. A link to the ins-site website (www.ins-site.co.uk) allows you to obtain personal quotations for term life and critical illness assurance. General insurance data is imported from Screentrade.

SPECIAL FEATURES

Corporate Profile Archives Amongst the unusual features of the site are these ratings, found in the Invest section. Public companies are rated by 'ethical expression', 'fat-cat quotient', financial record, share performance, attitude to staff, strength of brand, innovation, annual report and future prospects.

Collectibles is also found within the Invest section and provides introductions to the famous auction houses (Christies, Phillips and Bonhams). You can link to the Interactive Collectors website (www.icollector.com) for details of current online auctions and catalogues and a reference section containing archived catalogues, an art price guide, publications, associations and dealer and gallery guides.

Borrow has pages on personal credit rating and the implications of bankruptcy.

Insure contains valuable information on specialist insurance policies for sportsmen, antiques, mobile phones, special events and weddings. It also contains a salutary list of the Top 10 Financial Disasters courtesy of Cornhill Insurance.

Tax discusses the nuts and bolts of tax exile.

Each section functions as an extended guide, with any data subcontracted out to a third party (for example, MoneyNet, MoneyFacts). The guides are informative and intelligently written, as you would expect from The Times. The Achilles heel of infomediary sites is usually the pensions guide but this one stands up very well.

COULD DO BETTER

The absence of a portfolio tracker means that this site may not be first choice for investors. In addition, the layout is somewhat cramped. For some strange reason you can't maximise the display to fill your monitor space. The navigation bar tends to disappear from view as you scroll down the pages. This initially causes a bit of irritation, until you cotton on that it lies at the beginning and end of the page. Thereafter all is sweetness and light.

Overall this is an extremely interesting site, full of unusual and fascinating detail.

www.uk-invest.co.uk
UK-Invest

Overall rating: ★ ★ ★ ☆			
Classification:	Information	Readability:	★ ★ ★ ★
Updating:	Regularly	Reliability:	★ ★ ★ ★
Navigation:	★ ★ ★ ★	Speed:	★ ★ ★ ☆

UK R

This site is the investment and business channel of Freeserve. The content is a blend of news, live and delayed market data, expert opinion and analysis and investor education. The target readership seems to be the inexperienced investor, but the more seasoned market players will find much of value here.

Registration is only required if you want to use the portfolio tracker or play the investment game.

The left-hand navigation panel takes you to thirteen areas of the site: Share Search, Market Watch, What's New, Broadcasts, Opinions and Analysis, Your Money, World (market news), Weekend, Currencies, Equities, Education Centre, Tools and Archives.

The overhead navigation bar directs you to Live Share Prices, Share Clubs, the ISA Centre and Portfolio

SPECIAL FEATURES

The many attractive features include delayed share prices, interactive charts, company profiles and news from the London, Milan, US and Canadian markets provided by Stockpoint.

Daily news, including press clippings, company news, stocks to watch and investment and unit trust news.

Market Roundup is posted three times a day, and market indices and top gainers/losers are updated throughout the day.

Opinion and Analysis Regular and occasional guest columnists include 'Evil Knievil' (a legendary City short-seller), the formidable Mrs Cohen, and Alpesh Patel, a leading commentator on internet trading and e-commerce (in print and in sound). Past articles can be retrieved from the Archives.

Investment Challenge is a game with prizes for achieving the highest fantasy portfolio net asset value at given points in time. It is a great tool for giving novice investors hands-on experience in share trading, without taking any financial risks. You need to be registered to take part.

Stock Screener is useful for searching out shares by a host of criteria, such as price range, risk data, size/capitalisation, revenue and earnings data. This facility links up with the remarkable interactive Stockpoint graphics.

COULD DO BETTER

Your Money, the personal finance section, is heavily orientated towards investment. It is strong on ISAs, share clubs and investment and unit trusts, but it ignores life assurance and pensions altogether. Comparable sites like Interactive Investor International have strong leanings towards investment, but are more balanced. And why have a resident general insurance quotation service (www.insurancewide.com) and nothing on life assurance? The portfolio tracker only handles shares.

This is a bright, intelligent and thoroughly enjoyable site. The Investment Challenge game is a terrific innovation.

www.excite.co.uk/money
Excite Money and Investing

Overall rating: ★ ★ ★			
Classification:	Portal	**Readability:**	★ ★ ★ ★ ★
Updating:	Daily	**Reliability:**	★ ★ ★ ★ ★
Navigation:	★ ★ ★ ★ ★	**Speed:**	★ ★ ★ ★ ★

UK

Excite Money and Investing is a portal site on the Excite search engine. There is a bit of indigenous content on the home page in the form of the FTSE100, the Dow Jones indices and a Market Report, but apart from a portfolio tracker from Charles Schwab Europe, the rest of the site is powered by Interactive Investor International (III) . What you get is a sawn-off version of III (see p. 20), covering general insurance, investment, mortgages, pensions, saving and investment, and tax.

III is noted for the depth of its fund and share data, and this is precisely what you don't get here. Be content with lists of the leading unit trusts, investment trusts, pension and offshore funds. The Savings and Banking data has a bit more meat. Click on the top dog in each loan category and you get the chasing pack as well. The Mortgage section gives you the best of fixed, discounted and capped rates and first-time-buyer, cashback and 100 per cent loans.

The virtue of this site is its speed. Of course, there is always the hyperlink to III, but it's relatively heavy going. Besides, if you wanted the full Monty you wouldn't necessarily start from here, would you?

This is a quaint little site for those who like their information in digestible portions.

OTHER SITES OF INTEREST

LineOne Money
www.lineone.co.uk/money

This is the personal finance site on the LineOne ISP, a joint venture between British Telecom, News International and United News and Media. The site is noteworthy for its Jobs and Legal pages in addition to the usual coverage of best buys insurance, mortgages, pensions, savings, the stockmarket, tax and the obligatory portfolio tracker, which accommodates only shares.

Each section is subdivided into News, Guides, Tools (for example, calculators) and the resident Doctor Insurance/Mortgage/Savings/Pension, who is usually a luminary from the world of personal finance. This format greatly assists with navigation.

There is a particularly strong section on mortgages, with an encyclopaedic contribution from the Mortgage Doctor, who turns out to be IFA John Charcol. There is an impressive Property Directory listing sites covering anything from property databases to Neighbours at War (www.bbc.co.uk/education/neighbours).

The site imports its funds data from Interactive Investor International. However, the stockmarket quotes service is not very user friendly and was well behind the clock. The Guides could also be improved.

Compuserve Money
www.compuserve.com/money

This is an unremarkable site but it has one or two smart features. There is a handy tax guide residing on the home page and the share quotes come with nifty interactive charts powered by Teledata Borsen Information.

Money Web
www.moneyweb.co.uk

This is a no-nonsense site that spells out the nitty-gritty of pensions, life assurance, mortgages and investments in useful and accurate detail. Unlike most other sites, it doesn't treat you like a financial cretin. Money Web is compiled by former IFA, Ian Dickson and is sponsored by Scottish Friendly Assurance.

Blay's Guides (Savings and Finance)
www.blays.co.uk

This is a very handy best-buys site covering Utilities, Savings, Student Finance, Mortgages, Cards, Personal Banking, Business (banking, charge cards, fuel cards, and so on) and Telephones. Lightening fast.

Data Sites

Data sites are treated here as a subdivision of information sites in general, as they tend to have a much narrower focus. Some are confined to data only, in the form of tables and graphics, without any news or comment. Others have some additional features.

www.micropal.com
S&P Micropal

Overall rating: ★ ★ ★ ★ ☆			
Classification:	Information	**Readability:**	★ ★
Updating:	weekly	**Reliability:**	★ ★ ★ ★ ★
Navigation:	★ ★ ★ ★	**Speed:**	★ ★

UK

Standard and Poor's Micropal was founded in 1985 and is perhaps the leading independent fund information service, monitoring over 38,000 funds worldwide. This is the definitive site if you want to keep tabs on a unit trust, investment trust, life assurance or pension funds and offshore funds.

Registration is not required and it won't cost you anything to use this valuable site. Be warned, however, that navigation is not particularly easy or intuitive on this one. You need to take time to explore the system and learn the ropes.

A drop-down menu lists over 20 databases of domestic and foreign unit and investment trusts and (mostly) domestic life and pension funds. This menu remains visible wherever you are on the site. Click on the investment vehicle you want to be taken to the appropriate database.

The easiest way to get around is via the navigation bar at the top of the page that appears once you have logged on to the database section. This takes you to the Database Summary, Management Groups, Performance Tables and Fund Selector.

SPECIAL FEATURES

Database Summary displays the main fund categories. Fund categories contain fund sectors and fund sectors contain the individual funds.

Management Groups displays general information and performance data for all funds run by any management group.

Performance Tables contain summary performance information for each fund category; summary performance for all fund sectors within each fund category; and cumulative individual fund performance within each fund sector over 1, 2, 3, 5 and 10 years, together with volatility and Micropal star rating.

Use the Table Builder to display a specified number of funds in a sector either alphabetically, by growth rate. From within the Performance Tables you can click onto **Management Group** to find out more about the institution running a particular fund.

Fund Fact-Sheet provides more detailed fund performance analysis (cumulative performance, consistency, performance relative to the fund sector over six months) and other fund information.

Fund Selector is a search tool for compiling lists of funds using a more comprehensive set of filters It is very powerful and is the best method of generating lists of star performers by multiple criteria.

An encyclopaedia of managed fund information. This is an indispensable research tool for anyone (layman or professional) who is contemplating new investment in collective funds or who wants to monitor existing holdings.

www.market-eye.co.uk
Market Eye Internet

Overall rating: ★ ★ ★ ★ ★			
Classification:	Information	**Readability:**	★ ★
Updating:	Daily	**Reliability:**	★ ★ ★ ★ ★
Navigation:	★ ★ ★	**Speed:**	★ ★ ★

UK £ R

Market Eye is a site for dedicated 'non-professional' share investors, and claims to offer the same data and displays enjoyed by their professional counterparts. News and market reports are supplied by Datastream/ ICV, just like the pros we are told.

This is not the easiest site to navigate. There is a delphic three-tier navigation bar at the top of the screen which remains visible wherever you are on site. However, there is a useful demo that you can try out before you part with any dosh for the Premium Service.

SPECIAL FEATURES

There are two levels of service: a free **Investor Service** and a subscription **Premium Service**. Registration is mandatory for both.

The Investor Service gives you 15-minute delayed data for shares, derivatives, sectors, market indices and Forex. Although this is supposed to be a limited service, the level of detail is impressive.

Start with the on-site luminaries: David Schwartz the noted stock-market historian; John Piper, editor of Technical Trader the futures and options newsletter and Ben Turner and Andy Thacker of City Equities Ltd with their Penny Share Review.

Shares delivers 15-minute delayed prices (current, opening, high low and volume) augmented with interactive charts, customisable by date. Call up any share by its symbol, or click on the share name in the alphabetical listing. Download company fundamentals, and up to five years' worth of daily closing prices onto a spreadsheet. Click on the **Biggest Movers** button and observe the movers and shakers on the FTSE 100/250/350 by ups, downs and volume. Did the index move for you, darling?

If you want to trade, hit the Trading Floor and select an online stockbroker from James Brearley and Sons, Barclays Stockbrokers, FasTrade, Charles Schwab Europe and Union Cal.

Derivatives Historical, daily and tick data on all LIFFE instruments (futures and options). Previous exposure to the Caballa helps.

Sector Indices See how each sector of the stock market is performing. Click on any sector index and up pops a 1-year chart (well, most of time, anyway).

Market Indices FTSE 100/250/350/SmiCap/All Share; techMark 100/All; Eurotop 100/300, Ebloc 100, E300 Ex-UK, E300 Euro Bloc/Ex-Euro Bloc; ISE/Nikkei 50; DAX (XETRA); S&P 500. Click on any of these and you get performance charts for the year.

Also has CAC 40, Dow Jones, Nikkei 225, Hang Seng and SMI; FTSE AIM, FTSE SmCapExIT, FT Non Financial, FTSE Fledgling, FTSE Fledgling ExIT.

Forex Exchange rates for 18 currencies against sterling and the US dollar. Unexceptional but nice to find something on a human scale.

The basic Premium Service costs £23.50 per month (including VAT). What you get is the Investor Service with bells and whistles:

Latest News, Key Indices, Forex and **London Metal Exchange** prices are available on a summary page giving an overview of the markets in real time. Click on any index such as the FTSE 100 and you get to play with nine possible charts instead of just one on the free service. You can get delayed (yes delayed) equity and LIFFE data, plus fundamentals from Hemmington Scott.

Power search for any company or index and extract 5-year historical OHLCV (opening, high, low, closing and volume) data, nine charts and news.

Portfolios Create up to 50 portfolios of up to 50 'instruments' each - practically an orchestra - viewable by values, prices and trades

If you want all the above data in real time, you will have to pay extra real-time Exchange Fees as follows:

London Stock Exchange equity data	£ 6.23 p.m.
FTSE International (indices)	£ 6.35 p.m.
Paris CAC40 index	£ 2.35 p.m.
Dow Jones Industrial Index	£ 1.17 p.m.
LIFFE (futures and options)	£14.69 p.m.

Surprisingly, this site is fun to surf and you can learn a lot just by playing around with the free Investor Service. One for the anoraks.

www.hemscott.com
Hemmington Scott

Overall rating: ★ ★ ★ ★ ☆			
Classification:	Information	**Readability:**	★ ★ ★
Updating:	Daily	**Reliability:**	★ ★ ★ ★ ★
Navigation:	★ ★ ★ ☆	**Speed:**	★ ★ ★ ☆

UK £ R

Hemmington Scott was founded in 1985. It publishes guides and directories on UK public companies and supplies fundamental share data in print and on the internet to 'data vendors', such as E* Trade the online stockbroker

Hemmington Scott's renowned publications include The Hemscott Company Guide;The Pricewaterhouse Cooper's Corporate Register of directors of quoted companies; Company REFS (Really Essential Financial Statistics) for serious investors; Investing for Growth (an investment newsletter); and Treasury Management International (TMI), a magazine for treasury professionals.

In 1995 Hemmington Scott launched the UK Equities Direct website, a free 'investor-relations' investor service. In 1999 it launched Hemscott.Net Business, an Internet portal aimed at business and professional users.

This site will be of interest to direct equity investors who require fundamental data for share selection. The UK Equities Direct (www.hemscott.com) service gives you the following services free of charge:

A company reports ordering service; 5-year summary Profit and Loss Statements and Balance Sheets; 15-minute delayed share prices; 3,5, and 10-year share price graphics relative to the FTSE and sector; Brokers' consensus reports;

Directors details; Major shareholders; Registrars and advisers; and Key Dates.

The above data is available for fully listed companies, AIM and techMark listings, companies listed pending flotation, ADR stocks, and Traded Options.

Subscribers to Hemscott.Net Business (www.hemscott.net) get real-time AFX News, detailed broker forecasts and particulars of Directors' market dealings. You can register for Hemscott.Net Business free of charge if you connect to the internet using hemscott.net as your ISP. Otherwise it will cost you £10 per month + VAT.

You can link from Hemmington Scott to a panel of online stockbrokers to execute your trade. The current panel consists of E*Trade, Xest, TD Waterhouse and Halifax ShareXpress.

This is a dry-as-dust data site, but full of essential information for the dedicated share dealer. The personal finance section on Hemscott.Net Business turns out to be MoneyWorld

www.trustnet.co.uk
TrustNet Limited

Overall rating: ★ ★ ★ ★			
Classification:	Information	**Readability:**	★
Updating:	Daily	**Reliability:**	★ ★ ★ ★ ★
Navigation:	★ ★ ★	**Speed:**	★ ★ ★

UK R

TrustNet is another example of a dedicated data-only site. It displays information about UK and offshore managed funds, market indices and exchange rates.

TrustNet data is provided by TrustNet Limited in conjunction with Datastream/IVC and other third-party data vendors such as Financial Times Information Limited and Warburg Dillon Read.

TrustNet is narrowly focused and will appeal to the more sophisticated investor who requires an above-average amount of detail about managed funds. The data is provided free of charge and registration is only required if you want to use the portfolio tracker.

The site is basically split into two separate sections. The first reviews open-ended funds (unit trusts and OEICS), the second UK, US and offshore closed-end funds (investment trusts) and warrants. Data is accessible by fund name, performance and management group and sortable by region, sector and type. Every aspect of the funds is listed in quite astonishing detail.

SPECIAL FEATURES

Price and Performance data allows you to call up performance charts for one and five years and to examine dividend history.

Portfolio Summary lists the largest shareholdings and regional and sector weightings.

Peer Group Performance promises more than it delivers as you cannot display more than one performance history on a graph.

Portfolio Tracker Registered users can create multiple customised portfolios to track price and investment performance of selected funds. However, you can't enter the number of shares and units that you own and therefore cannot value your portfolio.

Indices will give you the low-down on anything from the Affarsvarlden All Share to the Zimbabwe Industrial. Did you know that there are about 46 FTSE indices alone out of 319? You learn something new every day!

Rates displays currency exchange rates for 139 currencies in terms of sterling and the US dollar, terribly useful if you want to know how many Vietnamese Dongs you will get for your bucks.

You don't exactly surf this one for thrills, but you can't deny the usefulness of much of the data. Overall, the site reviews 1,395 open-ended funds and 426 closed end funds. Log on when there is nothing else to watch on the Net. One thing is for certain, you won't have to queue for very long to get connected. Sound off in the investors' Forum and you could find yourself talking to yourself.

www.digitallook.com
Digital Look

Overall rating: ★ ★ ★			
Classification:	Information	Readability:	★ ★ ★ ★ ★
Updating:	Daily	Reliability:	★ ★ ★ ★ ★
Navigation:	★ ★ ★ ★ ★	Speed:	★ ★ ★ ★ ★

UK R

DigitalLook.com is a free service, researching UK quoted companies, reproducing news and providing investor alerts by e-mail or fax: in fact, everything you wanted to know but never knew existed about any UK plc, let alone were afraid to enquire about. Registration is mandatory and your are assigned your account number and password by e-mail.

SPECIAL FEATURES

Company profiles Latest prices, last trades, fundamentals from Hemmington Scott, performance graphs from Bloombergs and 'more digital research' from other sources.

News Wires from AFXpress and Bloomberg. Internet newsfrom CNet, Excite and Market Eye.

Bulletin Boards link to Interactive Investor International, The Motley Fool, Hemmington Scott, Market Eye, Raging Bull and Yahoo.

Tip Watcher and **Newspaper Watcher** are worth a look. You can research all the constituents of the techMark Index. And if you want to know what companies Jo Public is discussing, try the Most Talked About Shares, which gives you the hit rates on the various bulletin boards.

If at the end of it all you still can't make up your mind whether to buy, sell or hold, I wouldn't be a bit surprised!

www.stockpoint.com
Stockpoint

Overall rating: ★ ★ ★ ☆			
Classification:	Information	Readability:	★ ★ ★ ★
Updating:	Daily	Reliability:	★ ★ ★ ★ ★
Navigation:	★ ★ ★ ★	Speed:	★ ★ ★ ★

US

Stockpoint.com is a free American website devoted to the analysis and management of shareholdings covering US, Canadian, French, Italian and UK share markets. Use a power search panel on the right hand side of the screen to specify the country and the stock you wish to research by symbol or by name.

SPECIAL FEATURES

Stockpoint boasts one of the most innovative charting services that you will see anywhere:

Quick Charts allows you to plot the performance of any share at daily to 5-yearly intervals; compare performance with three other stocks of your choice and the FTSE; and plot up to seven indicators, such as on-balance volume, Bollinger bands, and relative strength. The Stockpoint Help Page is essential here.

Interactive Charts allows you to plot and compare share performance against three other stocks and the FTSE by the minute; click on any point of the graph and read off the historical share price at the time; drag on the vertical bar and watch the percentage change in the historical stock price from one minute, hour or day to the next.

What you do with this beautifully presented information is anybody's guess but it's great fun!

Chapter 3

Education and Advisory Sites

'advice, n. The smallest current coin.'

Ambrose Bierce: Cynic's Word Book (1906)

Getting financial advice on the internet can be a complicated and frustrating business. There is plenty of generic advice to be had but little in the way of regulated advice.

If you buy regulated financial products on the advice of an authorised firm of financial advisers, then you fall under the protection of the Financial Services Act and have the right to redress and compensation if the advice turns out to be inappropriate. However, if you buy without taking authorised advice, you normally have no right of compensation. The same principles of consumer protection apply whether the transaction proceeds on paper, by telephone or on the internet. Not all financial products are regulated: most term-assurance policies are unregulated.

The supervision of authorised firms is widely regarded by financial advisers as adversarial, oppressive and expensive, which is not to say that it is unjustified given their past conduct. Information sites and even Independent Financial Advisors (IFAs) will therefore go to great lengths to avoid bringing their online services under the authority of the FSA. This means that the bulk of online services either give you generic advice that is not product or provider-specific, with no attempt to transact business, or they are are execution-only, where no advice is sought or offered and the firm merely carries out your instructions. A few are confined to unregulated products like term assurance and (hitherto) mortgages. This is not a wholly desirable state of affairs. For a start, it is at least debatable whether consumers should forego advice in order to avoid paying commission or fees. Secondly, the range of online transactable products is restricted, with increased potential for 'misbuying'.

LIGHT AT THE END OF THE TUNNEL?

A few IFAs do provide fee-based full online advisory services. IFA Direct and Sort Limited provide an online 'fact-find' which forms the basis of their recommendations. If the client transacts through an execution-only service, commission is ofen rebated.

The uniqueness of Sort is that it separates advice from sales and that it is regulated on the quality of its advice only. For IFAs and revenue-hungry information sites who may be weighing up FSA authorisation, a three-stage version of the Sort model (with segregated information, advice and sales) may be the way forward.

On the other hand, the segregation of information, advice and sales could possibly undermine investor protection. The internet is not confined by national boundaries or sovereignty. It is not inconceivable that an advisor could establish a website outside the jurisdiction of the regulator and offer unregulated advice for a fee charged to a credit card. A precedent may already have been established in the gambling industry, where internet betting operations are based in Gibraltar to avoid UK betting tax. There may be trouble ahead...

www.financial-planning.uk.com
Financial Planning Horizons

Overall rating: ★ ★ ★ ★			
Classification:	Education	**Readability:**	★ ★ ★ ★ ★
Updating:	Daily	**Reliability:**	★ ★ ★ ★ ★
Navigation:	★ ★ ★ ★ ★	**Speed:**	★ ★ ★ ★ ★

UK

This site belongs to Financial Services Education for Consumers Limited, an independent body offering 'free education' in financial services. The site aims to increase the level of public awareness and understanding of financial services products.

Content is of the highest quality, and the site functions as a definitive financial-planning reference work for layman and professional alike.

SPECIAL FEATURES

The home page is the key to navigating the whole site, which can be enjoyed at different levels. A series of hyperlinks under **Contents of the Site** directs the layman to several sections:

Database lists important addresses, including professional bodies, regulators, government services, Inland Revenue).

Dates Important dates in the financial calendar, such as for filing tax returns under self-assessment.

Information Generic information about savings, investment, protection and mortgages.

Tools for assessing personal financial needs.

News Latest information on financial services.

Other features include a **Glossary** of financial terms, common **Financial Scenarios** and **Case Studies**.

SPECIAL FEATURES

Lifestages and **Life Crisis Points** on the panel on the left-hand side of the home page will allow you to explore topics in more depth. You will reach an index of 16 financial chapters which cover a typical 'life cycle' – from starting work, buying a first home, starting a family through to retirement planning, pre-retirement, retirement and death of a partner.

Each chapter is fully comprehensive, accurate, well organised and beautifully written. A typical chapter content will list generic product features, comparison of product types within the category and factors to be considered when choosing a product provider (for example, financial strength).

This site can be used for preparatory reading prior to consulting a financial adviser, or as a reference for checking the quality of financial advice already given. Best of all, it's free!

---

www.itsonline.co.uk
ITs Online

Overall rating: ★ ★ ★ ★ ★			
Classification: Education		**Readability:**	★★★★
Updating: Daily		**Reliability:**	★★★★
Navigation: ★★★★		**Speed:**	★★★★

UK £ R

ITs Online focuses on investment trusts, the poor relations of unit trusts in terms of popularity. This has had little to do with their intrinsic merits. Investment trusts are public limited companies whose business is to invest in the shares of the other plcs, and which simply do not have the vast marketing budgets available to retail fund managers.

An investment trust is a 'closed end fund', which means that there is a fixed number of shares in circulation. The price is therefore determined by supply and demand. This implies that it can trade at a 'discount' or 'premium' to its net asset value (NAV). In practice, UK investment trusts have tended to trade at discounts to NAV, to the vexation of their holders.

The discount is a decidedly mixed blessing. On the one hand it enables the investor to buy a pound's worth of assets for less than a pound, and to enjoy an enhanced dividend yield. On the other, there is the unfulfilled expectation that the discount will eventually narrow and yield disproportionate capital growth.

The endemic failure of UK investment trusts to eradicate the discount has led to desperate measures, not least of which has been a concerted 'buy back' campaign aimed at reducing the number of shares in circulation. Then at the dawn of the new millennium, the Association of Investment Trust Companies (AITC) hit on the unprecedented strategy of marketing them. 'IT's wonderful,' crooned the chic TV ads, and ITs Online is the website accessory.

The site is divided into two main subject areas: technical aspects of ITs and their applications, and practical aspects, namely choosing ITs and dealing in them.

Technical aspects are dealt with efficiently and there are interesting discussions of how ITs can be incorporated into pensions and the repayment of mortgages. However, the site is at its best when dealing with the matter of investment choice. This is a notoriously difficult area for investors. The problem of picking the right investment trust is identical to that of buying the right share; hardly surprising since ITs are shares.

SPECIAL FEATURES

Trust finder whittles down the seemingly infinite choice by way of a four-step process:

Goal selection asks you to choose between capital growth, income or growth and income.

Risk Preference asks you to specify what level of risk you want (high, medium-to-high, medium, low, very low).

Type of Trust allows you to state what type of trust you prefer. More than one type can be selected simultaneously and the choices include UK, international, smaller companies, venture and development capital, commodity, property, and emerging markets.

You are then asked to specify budget, investment frequency and vehicle (lump sum or regular contributions, ISA, savings plan or pension scheme).

The programme then creates a list of trusts that meet your criteria. You can click on any trust on the list to uncover a wealth of detail. For example, selecting Products and Performance gives you access to View Performance Charts where you can inspect the one and five-year performance of the trust in question compared to its NAV and benchmark, using graphics supplied by TrustNet (see p. 36).

Quick Search Use this as an alternative to Trust Finder if you already know the name of the trust or the management group. Finally, you can launch an Advanced Search whereby you specify your goal and the programme selects all the appropriate trust types. The onus is on you to delete trust categories that you don't want (for example, emerging markets). It's like Trust Finder without the training wheels.

The site offers a nice balance between investor education and practicality. It can be used by novice and experienced IT investors alike. The latter will benefit from the detailed trust information sections. However, the acid test of the site is whether it will persuade the public at large to buy Investment Trusts. The jury is out.

www.proshare.org.uk
ProShare (UK) Ltd

Overall rating: ★ ★ ★ ☆			
Classification: Education		**Readability:**	★ ★ ★
Updating: Daily		**Reliability:**	n/a
Navigation: ★ ★ ★		**Speed:**	★ ★ ★ ☆

(UK) (£) (R)

There is a list of relevant publications including the ProShare Investment Clubs Manual at £29.50 (including post and packing) which sets out the basics of setting up and running an investment club. There is also an online bookshop maintained by Global Investor International.

This site is essentially a shop window for ProShare (UK) Ltd and will be of interest to anyone considering setting up an investment club.

ProShare (UK) Ltd has three main fields of operation. Firstly, supplying independent information and services for the encouragement of private investors (particularly through investment clubs). Secondly, supplying teaching material for the National Investment Programme for Schools and Colleges. Thirdly, promoting employee share schemes by providing information, independent research and guidance to companies interested in implementing such schemes.

There is a three-and-a-bit page guide to the basics, highlighting affiliation to ProShare Investment Clubs, the benefits of which include a quarterly magazine called *Dividend*, a free copy of Hemington Scott's REFS (*Really Essential Financial Statistics)*, access to the ProShare Hotline and investment club seminars, and free membership for the first year.

The rest of the site deals with the National Investment Programme for Schools and Colleges and an introduction to Employee Share Ownership. The latter includes fact sheets, notice of seminars, training courses and workshop events, details of the government's New All-Employee Share Plan and information about membership of the ProShare ESSential Club (£325 per annum plus VAT) for assisting companies with fewer than 250 employees to set up and run employee share schemes.

Planning and Advisory Sites

FT Your Money is the successor to FT Quicken, the joint venture between the Financial Times and Intuit, creators of the respected Quicken personal finance software. The FT and Quicken have now gone their separate ways and FT Your Money was installed as heir apparent in December 1999.

The old FT Quicken site was always the poor relation of the main site ft.com, noteworthy for its exhaustive managed fund pricing service and little else. The site is owned by the Financial Times Group and pays its way out of advertising, selling content and by linking visitors to other sites.

The site has two levels: general pages which are accessible to all readers, and personalised pages where free registration is required. The latter is used to store personal data, calculations and agendas, a Personal Portfolio, To Do List and My Money (a personal home page).

A navigation bar at the top of the screen takes you to the personalised pages. But the best way around the site as a whole is via the Jump To drop-down menu which is visible on every page.

The approach is personal and interactive, with emphasis on quantitative answers to common financial problems rather than general guidelines. I counted no less than 11 calculators covering home buying, the cost of education (pre-school, primary, secondary, university), pensions, life assurance, income and expenses and savings. The preliminary questionnaires can be fairly detailed and you need to do some homework beforehand. The calculators lead naturally to several plans including: My Retirement, Education, Home buying and Creating Wealth.

SPECIAL FEATURES

Your Life incorporates guides to home buying, retirement, education and cohabitation.

Your Opportunities deals with personal goals, such as saving money, creating wealth, finding an adviser, getting organised and tax.

Your Decisions handles products such as mortgages, insurance, savings and credit, investments and pensions. The data is drawn from a variety of sources: savings and credit data is imported from MoneyNet; life assurance data is provided by MoneyeXtra and online-IFA Life-Search; investment funds data and share price quotes are provided by sister site FT.com. The reader is also referred to advisor and provider websites.

Number-crunching **calculators** accompany the topics covered in **Your Life** and **Your Opportunities**. Calculations can be stored by logging on to the personal pages.

The attention to detail can be quite astonishing. The Home buying section boasts four calculators (Buying Versus Renting, Mortgage Affordability, Repayment Versus Interest-only Mortgages, and Your Home as an Investment). There is a **Search** tool for finding solicitors, surveyors, financial advisers, removal and van hire firms, and builders and decorators by post code.

There are illuminating descriptions of eight different types of mortgages (variable, fixed, discounted and capped rate; cashback, flexible, euro and tracker) and the **Mortgage Finder** allows you to request information from multiple providers simultaneously.

Find A Home links you to a series of property market databases such as the AFT Property Finder (www.ft.com/property). You can also check out the quality of the neighbourhood by transferring directly to the Up My Street website (www.upmystreet.com).

Education is equally impressive. You can enter the current fees per child and specify an annual inflation rate to produce a schedule of future annual fees. Against this you can enter up to six investments with individual growth rates and maturity dates. The **Paying the Bill** calculator shows you how far your capital will go. Proceed to **My Education Plan** and research private primary and secondary schools by transferring to the SchoolsNet website (www.schoolsnet.com).

COULD DO BETTER

The **Research Fund/Share Performance** title is currently a misnomer, but you will soon be able to link to TrustNet for unit and investment trust prices. Whether these can be incorporated in the personal portfolio is a moot point, as only shares are currently admitted.

It is still early days, and perhaps a bit premature to be judging this site. However, first impressions are that it is eminently coherent, practical and a joy to explore. This is definitely one to watch over the next year.

www.investmentguide.co.uk
AAA Investment Guide

Overall rating: ★ ★ ★ ★			
Classification: Education		**Readability:**	★ ★ ★ ★
Updating: Regular		**Reliability:**	★ ★ ★ ★ ★
Navigation: ★ ★ ★		**Speed:**	★ ★ ★

UK £ R

If you are looking for a comprehensive guide to all aspects of investment and don't mind paying an annual subscription, look no further. The author is David Lewis, the former editor of *Money Mail* and *Money Management*, a contributor to *Which?* and now a freelance writer on personal finance. The site is divided into free and subscription pages.

SPECIAL FEATURES
Free pages/chapters currently include **Investment and Savings Strategy**, **Best Advice and How to Get It**, **Keeping Down Your Tax Bill** (part free), **Spread Your Money Around** and **Investment Summary**.

Subscription pages cover: **Capital Gains and Inheritance Tax**, **Turning Income into Capital**, **How to Invest in Stocks and Shares**, **Living and Working Aboard**, **Saving Towards a Pension**, **Wives Income and Investment**, **Children's Investment**, **Giving Money to Adult Children**, **Change in Plan** (redundancy, widowhood, divorce), and **Boosting Your Net Income**.

Be warned that as pages are updated they are frequently transferred to the subscription area. The annual subscription is £29.99 for viewing the whole guide online.

The following additional guides are available by email or on CD for viewing offline:

Shares – A Beginner's Guide to Making Money, £29.99 per annum.

The Money Code – A Beginner's Guide to Financial Security, £29.99 per annum.

You can have all three guides for £39.99 per annum.

You can view the free pages and browse the contents of the subscription chapters on the above websites before deciding whether to buy or not. This site is definitely worth a visit.

www.fool.co.uk
The Motley Fool

Overall rating: ★ ★ ★ ★			
Classification:	Education	Readability:	★ ★ ★ ★ ★
Updating:	Daily	Reliability:	n/a
Navigation:	★ ★ ★ ★	Speed:	★ ★ ★ ★

UK

If you want something completely different try The Motley Fool (or just plain The Fool), the UK version of the cult American site. Do not expect anything as mundane as managed funds performance tables, loans and savings rates, quotation or modesty. The Fool has much loftier ambitions, namely to 'Educate, Amuse, Enrich'.

The Fool is dismissive of commission-earning financial advisers. Fee-paid advisers are tolerated, in violation of the immortal 'Kin' Hubbard aphorism 'nothing dispels enthusiasm like an admission fee', which it once had the good sense to quote at the head of one of its web pages.

The Fool is utterly original, opinionated, iconoclastic, takes itself rather seriously and is generous with the self-praise. It recently took first prize in the Electronic Media category at the 18 Creative Freedom Awards ceremony, for amongst other things 'irritating independent financial advisers and fund managers by cutting them out of the loop'.

The writing style is distinctly jaunty. On the other hand, the humour sometimes gets in the way of a good read and the text can ramble on a bit. Paragraphing is also not one of The Fool's strongest suits.

It is a sprawling site, but if you stick to the navigation panel on the left-hand side of the screen you won't get too lost.

SPECIAL FEATURES

Fool's School is where you go to learn the art of investing 'the Foolish way'. Acquaint yourself with the **Ten Steps to Foolishness** which proclaims (inter alia) 'the miracle of compound interest', the folly of fixed deposits, the pre-eminence of direct equity investment, the habitual under-performance of active fund management and the pitfalls of money purchase pension plans and endowments.

The Fool is hot on direct share investment, partial to mechanical investment strategies (which it tries out in its **Foolish Footsie Workshop**) and obsessed with beating the FTSE. Collective investments such as unit trusts are scorned, save for Index Trackers. Not surprisingly, the **Portfolio Tracker** and '**Buy-to-hold Qualiport**' have no room for anything but shares.

Message Boards The Fool boasts some of the liveliest chat rooms and bulletin boards in all cyber-space, a true meeting place for the community of 'Foolish Investors'. What is particularly engaging is that most articles under **Fool's School**, **Personal Finance** and **Stock Ideas** contain hyperlinks that transport you directly to the message boards, to join the debate on the subject in question. Moreover, you can skip back as much as 365 days and forward again: great for trawling the message archives and picking up the threads of the argument.

The Fool is not above the occasional unintended howler but, happily, there are about four pages of disclaimers on site, if you can find the icon without a magnifying glass that is. Unfortunately, in the real world of financial advice there are no disclaimers!

It's both great fun and essential reading. Not to be missed.

www.sort.co.uk
Sort Limited

Overall rating: ★ ★ ★ ★			
Classification: Advice		**Readability:**	★ ★ ★
Updating: Regular		**Reliability:**	n/a
Navigation: ★ ★ ☆		**Speed:**	★ ★ ★

UK £

The remarkable thing about Sort is not so much the site contents but what Sort Limited does. Sort is a regulated independent financial adviser which sells advice rather than financial products. There are two levels of advice:

Financial Health Check (£99) quantifies shortfalls in your life assurance, critical illness assurance, income protection and retirement provision. It then calculates the indicative cost of putting them on track. Other calculations include: a suggested investment mix of cash, bonds and shares incorporating your risk preference, an estimation of your inheritance tax liability and a stab at the likely cost of providing index-linked long-term care.

Product Decision Service (£79) makes specific product and provider recommendations on mortgages, savings and investment, and pensions.

SPECIAL FEATURES

Central to the process is a comprehensive fact-find form that you complete and submit online. Sort uses the data to prepare a detailed report known as the **Financial Decisions Kit**. Included in the price is a 30-day consultation period during which you can discuss the content of the report with Sort's authorised advisers, by email or telephone.

The final stage in the process is when you act on the recommendations, using an execution-only broker who will rebate the lion's share of the commission. The term 'execution-only' means that advice is not sought from or given by the broker executing the deal. Sort does not receive any commission in respect of the placement of the business. Its only remuneration is the fixed fee that it charges for the advice.

OTHER FEATURES

For the rest, Sort functions very much as an information site. There is a series of guides covering mortgages, life assurance, pensions and investments. The best of them are the pensions and investment guides. The pensions guides seem to strike a reasonable balance between simplicity and substance. The investment guide provides a good synopsis of products (including National Savings, which seems to be ignored by most other information sites) with a useful classification in terms of risk and access.

Money Makeovers are real cases but do not approach the level of detail of the Financial Health Check.

The Top Products section turns out to be a very useful power search facility for unit trusts, investment trusts, pension funds and life assurance funds, courtesy of S&P Micropal.

The true merits of this site lie in the separation of advice from execution. The whole is greater than the sum of the parts!

www.mrscohen.co.uk
Mrs Cohen's Money

Overall rating: ★ ★ ★ ☆			
Classification:	Advice	Readability:	★ ★ ★
Updating:	Regular	Reliability:	★ ★ ★ ★
Navigation:	★ ★ ★	Speed:	★ ★ ★

UK

The redoubtable Mrs Cohen will be familiar as the eponymous heroine of the Channel Four programme Mrs Cohen's Money where she nagged and handbagged leading representatives of the financial establishment at weekly intervals. Now Mrs Cohen has her own SFA-regulated website, with 'a team of real experts...unparalleled on the internet'. So now you know!

The site is admirably clear and uncluttered. A navigation bar runs across the top of your screen. The home page directs you to other meatier sections of the site such as **Cohen Campaign**, **Cohen Pearls** and **Q&A**.

This site is pitched at the real beginner and there is no better teacher than a shining example. Follow Mrs Cohen as she ascends out of debt by trading her 'big house' for a smaller replacement and repaying a 'huge mortgage, a sizeable bank loan and a thumping great overdraft', and investing in...shares, what else?

'Ascendancy' is a common motif on advisory websites. Where The Motley Fool has its Ten Steps to Foolish Investment, Mrs Cohen invites you to **Climb the Investment Staircase**, a process that apparently begins at the age of 10+ and proceeds to 60+, whence you 'live happily ever after'. By now you will get the flavour of the site...

Unlike The Motley Fool, however, Mrs Cohen has no hang-ups about collective investments and active fund management. Having started from scratch herself, she would know that pooled investments such as unit trusts/OEICS (jumped-up unit trusts), investment trusts and pension funds are often the first exposure to asset-backed investments and a prelude to direct share holdings.

COULD DO BETTER

The only major gripe is that there are significant gaps in the content. A notable absentee is protection (life assurance, income protection, critical illness assurance, medical insurance). Insurance is the bedrock family prosperity, whether for the replacement of the breadwinner's income, contingency planning, the repayment of debt or the protection of one's estate against taxation. Given her emphasis on the basics of financial planning, Mrs Cohen should get her team of 'experienced financial journalists and qualified advisers' and start kicking a few backsides...again!

The virtue of this site is that much of it is eminently sensible stuff. The most detailed chapters cover savings versus investing, ISAs (advantages, disadvantages, decision time), pensions and picking a fund. For me, the most valuable chapters deal with the very basics: goal setting and budgeting.

Chapter 4

Commercial Transactions Online

In the previous chapters, we reviewed sites that largely give us information on personal finance topics. We now turn our attention to sites that enable us to transact over the internet. These fall into the following categories:

Internet Banking with short reviews of 16 'bricks and clicks' services and two stand-alone banks. At least four more stand-alone internet banks will make their debut in the UK this year.

Online Share Dealing Services including an overview of practical share dealing and reviews of 16 major services. Newcomers will be reviewed at future updates.

Online Insurance covers both general (motor, property, and travel) and life assurance.

Online Homebuying, with emphasis on internet estate agencies and independent mortgage sites.

Online Shopping, concentrating mainly on auction sites.

Trading Securely on the Internet

The internet is undoubtedly an efficient system for communication and dissemination of information. However, it is by nature an 'open system', originally designed for the sharing of information and to enable computers to communicate easily with one another. The open nature of the technology is a handicap, however, where confidentiality is required.

The fear of fraud (from interception or manipulation of credit-card data to breach of trade secrets and simple non-delivery of goods) is acknowledged as the single greatest impediment to the growth of e-commerce. The response of the e-commerce community is Public Key Infrastructure (PKI), a security system based on encryption of data.

PKI has three components:

Asymmetric data encryption (encoding or scrambling) and decryption based on the interplay of public and private keys.

Digital certificates which authenticate the identity of a party to an online transaction

Electronic signatures which associate the signatory with a message, as with a manual signature

ENCRYPTION

An encryption algorithm – the actual encryption engine – does the job of encoding your message. Public and private pairs of keys are used for unlocking the encryption algorithm and setting it to work.

The public key can be widely disseminated by e-mailing it to recipients or listing it in some public directory. The private key is confidential. The public and private keys have a mathematical relationship to each other. Any message encrypted with your public key can only be decrypted by using your private key, and vice versa.

DIGITAL CERTIFICATES

Digital certificates have been described as electronic ID documents and seek to verify that the transacting parties are who they claim to be. A digital certificate displays your name, serial number, expiry date and public key.

The digital certificates are issued by independent Certification Authorities (CAs) and can be purchased in the UK through such agencies as Royal Mail Viacode and BT Trustwise, who issue the public and private keys.

Purchasers are required to prove their identities in distinctly low-tech ways, such as by producing passports and driving licences.

DIGITAL SIGNATURES

A digital signature is in essence a message that has been 'hashed' (shortened and condensed) using a hashing algorithm, and encrypted using the sender's private key. The recipient uses the sender's public key to extract the hash and to marry it up with the hash on its records. The hashing/encryption process is also used simultaneously to verify the delivery of a message and demonstrate that it has not been tampered with.

In a nutshell, Public Key Infrastructure is designed to achieve the following objectives:

• Authentication of the identities of parties to an online transaction.

• Privacy of all information sent over the Internet

• Confirm the delivery and the integrity of the information transmitted (that is, to prove that the information has not been altered in transit)

• Non-refutability of contracts entered into over the internet. The only contentious issue concerns non-refutability of contracts. The convention is that a digital signature created using your private key is legally binding, but this principle has yet to be tested in the courts.

The E-Commerce Bill which is currently before parliament will establish the binding nature of digital certificates in law in the UK.

If you are confused but curious, visit the Interforum site at www.interforum.org. Interforum is a non-profit organisation, providing information and public information in internet technology.

Chapter 5

Online Banking

'A bank is a place that will lend you money if you can prove you don't need it.'
Bob Hope

There are currently 18 banks and building societies offering online banking services to the 'time poor' and 'temporally unchallenged' alike, enabling customers to call up their account balances, view past and current statements and perform everyday banking functions at any time of day or night, from their personal computers or Wireless Application Protocol (WAP) mobile telephones.

Barclays Online heads the league table of big hitters with 650,000 registered users. Egg has some 625,000 customers with access to the Internet. Other important players are Bank of Scotland Internet HOBS (350,000), Royal Bank of Scotland Direct Banking by PC (300,000), First Direct Access (180,000), Lloyds TSB (160,000) and NatWest On-line Banking (100,000).

Online Banking is a growth industry. Barclays Online is known to have revised its end-of-2000 target of 1m subscribers, and now expects to reach this figure by September. Egg is taking on new accounts at the rate of 3,000 a day, although the figure includes applicants for the Egg credit card.

Lloyds TSB is targeting 1m subscribers by the year end and has launched a pan-European stand-alone operation starting out in Spain, with the UK component due in place by the end of the year. Alliance & Leicester has announced plans for a stand-alone internet bank, which will be independent of the internet service that it launched for its existing account holders in January 2000. Abbey National has unveiled Cahoot, a stand-alone, 'interactive' operation scheduled for June 2000, with access through PC, WAP telephone and Digital TV. Smile (a division of The Co-operative Bank) and Intelligent Finance or IF (a division of the Halifax) are other examples of stand-alone internet banks, ostensibly competing directly with their own multi-channel siblings.

So, what's up? It seems that internet banking is polarising into two camps. The first sees online banking as an extra convenience channel for their branch and telephone customers to conduct their everyday affairs. The second sees online banking at the centre of e-commerce.

In short, the new breed of stand-alone bank wants you to buy 'stuff', be it consumer goods or financial products and services. The target market is the nouveau high-spending, high-borrowing class of customer who is comfortable with the technology.

Customers will be lured by attractive rates of interest on savings, mortgages and personal loans not available to rank-and-file branch and telephone customers, subsidised by the lower operating costs of online services. However, the very best rates and perks may be reserved for the most active account holders who contribute the most to the bank's profitability.

This may be e-commerce in the raw, but it is captive e-commerce. You will shop from a panel of retailers with whom your bank has struck a deal, sweetened perhaps by a discount on credit card transactions, as pioneered by Egg. Likewise your unit trusts may well come from the bank's own stable (or a narrow panel of chosen providers) and your shares will be acquired through the bank's affiliated dealing service.

The reward for sober-living, debt-averse customers who do not want to put all their eggs in one basket may be a second-class banking service. Oh brave new world!

Practical
Online Banking

Essentially, there are two kinds of services, PC Banking and Internet Banking. **PC Banking** enables you to operate your accounts from your own PC, loaded with the bank's dedicated software. **Internet Banking** gives you access from any computer linked to the internet. Internet Banking is considered to be the more advantageous because it allows you to operate your accounts from anywhere in the world.

Most online banking operations are internet services. Only First Direct and HSBC are exclusively PC at present, although have has an internet services pending. Bank of Scotland and Nationwide run both systems in parallel.

Online services differ in terms of scope. All but one display the details of your current and deposit accounts, some show your credit card transactions, personal loans and mortgage particulars as well, and a few display your holdings of their branded ISAs, PEPs, TESSAs and unit trusts (Virgin One will display the current value of your Virgin pension plan)

A key area of difference between the current array of online services is the degree of autonomy given to customers in running their accounts. This is particularly marked in the area of bill payments and transfers to third parties at other banks. Only Barclays, Nationwide, Royal Bank of Scotland, Smile and The Woolwich will allow you to set up third-party payments or transfers and standing orders without going through their customer services departments first.

Customer autonomy is a factor to take into consideration when choosing an online banking service. Ask yourself whether you want the bank to set up your automated payments, or whether you can manage by yourself.

Some online services permit the export of your data to personal financial management software packages like Microsoft Money and Intuit Quicken. This is useful for continuous account reconciliation, and for integration with details of assets and liabilities in general and deposits held at other institutions.

Security is of major importance with online banking. 128-bit Secure Socket Layer data encryption is standard.

Banking online is now universally free. There are no longer any joining fees or periodic subscriptions, so there is no disincentive to sign up. However, don't expect miracles. Online banking is extremely convenient but it can also be slow and irritating, especially at the set-up stage. The best is definitely yet to come.

Evaluating the competing services in advance is difficult, as you will not become aware of any shortcomings until you have signed on. The site demo should give you a feel for the scope of the service but there is really no substitute for first hand experience. Bulletin boards on the large information sites are often the best sources of informed opinion. Try the Online Banking Centre on Interactive Investor International (www.iii.co.uk) for up-to-the-minute whinging.

Remember that an online service is really only as good as the bank itself, so never transfer your banking arrangements simply for the online facilities.

www.smile.co.uk		
Smile		
Overall rating: ★ ★ ★ ★ ☆		
Classification: Internet Bank	**Readability:**	★ ★ ★ ★
Updating: n/a	**Reliability:**	n/a
Navigation: ★ ★ ★ ★	**Speed:**	★ ★ ★
UK R		

Smile is a division of the Co-operative Bank and was the first stand-alone online banking service in the UK (unlike Co-operative Bank Internet Banking, which is a complementary service to branch banking). Smile offers the full range of banking services (including telephone back up), but you can only open an account online.

Smile has won plaudits for its user friendliness and the generous rate of interest payable on the current account. You can access all your account and credit card details from one location, unlike say Barclays Online where you have a different set of log-on codes for your Barclaycard.

Setting up and managing standing orders and one-off money transfers is really easy. The system has jettisoned the Co-op's 'armchair banking' procedures, so that you can set up automated payments yourself. The only reservation is that you can't pre-schedule one-off inter-account transfers and third party transfers to other banks.

The interactive site demo is crystal clear, and gives you a realistic hands-on impression of the system.

www.rbs.co.uk		
Royal Bank of Scotland Direct Banking by PC		
Overall rating: ★ ★ ★ ★		
Classification: Internet Bank	**Readability:**	★ ★ ★ ★
Updating: n/a	**Reliability:**	n/a
Navigation: ★ ★ ★ ★	**Speed:**	★ ★ ★
UK R		

A solid all-round banking site that leaves the user to get on with things without having to refer back to the bank. The service is complementary to RBS branch and telephone banking.

You can view up to 50 RBS accounts, including TESSAs and ISAs. You can create standing orders and third party payments without troubling the bank, which provides a list of some 800 of the most common payees on a drop-down list for quick setting up.

Account data can be exported to Microsoft Money or Quicken.

With the Royal Bank winning the takeover battle for NatWest, can we expect that some of the no-nonsense Direct Banking style will rub off on NatWest Online?

www.virginone.com
Virgin Direct

Overall rating: ★ ★ ★ ★			
Classification: Internet Bank		**Readability:**	★ ★ ★ ★ ★
Updating:	n/a	**Reliability:**	n/a
Navigation:	★ ★ ★ ★	**Speed:**	★ ★ ★

UK R

The Virgin One account is a truly revolutionary product, which combines your current account and mortgage in a single package. Interest is only charged on your outstanding mortgage, minus the cash balance held in your account. Now it is available online.

You can view your net financial position at a glance, on the summary page and link easily to your Virgin deposit account, investments (ISA, PEP, unit trusts) and pension. A chart tracks the progress of your mortgage towards redemption date and a separate numerical entry calculates how far ahead or behind target you are.

The activity page allows you to inspect your last 30 days' transactions, and to search for older transactions. You can narrow down your search by filtering by direct debits, standing orders, or cheque size.

Despite the radical nature of the underlying banking concept, the online facility is on the conservative side. Virgin insists on setting up both your regular and one-off automated payments, though you can specify a date for the funds to leave your account or reach a destination account.

Your first consideration with this service is whether you are prepared to deposit your salary under the Virgin roof. If you are, you might as well have the whole bang shoot online.

www.barclays.co.uk
Barclays Online Banking

Overall rating: ★ ★ ★ ★			
Classification: Internet Bank		**Readability:**	★ ★ ★ ★
Updating:	n/a	**Reliability:**	n/a
Navigation:	★ ★ ★	**Speed:**	★ ★ ★

UK R

Barclays is the leading internet banking site by volume of subscribers. You can perform most routine banking functions online: which includes keeping an eye on all your Barclays accounts and shuffling your money between them; making direct payments to an individual or business with a UK bank account, by standing order or one-off transfer; viewing, amending or cancelling any standing order; and view ing your direct debits. Additionally, you can export your account data to Microsoft Money, or to a spreadsheet such as Excel; view your Barclaycard transactions; initiate share deals; and go shopping in Barclaysquare.

Linking to your Barclaycard requires another set of security codes and passwords, and can seem like an age. The onscreen display is rather pokey, and clicking on some of the buttons requires superior hand-eye co-ordination.

Barclays has no plans at present to launch a stand-alone, internet-only bank. It is wedded to creating an 'integrated financial portal' operation, that permits access to all services (banking, credit card, stockbroking, shopping, insurance) from a single site. It plans to have this in place by the year end.

The service does most things thoroughly but at a leisurely pace.

www.egg.com			
Egg			
Overall rating: ★ ★ ★ ☆			
Classification: Internet Bank		**Readability:**	★ ★ ★ ★ ★
Updating: n/a		**Reliability:**	n/a
Navigation: ★ ★ ★ ★		**Speed:**	★ ★ ★
(UK) (R)			

www.nationwide.co.uk			
Nationwide Building Society Online Banking			
Overall rating: ★ ★ ★ ☆			
Classification: Internet Bank		**Readability:**	★ ★ ★ ★
Updating: n/a		**Reliability:**	n/a
Navigation: ★ ★ ★ ★		**Speed:**	★ ★ ★ ☆
(UK) (R)			

Egg is the banking arm of the Prudential. It offers three savings accounts, mortgages and loans, and its own branded credit card, linked to an Egg Zone online shopping service with discounts available to Egg Card users.

The three Egg Savings Accounts on offer (in descending order of credit interest) are: internet access only; access by internet, telephone and mail; and full access with cash card.

You can view your last five savings account transactions online. Anything older is available by post. You can call up your current Egg credit-card statement and view the state of your loan account.

The glory of this site is the **Egg Shopping Zone** which embraces the spirit of the internet more completely than any other UK online banking operation, with the possible exception of Barclays Online. Customers who use the Egg Card in the Egg Shopping Zone get discounts of two per cent. A discount of one percent is available outside the zone.

Egg's main current competitor is first-e which currently shades it on the interest. However, Egg currently has the wider range of facilities, but it will have to watch out when first-e brings its current account and share dealing facilities online.

Nationwide provides a choice between a PC and an internet service. You need a lower computer specification for the former.

This is a flexible banking facility that works with your Nationwide FlexAccount (current account) and various card-based savings accounts (Smart Account, InvestDirect and Cashbuilder Card). You can view up to 90 days worth of transactions online and print off a mini-statement of the last 12 transactions. You can't view your credit card or your mortgage.

The system allows you to create automated payments by yourself and pay bills up to 30 days in advance. You can download account data to Microsoft Money.

Other facilities include online account application with 'intelligent' application forms and a quotation service for mortgages, credit cards and personal loans.

www.woolwich.co.uk
Woolwich Open Plan

Overall rating: ★ ★ ★ ☆			
Classification:	Internet Bank	**Readability:**	★ ★ ★ ★
Updating:	n/a	**Reliability:**	n/a
Navigation:	★ ★ ★ ★	**Speed:**	★ ★ ★ ☆

UK R

This internet banking site is a component of Woolwich Open Plan, an integrated banking and asset- management service.

Internet banking by PC enables you to view all your Woolwich accounts, from current and deposit accounts to unit trusts, mortgages and credit cards. You can transfer funds between your accounts and pay bills, instantly or on a prescheduled date.

There are several exciting developments pending. In April 2000, the Woolwich will launch interactive banking by WAP mobile phone, enabling all Open Plan customers to scrutinise account details, pay bills and transfer money over the internet, connected by a Wireless Application Protocol (WAP) mobile telephone.

An interactive digital TV banking facility is scheduled for the summer, which will provide virtually all of the functionality of internet banking by PC.

www.citibank.co.uk
Citibank Direct Access

Overall rating: ★ ★ ★			
Classification:	Internet Bank	**Readability:**	★ ★ ★ ☆
Updating:	n/a	**Reliability:**	n/a
Navigation:	★ ★ ★ ★	**Speed:**	★ ★ ★ ☆

UK R

Citibank Direct Access is somewhat limited in its functions. You can view your Citibank current and savings accounts online, but not your credit card or mortgage.

Inter-account transfers cannot be scheduled in advance. You can pay bills up to four months in advance, but you have to liaise with Citiphone Banking to set up a personalised payee list, which holds up to 99 names and their bank details, for one-off payments and standing orders.

You can download your accounts data to Microsoft Money, Quicken or to a spreadsheet.

UK Direct Access customers can transfer up to £10,000 per day to their Citibank accounts in France, Belgium, Germany Luxembourg and Greece, a handy facility for the habitual European traveller.

www.co-operativebank.co.uk
The Co-operative Bank Internet Banking

Overall rating: ★ ★ ★			
Classification: Internet Bank		**Readability:**	★ ★ ★
Updating: n/a		**Reliability:**	n/a
Navigation: ★ ★ ★ ★		**Speed:**	★ ★ ★ ★

UK R

This is a bread and butter online banking operation, which functions as a complementary service to conventional branch banking.

You can view your current account, Pathfinder (a flexible savings account), personal loans and Visa statements, all with the same set of codes and passwords. You can retrieve your last six bank statements and your last four credit-card statements.

The service is heavily dependent on armchair banking, which means that you have to contact the bank by telephone to set up new automated payments, such as standing orders and one-off third party transfers to other banks. However, once these have been set up, you don't need to call the bank to activate them in the future.

Armchair banking may once have been state-of-the-art, but it looks a little geriatric these days.

www.firstdirect.co.uk
First Direct PC Banking

Overall rating: ★ ★ ★			
Classification: PC Bank		**Readability:**	★ ★ ★ ★
Updating: n/a		**Reliability:**	n/a
Navigation: ★ ★ ★ ☆		**Speed:**	★ ★ ★ ★ ☆

UK R

First Direct is a division of HSBC and was the first telephone banking service to be launched in the UK. Direct Access is a PC banking service, designed to complement telephone banking. An internet service is pending.

Direct Access lets you view your current and deposit accounts, personal loan (Flexiloan) and First Direct Visa card account for the last four months. There is a nice touch to bill payments: you can specify a departure date for funds leaving your account or an arrival date in the destination account where allowance is made for clearance. You can't create, amend or cancel automated payments online.

On the other hand, you can open savings accounts online; apply for personal loans; request the First Direct Visa card and replacements; and download your data into Microsoft Money, Quicken and spreadsheets. You can also order foreign currency, travellers cheques and travel insurance or request a new PIN and paying-in books.

www.first-e.com
First-e

Overall rating: ★ ★ ★

Classification:	Internet Bank	**Readability:**	★ ★ ★ ★
Updating:	n/a	**Reliability:**	n/a
Navigation:	★ ★ ★ ☆	**Speed:**	★ ★ ★ ★ ☆

UK R

First-e is the first pan-European internet-only bank. It grabbed the headlines in November 1999 by offering 6.51% gross on its no-notice savings account, on balances of £1. First-e is a joint venture between Dublin-based ENBA Systems Ltd and Banque d'Escompte of Paris

The savings account is currently the only product ion offer from First-e, but an interest-bearing current account (now in pilot), a low-cost share dealing service and an independent mortgage and investment advice service are promised.

You can complete and submit your account application online, and will receive an email by return with a copy of your application and a declaration stating that you are not a resident of France or the Irish Republic (so that you can receive interest gross). You print off and sign the forms and return them by snail mail with proof of identity and residence.

The only route for making deposits is by e-transfer. Cash and cheques are not accepted at present but this may change when the current account comes online.
The first-e interest is paid without deduction of tax. UK taxpayers must remember to declare their first-e interest on their returns to the Inland Revenue.

First-e is regulated by Banque de France. Funds are covered by the French National Bank's Deposit Guarantee Fund up to 70,000 Euros (about £45,000).

Clients have to enter their usernames and passwords to access the system and enter a unique transaction number (TAN) when moving funds out of the account. TANs get sent out to you in batches of 30 by secure e-mail, and are used once only.

www.lloydstsb.co.uk		
Lloyds TSB Online		
Overall rating: ★ ★ ★		
Classification: Internet Bank	**Readability:**	★ ★ ★ ★
Updating: n/a	**Reliability:**	n/a
Navigation: ★ ★ ★ ★	**Speed:**	★ ★ ★ ★
(UK) (R)		

Another internet banking service with the heavy hand of the bank ever present. View your current, savings and investment accounts, but not your credit card or Lloyds-TSB mortgage.

Forget about setting up automated payments by yourself, and you have to enter your password every time you want to activate a bill payment, transfer or standing order.

Online account holders can get discounts on Dell computer hardware.

www.natwest.co.uk		
NatWest On-line		
Overall rating: ★ ★ ★		
Classification: Internet Bank	**Readability:**	★ ★ ★
Updating: n/a	**Reliability:**	n/a
Navigation: ★ ★ ★ ★	**Speed:**	★ ★ ★ ★
(UK) (R)		

NatWest On-line has finally made the transition from PC to internet service, and has dropped the anachronistic £30 charge. However, nothing much else seems to have changed, and it is the same old NatWest under a new lick of paint.

You can view your current and savings account, cash ISA and credit card, but you can't set up your own automated payments without the bank's guiding hand. What's more, this is one of the few services other that does not permit you to amend or cancel standing orders.

On the credit side, you can download your data into a variety of personal financial management packages: Microsoft Money, Quicken, Sage and spreadsheets.

With a bit of luck, Royal Bank of Scotland will bring this lot up to speed.

www.alliance-leicester.co.uk
Alliance & Leicester Internet Banking

Overall rating: ★ ★ ☆

Classification:	Internet Bank	**Readability:**	★★★★
Updating:	n/a	**Reliability:**	n/a
Navigation:	★★★★	**Speed:**	★★★

(UK) (R)

www.bankofscotland.co.uk
Bank of Scotland Home and Office Banking (HOBS)

Overall rating: ★ ★ ☆

Classification:	PC/Online Bank	**Readability:**	★★★☆
Updating:	n/a	**Reliability:**	n/a
Navigation:	★★★☆	**Speed:**	★★★☆

(UK) (R)

This service was launched in January 2000 as an internet channel for the Alliance and Leicester's two million existing account holders.

You can view your current and savings accounts but not your mortgage or credit card transactions. All bill payments and transfers have to be 'mandated' by customer services, and you cannot amend or cancel standing orders online.

The site is quite attractive, with dedicated bill-payment icons for regular bills such as gas, electricity, telephone and water, but the site demo is most uninformative.

However, all this is clearly the opening skirmish in a grander campaign. The Alliance and Leicester has announced that it will be launching a stand-alone internet bank later in the year, under separate management and with its own independent product range.

HOBS is the oldest online banking service, having started out in 1985 by beaming account data down the telephone line to a screenphone.

Now HOBS is in transition. The old PC service is making way for a spanking-new internet operation. The PC service will not be abolished outright, but will probably be allowed to wither on the vine.

The internet service is a bit betwixt and between at present and not all the planned facilities are in place. There is currently no functionality at all for automated payments, but you will be allowed to set up your own third-party transfers from March.

BOS is also running a Wireless Application Protocol (WAP) mobile phone pilot, just like the Woolwich but without the razzmatazz. It looks like it means business.

One word of advice: don't even contemplate downloading the site demo. Life is much too short!

www.nbps.co.uk		
Norwich & Peterborough NetMaster		
Overall rating: ★ ★ ★		
Classification: Internet Bank	**Readability:**	★★★★
Updating: n/a	**Reliability:**	n/a
Navigation: ★★★★	**Speed:**	★★★★
UK R		

www.halifax-online.co.uk		
Halifax Online		
Overall rating: ★ ★		
Classification: Internet Bank	**Readability:**	★★★★
Updating: n/a	**Reliability:**	n/a
Navigation: ★★★★★	**Speed:**	★★★★
UK R		

A limited service enabling you to view and administer your Norwich and Peterborough current and savings accounts, but not your mortgage.

The system is very easy to get around and there is a very clear demo to play with before you sign on.

You have to ask the National and Peterborough to set up your standing orders and bill payments, and inter-account transfers can't be pre-scheduled.

Another narrowly based service for managing your Halifax current account only. You can't view or manage your other Halifax accounts (mortgage, credit card or savings).

The system is in its infancy, and not all the facilities are in place. Transferring money to your other Halifax accounts is pretty laborious. You have to get the back office staff to set up the facility for you, just as you do when transferring to a third party.

Predictably, you can't set up automated payments by yourself, and you can't schedule bill payments or funds transfers in advance.

The Halifax will be launching a stand-alone online bank later this year, called Intelligent Financial or IF. It promises a banking revolution. We shall see...

www.banking.hsbc.co.uk
HSBC PC Banking

Overall rating: ★ ★ ★			
Classification: PC Bank		**Readability:**	★ ★ ★
Updating:	n/a	**Reliability:**	n/a
Navigation:	★ ★ ★	**Speed:**	★ ★ ★

UK R

This is currently a PC banking service, which means that you can only operate it using a computer loaded with dedicated HSBC software.

The service is somewhat limited at present, with no facility for automated payments. This means that you cannot create, view, amend or cancel standing orders or direct debit mandates online.

Word is that the service will be brought up to speed when it converts to an internet banking operation in the late summer.

HSBC hit the headlines last year with the launch of a digital TV banking service, which allows you to call up your account data and perform basic banking functions from the comfort of your sofa. This should not be confused with PC or internet banking, which is performed from the discomfort of your personal computer.

	Alliance & Leicester Internet Banking	Bank of Scotland (HOBS)	Barclays Online Banking	Citibank Direct Access
URL	www.alliance-leicester.co.uk	www.bankofscotland.co.uk	www.barclays.co.uk	www.citibank. co.uk
Type Of Service	Internet	PC+ Internet	Internet	Internet
Accounts to view	current	current, deposit/savings loan, currency accounts, mortgage, Visa, Mastercard, affinity cards	current, deposit/savings	current, deposit/savings
View/print statements	last 46 days	PC last 3 months Internet: last 6 weeks	last 6 weeks	Up to 6 months
View credit cards	No	PC last 3 months Internet: last 6 weeks	last 6 months	No
Inter-account transfers	Up to 364 days in advance	Up to 30 days in advance	Up to 2 years in advance	Yes, but not in advance
Set up third party payments	offline	PC: No Internet: pending	online	offline
Pay bills	Up to 364 days in advance	Up to 30 days in advance	Up to 2 years in advance	Yes, unlimited in advance
Standing Orders	view	PC: view Internet: No	create/view/ amend/ cancel	view/amend/ cancel
Direct Debits	view	PC: view Internet: No	view/cancel	view
Download to personal financial management software	mini-statement to a spreadsheet	PC: MS Money and Quicken Internet: pending	MS Money, Sage Excel	MS Money, Quicken, Spreadsheets
Banking hours	24 hours	6 a.m. to 1 a.m.	24 hours	24 hours

The Co-operative Bank Internet Banking	Egg	First Direct PC Banking	first-e	Halifax Online
o-operativebank.co.uk	www.egg.com	www.firstdirect.co.uk	www.first-e.com	www.halifax-online.co.uk
Internet	Internet	PC Internet Pending	Internet	Internet
current, savings, loan, Visa card	savings accounts, mortgage, credit card	current deposit/savings Flexiloan Visa card	"Savings only. Current, mortgage and sharedealing accounts due in 2nd quarter"	current
last 6 statements	mimi-statement: last 5 transactions	100 working days	full account history	last 60 entries
last 4 statements	last 3 statements	100 working days	n/a	No
Yes, but not in advance	Yes, but not in advance	Up to 12 months in advance	"Yes, no time limit"	As bill payment only; not in advance
offline	online to own nominated account only	offline	online	offline
Yes, but not in advance	n/a	Up 12 months in advance	up to 5 years in advance	Not in advance
view/amend/ cancel	n/a	view	n/a	view/cancel
view/cancel	n/a	view	n/a	view/cancel
No	No	MS Money, Quicken, Spreadsheets	No	No
24 hours	24 hours	24 hours	24 hours	24 hours

	HSBC	Lloyds TSB Online	Nationwide	NatWest Online Banking
URL	www.banking.hsbc.co.uk	www.lloydstsb. co.uk	www.nationwide.co.uk	www.natwest. co.uk
Type Of Service	PC Internet pending	Internet	Internet (or PC)	Internet
Accounts to view	current, deposit/savings	current, deposit/savings	current and cardbased savings accounts	current deposit/ savings loans
View/print statements	last 65 days entries	current plus last statement	last 90 days entries.	Print off last 12 entries
View credit cards	last 2 months bills + subsequent transaction (max 90)	No	No	last 50 entries
Inter-account transfers	Up to 45 days in advance	Yes but not in advance	Up to 30 days in advance	Up to 40 days in advance
Set up third party payments	online	offline	online	online
Pay bills	Up to 45 days in advance	Up to 12 months in advance	Up to 30 days in advance (Max £5,000)	Up to 40 working days in advance
Standing Orders	n/a	view/amend/ cancel	create/view/ amend/cancel	view
Direct Debits	n/a	view	view/cancel	view
Download to personal financial management software	OFX and ASCII compatible formats only	MS Money Quicken	MS Money	MS Money Quicken Sage spreadsheets
Banking hours	24 hours except Sundays (00:00 - 08:00)	04:00 to 00:00	24 hours	24 hours

Norwich & Peterborough	Royal Bank of Scotland Direct Banking by PC	smile	Virgin One	Woolwich Open Plan
www.npbs.co.uk	www.rbs.co.uk	www.smile. co.uk	www.virginone .com	www.thewoolwich .co.uk
Internet	Internet	Internet	Internet	WAP mobile telephone (pending)
current, deposit/savings	current deposit/savings TESSAs ISAs	current, no-notice savings, credit cards, personal loans, mimi-cash ISAs	Virgin One current account and mortgage, deposit account, PEPs/ISAs, unit trusts, pensions	current, savings, personal loans mortgage, unit trusts, credit card
last 40 entries	last 6 months	last 6 months	last 12 months	last 30 days, Search faciility for older transactions
No	No	last 12 months	full account history	Balance currently Transactions pending (summer)
Yes, but not in advance	Up to 120 days in advance	Not in advance	Up to120 days in advance	Not in advance
offline	online	online	offline	online
Up to 3 years in advance	Up to 120 days in advance	Not in advance	Up to 120 days in advance	Up to 6 weeks in advance
view/amend/cancel	create/view/ amend/cancel	create/view/ amend/cancel	view/amend/ cancel	view/ amend
view/cancel	view/ cancel	view/ cancel	view/ cancel	view
No	MS Money Quicken	No	MS Money and Quicken both pending	MS Money for Internet service only
24 hours	24 hours	24 hours	24 hours	24 hours

Chapter 6

Online Share Dealing

'A broker is a man who takes your fortune and runs it into a shoestring.'

Alexander Woollcott

Online Share Dealing

Financial Services is expected to become the most popular online sector by the end of 2003, with online share dealing forecast to be the largest activity by value of transactions. A glimpse of the potential level of interest occurred over the turn of the millennium, when speculative frenzy seriously overloaded the dealing systems.

Internet share dealing is evolving rapidly. There are currently two basic types of service:

Order routing where your instructions are effectively emailed to a stockbroker who executes the trade.

Straight-Through-Processing (STP) where you deal directly with the market and execute the trade yourself in real-time, using the website of the stockbroker hosting the service.

Most of the services reviewed in this chapter are either STP systems or are in the process of upgrading to STP. Services also differ in respect of the quantity and quality of market information that they carry on site. The most lavish (Stocktrade, DLJ Direct, E*Trade, TD Waterhouse) claim to display the same quality of information enjoyed by city dealers.

THE LIMITATIONS

How much of this is pure hype? There is no guarantee that you will get better prices by trading directly with the market than by sending your order to a stockbroker or using an advisory service. A recent academic study from America suggests that online traders do worse than offline traders, despite the cost advantages of the former.

You may well find that the range of tradable securities is more limited with an STP service. With most online services you can only trade in the securities on their dealing lists, which may exclude gilts, corporate bonds and managed funds. However, a classic order router such as Caves-on-the-Net will deal in anything for which it can find a City market maker (at online commission rates, of course).

Whether you need half the market information that some sites display is also open to question, although if you are a serious investor you may appreciate having all the news and data centralised in a single location rather than having to gather it from a range of sites.

The attraction of online dealing is the low cost, but the price means the services are execution-only. In plain language, you can't get advice from the broker.

PRACTICAL ONLINE TRADING

Setting up You register with an online brokerage, a procedure normally initiated on the web but ultimately requiring the return of paper by snail mail. You are issued with a password and PIN by return. Digital signatures will eventually bring the whole process online once the E-Commerce Bill is passed.

Normally you have to deposit money in the broker's cash management account before you can start trading. Money-laundering safeguards can hold things up, but in practice the process usually takes just a few days. DLJ Direct is exceptional in allowing you to trade on receipt of your uncleared cheque. Barclays, NatWest and Halifax will allow you to use accounts at other institutions, with settlement by direct debit or credit.

Dealing You can usually buy to the limit of the credit balance on your cash-management account. Disposals are credited to the account. TD Waterhouse will allow you to trade against 25 per cent of the value of the transaction held in cash or shares. Killik & Co allows you to trade on margin against the security of eligible assets in their custody (minimum £20,000), at 2 to 3.5 per cent per annum over Bank of Scotland base.

The trading process is very much the same on each site. You first tell the program whether you are buying or selling a quantity of shares in a given company (for example, 100 shares in DotCom Inc), or investing or realising/raising a specific monetary consideration (for example £1,000 of DotCom Inc).

If you are trading directly on the market, you call up a stock-price quote by entering the EPIC symbol. If you don't know the EPIC symbol, you can look it up by entering the first few letters of the company name and picking it out on the drop-down list of available stocks. The system generates a real-time quote, which is held for a short time, usually about 15 or 20 seconds. You accept the quote by placing the deal. Otherwise it lapses. You should receive almost immediate confirmation of your order by email and can trace its progress on the Order Status page on the site.

Orders are normally executed at best unless you specify price limits (limit orders). Limit orders are helpful if you have better things to do with your time than hang about on the internet in the hope that market prices will stray inside your parameters. They are also useful if you are placing orders outside normal trading hours. Limit orders are usually held until the close of trading.

Some STP services do not support limit trading (for example DJL Direct, E*Trade) since clients can effectively impose their own limits by declining to deal at the quoted price.

Charges The main charge is dealing commission which is usually calculated as a percentage of the value of the trade, with specified minima and maxima. Some brokers charge a flat dealing fee.

For some services there is an annual registration charge, to cover the cost of sponsored CREST membership, or in exchange for lower dealing rates for frequent traders. Finally, you pay stamp duty at 0.5 per cent on your deals, and a Panel on Takeovers and Mergers (PTM) levy of 25 pence for trades over £10,000.

Custody of your shares Your shares are usually held electronically and registered in the broker's nominee account, although you retain beneficial ownership. There are no share certificates to delay settlement which occurs in five working days following a transaction (T+5) if conducted through CREST (the electronic settlement system), and in T+10 days for certificated securities. Barclays is an exception where all deals are certificated.

NatWest Stockbrokers, James Brearley and Sons, Goy Harris Cartwright, Stocktrade and Xest offer sponsored membership of CREST. Your shares are registered in your name, but still held electronically. You receive dividend vouchers, company accounts and other tokens of shareholder rights.

There is generally no charge for transferring securities into a nominee account (with the exception of Redmayne-Bentley). However, transferring out can cost you £10 or more per holding.

When you sell your shares, you can usually trade immediately with the proceeds, prior to formal settlement.

The Big Hitters

The following sites represent the main online share dealing players in the UK at the time of writing. A major emerging trend is the development of Pan-European exchanges, which will permit online dealing across national borders on a common trading platform. The effect of this will be to widen the range of shares that can usually be traded online, and reduce the cost of online share dealing.

The most recent of these exchanges, Jiway (whose name derives from the Chinese word for wisdom), will be based in London. Jiway is expected to be operational by September 2000.

NASDAQ and Tradepoint will be launching their own European exchanges, and eight other 'traditional' European bourses are planning to establish a common trading platform by November 2001, although the Jiway initiative is expected to force the pace.

www.dljdirect.co.uk
DLJ Direct

Overall rating: ★ ★ ★ ★ ★			
Classification:	STP	Readability:	★ ★ ★ ★
Updating:	Frequently	Reliability:	n/a
Navigation:	★ ★ ★ ☆	Speed:	★ ★ ★ ★ ★

UK £

DLJDirect is the UK online dealing service of Donaldson, Lufkin and Jenrette of Wall Street. The site was runner up to FT.com as Find's (www.find.co.uk) financial services website of 1999.

The site provides a dealing platform (STP) for real-time, execution-only equity trading on the London Stock Exchange (LSE) and American exchanges. A feature of this site is the number of highly interactive pages including:

UK Company Digest for real-time quotes, fundamentals and broker forecasts, news and interactive charts that allow you to plot up to four share prices/indices on a single chart at a variety of time intervals; from five minute intra-day through to ten year monthly.

Model Portfolios for monitoring up to 20 portfolios of 20 holdings each at previous day's closing prices.

Customised Personal Stock Ticker, which runs continuously along the bottom of your screen, giving you price updates of your chosen shares at 15 minute intervals irrespective of whether you are logged on to DLJ or not. The ticker symbol also acts as a navigation tool, providing quick access to real-time prices, charts, and news and reports.

Trading instructions are given in terms of a volume of shares only (not monetary consideration). Real-time quotes are held for 30 seconds. Dealing is at best only, but you can preview your order to inspect the monetary outlay including the itemised charges.

You may place market orders outside trading hours to be executed at best on the next trading day. However, the system does not currently support limit orders, although this facility is due to be in place by spring 2000.

Trading commission is 0.75 per cent with a minimum of £14.95 and a maximum of £37.50. Your first month's trading is free.

Client funds are held on deposit at 1 per cent below the Bank of Scotland base rate. There is no minimum deposit or balance required. Settlement is formally T+5 days, but the proceeds of sales are immediately available for further trading.

www.etrade.co.uk
E*Trade UK

Overall rating: ★ ★ ★ ★ ★			
Classification:	STP	**Readability:**	★ ★ ★ ★
Updating:	Frequently	**Reliability:**	n/a
Navigation:	★ ★ ★ ☆	**Speed:**	★ ★ ★ ☆

UK £ R

E*Trade UK was founded in 1998 as a joint venture between US online investment services provider E*Trade Group Inc and Electronic Share Information (ESI) Ltd, a British provider of internet financial services. In January 2000, E*Trade Group Inc acquired the remaining shares of E*Trade UK.

To quote the company: 'E*Trade UK vision is to empower self-directed investors to make informed decisions with anytime, anywhere access to the world's major investment markets, with comprehensive information, research, investment tools and customer services, and with revolutionary flat rate charges.'

There are three levels of E*Trade UK membership:

Free Membership, which entitles you to 15-minute delayed LSE price quotes, news headlines, company fundamentals and a personal stockwatch list. Registration entails establishing a user ID and a password.

Research Membership costs £5 plus VAT per month and entitles you to a wider range of news services (AFX, RNS, News Archive), company information (profiles, key fundamentals, financials) and market information (such as 15-minute delayed prices, charting, stockwatch and indices).

Research Plus Membership costs £14.95 plus VAT per month and gives you all the facilities of Research plus real-time market prices and news. In addition you can access premium services such as Price Histories, Hemmington Scott Company REFS and BARRA's Estimates Directory on a pay-per-view basis.

Trading Membership costs £25 per half year and gives you real-time, execution- only dealing in UK shares and includes free membership of Research (worth £60 per annum plus VAT). You can upgrade this to Research Plus for a further £9.95 plus VAT per month.

The minimum initial trading deposit is £1,000, which you can pay by cheque, direct debit or stock transfer with your account application. Thereafter, funds are transferred into your trading account by a direct-debiting mandate linked to a nominated bank account, which you activate from within the E*Trade site. Interest on your trading account rises directly with the size of your balance, based on The Royal Bank of Scotland Corporate Money Market Rate.

E*Trade has a distinctive tariff of dealing charges which rewards the frequent trader. Trades of £1,500 or less cost £14.95 to execute. Trades over £1,500 depend on the number of deals you have executed in the past. Once you have executed 25 trades the cost goes down to £14.95 each.

Formal settlement is in T+5 days, but in practice you can trade immediately with the proceeds of a sale.

www.stocktrade.co.uk
Stocktrade

Overall rating: ★ ★ ★ ★ ★			
Classification:	STP	Readability:	★ ★ ★ ★
Updating:	Frequently	Reliability:	n/a
Navigation:	★ ★ ★ ☆	Speed:	★ ★ ★ ☆

UK £

Stocktrade is the online execution-only dealing service of Brewin Dolphin Securities and claims to be the first 'truly live' retail internet dealing system in the UK.

Stocktrade is a Straight Through Processing (STP) system enabling 'live dealing in a live environment'. The system permits free access to market prices, dealing at real-time quotes, real-time portfolio valuation and near-instantaneous settlement.

The trading page requires you to call up a real-time quote, which is held for 15 seconds. You can trade by volume of shares or by monetary consideration. Although the system does not formally allow limit trading, you can apply your own price limit by declining to deal at the quoted real-time price.

The glory of this site is the Knowledge Centre, which links up to Interactive Investor International (see p.20) to provide you with:

Interactive graphical analysis of company share prices, including comparison with other shares in the same sector and the FTSE indices.

Company news stories

Key financial data (major shareholders, income statements, assets, liabilities, cash flow, key ratios).

The **Knowledge Centre** is free of charge to investors who execute at least four trades in every two month period.

Client funds are placed on deposit at one per cent per annum below Bank of Scotland base rate, paid quarterly. Although there is no minimum initial deposit or running balance, you can't buy without sufficient funds in your deposit account. Your shares are held in your name in a sponsored Crest account, for which you pay £10 per annum. Settlement is formally T+1, but in practice you can trade immediately with sale proceeds.

There are two levels of dealing charges. Regular Traders deal at 0.4 per cent (£14.50 minimum) and Star Traders at 0.2 per cent (£14.50 minimum). You become a Star Trader when you have executed 50 deals.

www.tdwaterhouse.co.uk
TD Waterhouse

Overall rating: ★ ★ ★ ★			
Classification: STP		**Readability:**	★ ★ ★
Updating:	Frequently	**Reliability:**	n/a
Navigation:	★ ★ ★	**Speed:**	★ ★ ★

UK £ R

TD Waterhouse is the online share-dealing arm of TD Waterhouse Investor Services (Europe), a subsidiary of the TD Waterhouse Group Inc which operates the third largest online discount brokerage service in the world.

This site supports STP execution-only dealing in most securities listed on the London Stock Exchange. There are three levels of access to this site:

Public User, which permits access to the home page and the site demo.

Registered Members, which provides price quotes and news delayed by at least 20 minutes, a stockwatch portfolio facility and stock alerts.

Customer, which supports real-time dealing and price quotes, portfolio viewing at previous day's closing prices plus all the benefits of registered membership.

You need to open a TD Waterhouse Cash Management account and a nominee account for custody of your securities. Deposit interest is paid at two per cent per annum below the NatWest base rate. You can transfer existing securities into your nominee account without charge. You need to hold a minimum cash balance or fully paid-for securities of at least 25 per cent of the value of any trade in order to be able to place a purchase order.

Real-time stock quotes are held for 15 seconds. If you fail to verify your order, the system will automatically generate up to two more 15-second real-time quotes. Thereafter you have to re-enter the trade details from scratch.

Standard dealing commission is 1 per cent up to £1,999 (minimum £12.95) and £19.99 plus 0.02 per cent thereafter. For frequent traders there is a flat commission of £14.95 for deals up to £100,000, and £14.95 plus 0.05 per cent thereafter. A minimum of 15 trades per annum is required and a charge of £65 may be levied for fewer trades.

Settlement is T+5 days for CREST-eligible securities, and T+10 otherwise. In practice, you can use the proceeds of a sale as immediate collateral for further trades.

A feature of this site is the rich **The Markets** section which displays a wealth of market information including charts and overviews of selected companies; a portfolio (real or fantasy) window that you can launch from within other pages on the site; and the performance of the constituents of the FTSE 100 and 250 at market close.

www.schwab-worldwide.com/Europe
Charles Schwab Europe

Overall rating: ★ ★ ★ ★			
Classification: STP		**Readability:**	★ ★ ★
Updating:	Frequently	**Reliability:**	n/a
Navigation:	★ ★ ★ ☆	**Speed:**	★ ★ ★ ☆

UK £

Charles Schwab Europe is a subsidiary of the Charles Schwab Corporation and provides real-time (STP) execution-only equity dealing facilities on the London Stock Exchange, AIM and American exchanges.

There are two main levels of service:

MarketMaster is for the occasional trader. It provides online trading at real-time prices and 'simplified' portfolio management (at the previous day's closing prices). You pay 0.9 per cent for a deal up to £2,500, 0.75 per cent for the next £2,500 and 0.1 per cent over £5,000 (minimum £15; maximum £75), plus administration charges.

Frequent Traders Club is a similar service except that you pay an annual subscription of £60 and execute trades of any size at a flat £19.50 a time.

Investment Clubs can deal for a minimum of £12 and a maximum of £26 per trade.

You can set up a Stocks and Shares ISA online, and transfer all your PEPs into a Charles Schwab self-select PEP. A separate scale of administration charges applies.

Deals are specified by share volume or monetary consideration, at best or at limit.

All clients get Reuters Investor Service for free, providing 20-

minute delayed share prices for UK shares and news. For an extra £10 per month you can subscribe to Reuters Premium Service which gives you more in-depth news, international stock coverage, currency rates, international interest rates, charting, and up to eight portfolio trackers holding ten stocks each.

Cash deposits for trading are held in an interest-bearing deposit account paying between 0.5 and 4.25 per cent per annum. Your assets are held in a nominee account. Settlement is formally T+5, but you can usually deal immediately with sales proceeds.

Your first thirty days of trading are commission-free.

www.caves.co.uk
Caves-on-the-Net

Overall rating: ★ ★ ★			
Classification:	STP	Readability:	★ ★ ★ ★ ★
Updating:	Frequently	Reliability:	★ ★ ★ ★ ★
Navigation:	★ ★ ★ ★ ★	Speed:	★ ★ ★ ★ ★

UK £

This site belongs to independent stockbrokers Cave and Sons Ltd, established 1906. It is a classic example of an order-routing service, being little more than a traditional stockbroker operating by email.

Lest you snigger, it should be said that you can trade online in a much wider range of securities (at online dealing commission rates) than many of the state-of-the-art services: domestic and foreign equities, gilts, corporate bonds, unit trusts, ISAs – in fact in anything where Caves can find a London market maker.

You sign the terms of business and send off your cheque to be deposited in your Cave dealing account at the Bank of Scotland. You can trade at best (by share volume or monetary consideration) or at limit. Your shares are held in a Cave nominee account and non-certificated securities are settled in T+5 days. You are not trading in real time, but do you care? If you must have market information you can use the links to Bloomberg, Pointcast and Reuters for news on UK stocks, and BBC and Market Eye for UK share prices.

Dealing commission is £5 plus 1 per cent up to a maximum of £35. ISAs cost a bit more to deal in and (together with PEPs) attract annual administration fees of 0.5 per cent per annum (minimum £15), but Caves will rebate up to one third of unit trust commission received.

www.halifax.co.uk/sharedeal
Halifax ShareXpress

Overall rating: ★ ★ ★ ★			
Classification: STP		**Readability:**	★ ★ ★ ☆
Updating:	Frequently	**Reliability:**	n/a
Navigation:	★ ★ ★ ☆	**Speed:**	★ ★ ★ ☆

UK £ R

Halifax ShareXpress is the online and telephone execution-only share-dealing service of the Halifax Group plc. The online service is an STP system enabling dealing in UK registered companies quoted on the London Stock Exchange and AIM, which are settled with CREST.

The information sections of the site display 15-minute delayed market prices, company information, stock market news and world indices. Account holders enjoy real-time trading with real-time price quotes, and can view their portfolios and account information online.

Registered users can place immediate, delayed, and limit orders. Immediate orders are executed during market hours. Delayed orders are placed outside market hours and are executed as soon as possible during the course of the next working day.

You can issue instructions to trade for a specific value of shares (invest and raise) or for a specific volume of shares (buy and sell). Limit orders specify a maximum buying price or a minimum selling price. The trade is executed when the actual price falls within the client's limit.

You nominate an account with an approved UK bank for trading, which need not necessarily be the Halifax. Payment for share purchases is made by automated payment (direct debit mandate, debit card or BACS). The proceeds of share sales are deposited to this account. The settlement basis is T+5 days.

All your share purchases are held electronically in the name of HSDL Nominees Limited. There is no charge for the use of the nominee service even if you transfer in shares and other securities not acquired through the Halifax service.

Online dealing commission rates are: £12.50 for deals up to £2,500, £22.50 for deals between £2,501 and £60,000, and £50 for deals above £60,000.

For shares that are sheltered in an ISA there is a quarterly administration fee of 0.125 per cent (minimum £6.50; maximum £25).

www.natweststockbrokers.co.uk

BrokerLine Internet

Overall rating: ★ ★ ★ ★

Classification:	Order Routing	**Readability:**	★ ★ ★ ☆
Updating:	frequently	**Reliability:**	n/a
Navigation:	★ ★ ★ ☆	**Speed:**	★ ★ ★ ☆

UK £

BrokerLine Internet is the telephone and internet dealing service of NatWest Stockbrokers. It enables you to:

Trade in UK listed shares and gilts on the internet.

View prices of UK securities, displayed 15 minutes in arrears.

Call up share-price histories of specific UK companies, including charts, and access company news and information.

BrokerLine Internet is essentially an order routing system. Your trading instructions are transmitted to NatWest Stockbrokers who execute the trade. The costs of dealing in UK shares are the same by internet and telephone. Securities that cannot be traded online may be tradable through the telephone service, for example international equities, Eurobonds and unit trusts.

Trades are expressed in terms of share volume or monetary consideration. You can specify whether a consideration includes or excludes dealing charges and levies. Limit orders are held until close of business. Deals submitted after trading hours are processed the following day.

Share dealing commission is 1 per cent for the first £4,000 (minimum £15) and 0.1 per cent thereafter. There is a separate scale of dealing charges for gilts.

You can choose between using the NatWest nominee service or the sponsored CREST membership for custody of your securities. In both cases, settlement is T+5 days. Deals in certificated securities are settled in T+10 days. Settlement is by direct debit or credit from or to a bank account of your choice.

www.barclays-stockbrokers.co.uk
Barclays Internet Dealing

Overall rating: ★ ★ ★ ☆			
Classification: STP		**Readability:**	★ ★ ★ ☆
Updating: Frequently		**Reliability:**	n/a
Navigation: ★ ★ ★ ☆		**Speed:**	★ ★ ★ ☆
UK £			

This is Barclays Stockbrokers' online execution-only (STP) service for trading in LSE-listed shares. Other securities, such as gilts and warrants, are tradable through a telephone dealing service at a different scale of commission.

Barclays Internet Dealing gives you real-time share quotes and dealing with a Price Improver, which claims to guarantee you 'the optimum price for buying and selling your shares'.

You are not required to make any specific deposits with Barclays to fund your purchases. Instead you set up a direct debit mandate at your own bank or building society, and the costs of your purchase are debited ten business days from the date of the transaction. You are given an initial trading limit of £7,500, which is increased once a credit reference is received from your bank or building society. The maximum deal size is £20,000.

There is no nominee service for keeping custody of your shares. All share holdings are certificated and forwarded to you within two to three weeks. Settlement is T+10 days.

You can buy or sell by volume of shares or by monetary consideration. Real-time price quotes are held for 15 seconds. Meanwhile, the Price Improver links up with other market makers to identify the most competitive price on the market, which is the price at which the deal is struck.

Deals are confirmed immediately online.

There is no online facility for limit price orders, although you can place them by telephone (minimum £3,000), at the telephone service commission rate.

The commission rate for internet dealing is 1 per cent, with a minimum charge of £11.99 and a maximum of £39.99.

An enhanced version of the service will be online by April 2000.

www.e-cortal.com
E-Cortal

Overall rating: ★ ★ ★ ☆			
Classification:	STP	Readability:	★ ★ ★
Updating:	Frequently	Reliability:	n/a
Navigation:	★ ★ ★	Speed:	★ ★ ★

FR £ R

E-Cortal is the online trading service of Cortal Bank, a subsidiary of Paribas. The share dealing facility is known as the World Stocks Shop, a (partial) STP service providing market price quotes and online share trading in the constituents of 15 indices on 9 major European and North American stock markets, namely:

Frankfurt (Dax, MidDax), Madrid (Ibex and Spain Ma), Amsterdam (AEX 25, All Shares Index), Milan (MIB 30, Milan Telematico), London (FTSE 350), Zurich (SMI, SPI), Paris (all listed securities), NYSE (S&P SuperComposite 1500), and NASDAQ (S&P SuperComposite 1500).

Real-time price quotes are available for French shares and are pending for the NYSE and NASDAQ. All other quotes are currently delayed by about 15 minutes. You can deal at best (market-price orders) or at limit.

Although the E-Cortal operation is based in Paris, the UK investor can use the service with comparative ease. Registration entails filling in an online questionnaire. Thereafter you download, print off, and sign a personalised application form and return it together with proof of identity (preferably a copy of your passport) to a London postal address.

You will need to set up a cash trading account. There is no minimum deposit but the funds must be sufficient to cover any trades. The cash trading account is denominated in euros, but you can write a sterling cheque and it will be converted without currency commission.

A monthly subscription fee of six euros is debited to your cash trading account. There are separate scales of dealing charges for market-priced orders and limit orders conducted over the internet. You can also deal by freephone, fax or snail mail.

A £5,000 market-price trade ('at best') will cost you about 30 euros (£18.50) including tax. A £5,000 limit-price deal will set you back 65 euros (about £40) including tax. Settlement is immediate and sales proceeds are credited to your trading account.

The E-Cortal website is rather slow at present, and key sections (including the site demo) are still under construction.

www.fastrade.co.uk
FasTrade

Overall rating: ★ ★ ★ ☆			
Classification: Order Routing		**Readability:**	★ ★ ★ ☆
Updating: Frequently		**Reliability:**	n/a
Navigation: ★ ★ ★ ☆		**Speed:**	★ ★ ★ ☆

UK £

FasTrade is the execution-only online dealing service for Torrie & Co of Edinburgh. Investors can use this site to deal in domestic equities (including share ISAs), and to display them alongside foreign equities, UK government stock, corporate bonds and (non-share) ISAs and PEPs held by Torrie Nominees on their behalf. FasTrade is currently an order routing system, but is in the process of being upgraded to STP.

You are required to open a FasTrade Deposit Bank Account and may only buy to the limit of cleared funds held in this account. Any dividends generated will be held in an interest-bearing FasTrade Deposit Income Account and transferred to your FasTrade Deposit Bank Account half-yearly. Interest is paid at a variable margin below the Bank of Scotland base rate.

FasTrade will only sell securities held in your FasTrade Stock Account. You can transfer existing stock and funds into your stock account. The necessary CREST Transfer form (for equities) and Stock Transfer forms (for unit trusts and Treasury stock) can be downloaded and printed. The assets in your stock account are registered in the name of Torrie Nominees for efficient administration and settlement.

The FasTrade Stock Account is free for portfolios up to £100,000 and costs 0.01 per cent per quarter thereafter. The nominee service for UK securities is free for portfolios under £100,000.

There are currently no direct live share-price quotes to be found on this site. Instead, there are links to The Motley Fool, Moneyworld and Market-Eye websites for 20-minute delayed prices. Real-time prices are expected to be on site by March 2000.

You can express your trade in terms of a volume of shares or by monetary consideration, at best or at limit.

Formal settlement is in T+5 days. In practice settlement is virtually instantaneous because you can't buy without having the funds in your deposit account and you can reinvest sales proceeds immediately.

Charges are fairly modest. There is no joining fee and a trade in domestic shares costs 0.5 per cent, with a minimum charge of £15 and a maximum of £30 for trades under £40,000. Deals in excess of £40,000 cost £30 plus 0.1 per cent.

www.ghcl.co.uk
GHCtrader

Overall rating: ★ ★ ★ ☆			
Classification: Order Routing		**Readability:**	★ ★ ★ ☆
Updating: Frequently		**Reliability:**	n/a
Navigation: ★ ★ ★ ☆		**Speed:**	★ ★ ★ ☆

UK £ R

GHCtrader is the execution-only, online dealing service of stockbroking and investment house Goy Harris Cartwright and Co Ltd. At present you can only trade in fully listed LSE and AIM stocks and gilts, though further services are planned.

GHCtrader is currently an order routing system, but will evolve to an STP system by summer 2000. Registration currently takes place entirely offline, but plans are afoot to put the application forms on site for online registration, and eventually to accept digital signatures.

You can buy and sell by share volume or monetary consideration. Limit orders are held for a day. Client funds are held on deposit at Lloyds TSB and interest is paid quarterly. Funds for purchases must be available on deposit when the deal is placed. Sales are credited on the day of settlement.

All CREST-eligible securities are held in a sponsored account. Residual shares are held in GHC custody also in the name of the holder.

Settlement is T+5 for non-certificated holdings. Residual shares are settled in T+10 days. The annual fee of £35.25 includes sponsored Crest membership. Dealing commission is a flat £20.

www.killik.co.uk
Killik & Co Online Dealing

Overall rating: ★ ★ ★ ☆			
Classification: Order Routing		**Readability:**	★ ★ ★ ☆
Updating: Frequently		**Reliability:**	n/a
Navigation: ★ ★ ★ ☆		**Speed:**	★ ★ ★ ☆

UK £ R

Killik & Co Online Dealing is the share dealing service of stockbrokers Killik & Co. The service is complementary to Killik's advisory dealing facilities, but permits dealing in LSE shares only.

The service is execution-only, but clients are assigned a personal broker 'who will remain on hand to answer any queries you may have or to give advice regarding your investments.' The service is an 'add-on' facility for clients who normally take advice from their personal broker.

To be able to deal online, you must hold a minimum of £10,000 in cash and securities. A portfolio viewing facility (at last closing prices) is available to all clients.

The service allows clients to trade directly with the market during trading hours. Trading is at best and you have 30 seconds to accept a price quote. The Marker Orders facility enables clients to place limit orders outside trading hours. These are transmitted to Killik dealers and executed on a first-come-first-served basis.

The maximum single order is £15,000. Clients wishing to deal in larger amounts online will have to place multiple trades. There is no minimum deal size.

You have to open an interest bearing Dealing Account for

holding trading funds. There is no minimum initial deposit or cash balance, save that required to fund your trades. Once you have amassed £20,000 in eligible securities (mainly FTSE 350 stock) you can graduate to the Killik & Co Cash Account with a chequebook and credit card. You can use this facility to borrow against the security of your portfolio to buy more shares (margin trading), from two per cent above the Bank of Scotland base rate.

Securities are held in a Killik nominee account but a minority of Killik clients have sponsored membership of CREST. Settlement is formally T+5, but you can usually deal immediately with the proceeds of sales, depending on the stock traded.

The commission rate is a steep 1.25 per cent, but below the normal 1.65 per cent on deals to £15,000. However, the £15,000 deal limit is a deterrent to the larger investor as the normal Killik dealing rate for the excess is only 0.5 per cent.

Killik & Co Online Dealing should be regarded as a complementary service to share investors whose primary requirement is dealing with advice.

www.redm.co.uk
REDM

Overall rating: ★ ★ ★ ☆			
Classification:	Order Routing	**Readability:**	★ ★ ★
Updating:	Frequently	**Reliability:**	n/a
Navigation:	★ ★ ★	**Speed:**	★ ★ ★ ☆

UK £ R

REDM is the online share-dealing service of independent stockbrokers Redmayne-Bentley. Only shares quoted on the LSE are traded. You can view real-time prices, but your order is routed through to REDM dealers who execute the deal on your behalf. You can register as a user or trader. Users get free access to 15-minute delayed market prices. Traders can deal at best or at limit at real-time prices, with orders based on monetary consideration or volume of shares.

Registering as a trader requires an initial deposit of £1,000 plus your first quarterly subscription (£15 + VAT). Funds are deposited at Yorkshire Bank at two per cent per annum below base rate.

You are expected to hold sufficient funds in your deposit account to pay for your purchase, but at a pinch cleared funds are required by settlement date. Your deposit account is credited with the proceeds of sales on settlement date.

Transactions up to £2,590 cost £12.95. Thereafter you pay 0.5 per cent to a maximum of £39.95. You can select settlement from T+3 to T+20 online. Orders are confirmed by email. All shares purchased through the REDM service are registered in the name of Redmayne (Nominees) Limited at no cost. Other holdings may be transferred into the nominee service at £5 per holding.

www.xest.com
Xest

Overall rating: ★ ★ ★ ☆			
Classification:	Order Routing	**Readability:**	★ ★ ★ ★ ★
Updating:	Frequently	**Reliability:**	★ ★ ★ ★ ★
Navigation:	★ ★ ★ ★ ★	**Speed:**	★ ★ ★ ★ ★

UK £ R

Xest is the execution-only online dealing arm of stockbrokers Charles Stanley and Co Ltd. The service supports dealing in stocks and shares listed on the LSE or AIM. There are two levels of registration:

Free Site Membership which gives you free access to delayed share prices, general market news, stock news, five year graphs and key indicators.

Xest Membership for dealing, real-time price quotes and portfolio viewing at previous days closing prices.

Xest is an order routing service, but plans are well advanced for upgrading the service to STP. At present, you enter your buy/sell instruction for a quantity of shares at best or at limit. Your order is transmitted to Xest's dealers and limit orders are executed on a fill or kill basis. If the complete order cannot be executed immediately, it is rejected.

There is a registration fee of £20, which takes you to 1st April 2000, and £45 per annum, including the cost of Sponsored CREST membership. There is a flat dealing charge of £20. Client funds are held in a Cash Management account and earn between 4 and 5.55 per cent per annum gross. Settlement is T+5 days although sales proceeds can be used for immediate dealing.

www.brearley.iii.co.uk
James Brearley & Sons (ICON)

Overall rating: ★ ★ ★			
Classification:	STP	**Readability:**	★ ★ ★
Updating:	Frequently	**Reliability:**	n/a
Navigation:	★ ★ ★	**Speed:**	★ ★ ★

UK £ R

This execution-only STP share dealing service is known as ICON.

The trading system carries the hallmarks of its creator, Interactive Investor International, and offers real-time market quotes, dealing, portfolio valuation and a watch list of shares. There is no current facility for setting up ISAs online and you can't yet place orders outside market trading hours or submit limit orders, although these features are due to be added in the near future. Trading in foreign equities and managed funds are also known to be on the agenda.

You deal by clicking on a drop-down list of available shares and entering the number of shares to buy/sell. You have 15 seconds to accept a real-time price quote and to execute the trade. Your transaction is displayed instantly on your portfolio details.

Trading funds are deposited at the Bank of Scotland and earn 0.75 per cent below the Bank of England base rate, with no bank charges. Shares are held in a CREST sponsored nominee account. Formal settlement is T+1, but you can trade immediately with the proceeds of sales.

There is an annual registration fee of £25 plus VAT. Trades are executed at a flat £20.

DEALING SERVICE	TYPE OF SERVICE	MAIN FEATURES
Barclays Stockbrokers	STP	Execution-only real time dealing in UK shares Price Improver Service
Cave & Sons	Order routing STP pending	Execution-only dealing in UK shares trusts, ISAs, PEP and ISA transfers
Charles Schwab Europe	STP	Real-time, execution-only dealing in UK and US shares Price improver service Free Reuters Investor Services Reuters Investor Premium Services for £10 p.m
DLJ Direct	STP	Real time, execution-only dealing on UK and US markets.
E-Cortal	STP	Dealing on 9 international exchanges. Real-time quotes for French markets, pending for NYSE and Nasdaq ; others delayed by about 15 minutes.
E*Trade	STP	Real time execution-only dealing in UK equities. Free membership of RESEARCH. Membership of RESEARCH PLUS for £9.95 p.m. for real time quotes and add-on premium services. E-mail alert for corporate actions and dividends.
Fastrade	Order routing STP pending	Execution-only, dealing-only service in domestic and foreign equites, UK Government stocks, UK Corporate Bonds ISAs and PEP transfers
GHCtrader	Order routing STP pending	Execution-only dealing in LSE-listed companies, foreign companies corporate, government, public agency and municipal bonds and warrants, as listed in the GHCtrader internet dealing pages

| UPFRONT COSTS | SHARE DEALING COMMISSION | | | SETTLEMENT TERMS |
	£1K	£5K	£10K	
Free	£11.99	£39.99	£39.99	T+10
Free	£15.00	£35.00	£35.00	Settlement T+5 days for unit certificated stock, T+10 otherwise. Sales proceeds can be reinvested immediately
MarketMaster Admin fees: £1 per quarter per stock (min £5 - max £30)	£15.00	£41.25	£46.75	T+5 days. Proceeds credited to cash account imediately, for further trading prior to formal settlement
Frequent Trader £60 p.a. (no admin fees)	£19.50	£19.50	£19.50	
Free	£15.00	£37.50	£42.50	T+5 days. Proceeds credited immediately for further trading, prior to formal settlement.
Subscription E6 p.m. debited to trading account	Euros 19.5 (market-price orders) Euros 35 (limit-price orders)	Euros 30	Euros 59	Immediate settlement.
	E42.21 (limit-price orders)	Euros 64.89	Euros 129.57	
Admin fees: £25 per half year	£14.95	First 10 trades @ £24.95 next 15 @ £19.95; thereafter @ £14.95 Alltrades cumul\tive		T+5 days. Proceeds credited immediately for further trading, prior to formal settlement
Free	£15.00	£25.00	£30.00	T+5. Immediate in practice
Annual Fee: £35.25	£20.00	£20.00	£20.00	Settlement T+5 for Crest-eligible stocks; T+10 otherwise. Sales proceeds credited to deposit account on settlement day.

DEALING SERVICE	TYPE OF SERVICE	MAIN FEATURES
Halifax ShareXpress	STP	Real-time market prices and execution-only dealing in UK shares settled through Crest, including those sheltered in ISAs "
James Brearley & Sons	STP	Real-time, execution-only dealing in UK equities. Real-time market prices, portfolio display and "watch list
Killik & Co	STP during market hours	£10,000 minimum in cash and securities Real time, execution-only dealing in UK shares Assignment of personal broker
NatWest Stockbrokers	Order routing	Execution-only dealing in UK equities & gilts
REDM	Order routing	Execution-only daking in shares listed on the LSE
Stocktrade	STP	Real time, execution-only dealing in UK shares Real-time portfolio valuation Free access to Knowledge Centre for regular traders
TD Waterhouse	STP	Real-time price quotes and execution-only dealing in LSE listed securities Stockwatch portfolios (delayed prices) Stock alerts
Xest	Order routing STP pending	Real-time execution-only dealing in stocks and shares listed on the LSE or AIM

UPFRONT COSTS	SHARE DEALING COMMISSION			SETTLEMENT TERMS
	£1K	£5K	£10K	
Free	£12.50	£22.50	£22.50	Settlement T + 5
5 p.a.+ VAT registration fee, including sponsored membership of Crest"	£20.00	£20.00	£20.00	Settlement T + 5 but sales proceeds can be reinvested immediately
£10 p.a. custody charge	£32.50	£65.00	£127.50	"Formal settlement T+5 Immediate dealing, prior to formal settlement."
Free	£15.00	£41.00	£46.00	T+5 for nominee or sponsored CREST membership. T +10 days otherwise
£15 + VAT joining fee £5 per holding transfer-in fee to nominee account	£13.00	£25.00	£39.95	Settlement negotiable: T+3 to T+20
£10 p.a. for Sponsored CREST membership	Regular trader £14.50	£20.00	£40.00	T+1 day. Sales proceeds can be reinvested immediately
	Star trader £14.50	£14.50	£20.00	
Free	Standard £12.95	£25.99	£35.99	Settlement:non-certificated T+5; certificated T+10 Sales proceeds can be used as immediate collateral for further trading
	Frequent Trader £14.95	£14.95	£14.95	
20 initial registration to 1 April, thereafter £45 p.a. (includes CREST Sponsored Membership)	£20.00	£20.00	£20.00	Selling: T+ 5 days. Sales proceeds available for further dealing prior to formal settlement

Chapter 7

Homebuying

'*In the midst of life we are in debt.*'
Ethel Watts Mumford, Oliver Herford and Addison Mizner:
Altogether New Cynic's Calendar (1907)

Online Estate Agents

Terrestrial estate agents typically charge between 1.5 and 2 per cent for selling your home. A recent phenomenon is the emergence of the online real-estate broker, claiming to be able to pass on the economies of the internet to sellers. The classic example is Link Up which takes a flat commission for all properties on its books which are sold within 8 weeks of listing.

Other services like Home Directory, Fish4Homes, Home Pages and Home2Home, however, are not estate agents themselves but act as bulletin boards for brokers to post details of the properties on their books.

HouseWeb and Easier attempt to cut out estate agents altogether by accepting advertisements directly from the general public and foregoing commission. HouseWeb charges £40 per annum for an advertisement and makes money from affiliated property-related service providers like solicitors and conveyancers, surveyors, relocation agents and mortgage lenders and intermediaries. Easier offers a completely free service and does not even charge for advertising property on its site. It is totally reliant on income from its affiliated business partners.

The drawback with the commission-free services is that they currently have relatively few properties on their books, whereas Fish4Homes, for example, has some 96,000 listed properties.

www.home2home.co.uk			
Home2Home			
Overall rating: ★ ★ ★ ★ ☆			
Classification:	Information	Readability:	★ ★ ★ ★
Updating:	Regularly	Reliability:	★ ★ ★ ★
Navigation:	★ ★ ★ ★	Speed:	★ ★ ★ ☆
UK			

This is a buyer-friendly information site dealing with all aspects home buying. The features include:

Finding a home using a power search tool, with displays of properties submitted by estate agents – an estate agency of estate agents, as it were. Unlike Easier, this service does not attempt to cut out intermediaries.

Search tool for finding mortgages (John Charcol), solicitors (National Solicitors' Network), home insurance (Find net directory), professional associations, restaurant guides and house price indices.

Area information Select the residential area of your choice and view local history, character, communications, estate agents, schools, property prices, and council tax rates.

Guides Buyers', sellers', moving, renting and letting guides.

Mortgage quotation service provided by John Charcol Online (see p. 101).

Shoppers' sourcing catalogue for household goods.

Magazine An online home interiors and style magazine.

Pending developments include online conveyancing and mortgage application, and, no doubt, more e-commerce.

Home2Home is information-rich and very nicely laid out. Bookmark it!

www.homedirectory.com
Home Directory

Overall rating: ★ ★ ★ ★

Classification:	Information	**Readability:**	★ ★ ★ ☆
Updating:	Regularly	**Reliability:**	★ ★ ★ ★
Navigation:	★ ★ ★	**Speed:**	★ ★ ★ ☆

UK

An innocuous looking home page hides a wealth of useful information and links:

Property search by location Property thumbnails for sale or rental are accompanied by links to the estate agents. Add a property to your shopping basket for future reference

Choosing an area A panel of links to other sites covering education, employment, Local government, maps, transport, local information and Up My Street.

Mortgages This section provides quotes from John Charcoal, Emfinance, Guardian Finance and Lenderslake; mortgage comparisons and life assurance quotes by MoneyeXtra, a mortgage overview by MoneyNet ; Your Mortgage (an online magazine); the Find net directory and links to the top 20 mortgage lenders' sites

Financial links to Financial Planning Horizons, MoneyWeb, and IFA Online, a division of Burns-Anderson Independent Network plc.

Virtual tours of some 93 London areas, plus Cardiff, Colchester and Edinburgh.

Another information-rich site although not quite as user friendly as Home2Home. The 360-degree virtual tour is a great feature, although the pics take a long time to download.

www.easier.co.uk
Easier

Overall rating: ★ ★ ★ ☆

Classification:	Information	**Readability:**	★ ★ ★
Updating:	Regularly	**Reliability:**	★ ★ ★
Navigation:	★ ★ ★ ★	**Speed:**	★ ★ ★ ☆

UK R

Easier may be described as an 'anti-estate agent' site, with a mission to 'revolutionise the way homes are bought and sold'.

Easier enables you to advertise your property on the internet without charge and claims to earn its keep from its unspecified business partners. A ramble through the encyclopaedic questions and answers section of the site identifies the National Conveyancers Network as one such partner, from which it may be deduced that these are drawn from providers of property-related services seeking volume business.

Easier lives up to its name in the form of a site that is easy to understand and to navigate. Essentially, the site is divided into **Sell Your Home** and **Buy Your Home**. Both prospective sellers and buyers are required to register. You can't browse without registering.

Sell Your Home enables you to list the details of your property, attach a description with a photograph, modify the details and withdraw your property from the market. Property listing is rather comprehensive and should deter all but serious sellers.

Buy Your Home contains a search tool with a fairly detailed set of filters: type of property, price range, post code and garage/garden. Properties that survive your initial search criteria come up on a list, which you can sort by newest listing, highest price first or lowest price first. You may subsequently opt for an advanced search, which entails more detailed criteria, the success of which also depends on how much detail the vendors have provided. You can store your search criteria for future use.

If you wish to make contact with a seller you must click on the send contact details button. The vendor's address is not disclosed. Your particulars are simply e-mailed to the vendor so that he/she can make contact with you.

The other noteworthy feature of the site is the detailed question & answers section, which would be extremely unwieldy were it not for the search tool which directs you to the relevant sections of the text.

This is a nice, unfussy site that could provide a really valuable service. Unfortunately, it is somewhat coy about its business partners on which its commercial future depends.

www.houseweb.com
Houseweb

Overall rating: ★ ★ ★ ☆			
Classification:	Information	Readability:	★ ★ ★ ☆
Updating:	Regularly	Reliability:	★ ★ ★ ☆
Navigation:	★ ★ ★ ☆	Speed:	★ ★ ★ ☆

(UK)

Houseweb is primarily an information site for a wide range of property transactions. You can also use it to initiate quotations for life and general insurance.

Advertise your main residence and holiday home for sale, rent or exchange at £40.

Search for a property to buy, rent or exchange (including holiday homes).

Guides Generic guides on selling, buying, mortgage, insurance, and moving and exchanging.

Life assurance quotes from ins-site, and general insurance quotes from Screentrade.

Link to panels of insurance services, mortgage services, solicitors and conveyancers, relocation agents, removal firms, van and car hire rental companies, and a shopping channel currently comprising QXL (the online auctioneer) and BarclaySquare.

Best buy mortgages Review the selection of fixed rate - with or without redemption penalties, variable, variable discounted, capped and first time buyer variable.

Houseweb is a bit thin on the mortgage best buys, but the property exchange and holiday homes sections give this site an international dimension.

www.fish4homes.co.uk
Fish4Homes

Overall rating: ★ ★ ★

Classification:	Information	**Readability:**	★ ★ ★
Updating:	Regularly	**Reliability:**	★ ★ ★
Navigation:	★ ★ ★	**Speed:**	★ ★ ★ ★

UK

Fish4Homes is part of a network of four consumer web-sites including Fish4Cars, Fish4Jobs and an online directory. The sites have been developed by six regional newspaper groups.

Fish4Homes is a free service, which enables you to search for properties for sale or rent. The site claims to have over 96,000 properties on its database.

Other useful features of the site include mortgage quotation services by John Charcol, Alliance & Leicester, Bank of Scotland and Egg.

www.homepages.co.uk
Home Pages

Overall rating: ★ ★ ★ ★

Classification:	Information	**Readability:**	★ ★ ★ ★
Updating:	Regularly	**Reliability:**	★ ★ ★ ★
Navigation:	★ ★ ★	**Speed:**	★ ★ ★

UK

Home Pages is a sister site to MoneyeXtra (see p. 23).

The meat of the site is in the Compare section, where you can search for property by price, location, and number of bedrooms; life assurance; home insurance; personal loans and mortgages.

All insurance and mortgage data is drawn from the MoneyeXtra site itself. Properties are displayed with photographs and thumbnail sketches, along with the relevant estate agent details. You can click on for useful DfEE local information: area map, primary and secondary schools and colleges, house prices, council tax rates, surveyors, solicitors, removal firms and builders.

The 360-degree moving property virtual tours are great but they take a long time to load.

The site is nicely compact with a clear navigation side panel. However, it can be agonisingly slow at times.

Mortgage Services

The emphasis in this section is on Internet mortgage services that are either independent or quasi-independent in the sense that they represent more than one provider.

Such services do not execute the mortgages themselves, but provide information and quotations, and initiate the transaction process by linking borrowers to the providers.

The sites are targeted at different segments of the market. Promise deals in remortgages only, and uses the fact that it is a less risky class of lending to cut interest rates and dispense with some of detail normally required with mortgage applications. However, it is the least independent of the services, as it represents only two providers.

Flexemortgage deals in a narrow class of loans which is principally but not exclusively of interest to existing borrowers seeking remortgages on more flexible terms.

Only John Charcol and newcomer E-Loan can really lay claim to true independence at present. Moneysupermarket may mature into an independent site, but the range of mortgages for which you can apply online is still quite narrow.

The most interesting developments in online mortgages are happening in the USA at present, where the reverse auction mortgage is taking hold. These strange beasts enable borrowers to put their mortgage terms out to tender on the Net, and force the providers to compete for the business by bidding down the APR. For more details see p. 117 (shopping and auctions chapter).

---

www.eloan.com/uk			
E-loan			
Overall rating: ★★★★★			
Classification:	Intermediary	Readability:	★★★★★
Updating:	Regularly	Reliability:	★★★★
Navigation:	★★★★☆	Speed:	★★★★
UK R			

E-LOAN Ltd is the UK mortgage arm of E-LOAN Inc, providing information on mortgages, credit cards and small business loans. This is an information site designed to enable potential borrowers to choose a suitable mortgage, and to initiate applications online. The site purports to be totally independent and provides access to products from over 40 lenders.

Make no mistake, this site is a class act. It is well designed, clearly written, educative, thorough and easily navigable. An overhead navigation bar enables you to select between Purchasing your Home and Remortgage Your Home. Down the left hand side of the page is another navigation panel that contains Products and Tools to Manage Your Debt. Products comprises fixed, variable, capped, discounted and flexible mortgages. The tools are a series of calculators (Mortgage Payment, How Much Can I Afford? Extra Regular Repayment and Extra Lump Sum Repayment) and a detailed power search facility called Select a Mortgage.

The application process has the following stages:

Select a Mortgage Use this feature for guidance on the most suitable type of mortgage. This entails filling in a detailed (but not onerous) questionnaire starting with the purpose of the mortgage and progressing through future plans (How long do you plan to keep this mortgage? Would you like to pay your mortgage off more quickly?), property details, loan size, income prospects, expectations of future interest rates and attitude to risk. Each question is accompanied by a 'Why is this important?' hyperlink.

The programme produces a list of mortgage types that are consistent with your income, preferences and goals (such as variable rate, flexible and 3-year discounted)

Search Click on this button and you get a table of 10 offers for each recommended loan category, itemised by payable rate, monthly payments, standard rate, APR, customer fees, cashback, mandatory insurance, redemption fee period and product details. You can sort each table in descending order of merit by payable rate, monthly payment, APR, and customer fees.

Product details allows you to view the mortgage terms, rate and payment forecast over 10 years and estimated completion costs for any loan listed. Finally, check the Tick to Compare box adjacent to each offer to select any number of mortgage offers, and compare them (in pairs) by terms, mortgage payment, mortgage interest and early redemption penalty, over any period up to 10 years

Apply Click this button on the left of your chosen mortgage to commence the online application. This part is a bit of a slog, but the programme really means business and you are going to have to provide these details anyway.

Submit your application online and wait for an E-LOAN consultant to contact you.

Learn About Mortgages These pages contain the clearest exposition of different mortgage types anywhere, along with a useful Pros and Cons table of each loan type. The calculators are unfussy and informative.

The only quibble is the absence of a practical guide on homebuying. However, this is the clear number one mortgage search site at present. Different league!

www.charcolonline.co.uk
Charcol Online

Overall rating: ★ ★ ★ ★ ☆			
Classification: Advisor		**Readability:**	★ ★ ★ ★ ☆
Updating: Regularly		**Reliability:**	★ ★ ★ ★
Navigation: ★ ★ ★ ★ ☆		**Speed:**	★ ★ ★ ★

UK R

John Charcol is a leading independent mortgage advisor and IFA, and claims to place over £2bn of mortgage business per annum. Charcol Online was awarded third place in the Find's (www.find.co.uk) Financial Services Website of 1999, behind FT.com and DLJ Direct.

Charcol Online aims to help you a suitable mortgage product and to apply for it over the Internet. The site is divided into four distinct sections:

Buying a Home A practical guide to the home buying process covering selling your home, choosing a mortgage, finding a solicitor, choosing a property, conducting a survey, exchanging contracts, competing and moving in.

Finding the Right Mortgage A mortgage wizard collects data about your preferences in respect of: mortgage type (repayment, interest-only, discounted, capped, cashback), flexibility, redemption fees, overhang and compulsory insurances; your existing property if you are re-mortgaging; and your disposable income.

The wizard then generates a table of suitable schemes (Mortgage Options) by lender, type, description, APR or payments (you select which), offer term, redemption details, and compulsory insurances. You can view the details of specific offers by clicking in the View Details column.

You can check whether you meet the lenders' criteria by clicking on the Do I Qualify? button at the bottom right of the page. You are transported to the Eligibility section where you are quizzed about your UK residence, the prospective property and your employment. The program then adds a red tick against each mortgage option listed in the table for which you qualify.

Finally, you can apply online by clicking on the Apply Now button, adjacent to any listed mortgage offer for which you are eligible.

Rapid Re-Mortgage calculates whether it is worthwhile for you to re-mortgage at all, and lists some special re-mortgaging deals negotiated by John Charcol. You can check your eligibility and apply online as with Finding the Right Mortgage.

Best Buys displays the best fixed rate, capped and discounted mortgage products by lender, rate (and APR), offer term, redemption penalty, and compulsory insurances

Quick Calculators work out monthly payments for any loan size and interest and how much you can borrow on the strength of your income.

This an impressive functional site, well organised and easy to navigate. However, it lacks the superb interactivity of E-LOAN and contains no guide to mortgage products.

www.emfinance
Emfinance

Overall rating: ★ ★ ★ ☆			
Classification:	Intermediary	Readability:	★ ★ ★ ☆
Updating:	Regularly	Reliability:	★ ★ ★ ★
Navigation:	★ ★ ★ ☆	Speed:	★ ★ ★ ☆

UK R

Emfinance is a new joint venture with The eXchange Holdings plc, the leading provider of information and quotation material to UK IFAs. Emfinance describes itself as 'a leading web-centric financial information provider' and claims to be completely independent. It aims to assist prospective borrowers to find a suitable mortgage and to apply online. Its funds come from a panel of lenders, which include Bristol and West CMS, Birmingham Midshires MSL, Market Harborough Building Society, The Mortgage Business, West Bromwich Building Society and Woolwich plc. Alliance and Leicester, Royal Bank of Scotland and HMC are set to join and the intention is to expand the panel extensively.

NEW CLIENTS

The first port of call is the Mortgage Calculator, which works out whether an emfinance mortgage can save you any money. You can refine your search for the best money-saving product by eliminating (unchecking) any of the following options: fixed, capped, flexible, cashback, LIBOR, discounted, base-rate racker, no proof of income required, standard variable rate.

The programme then displays a table of mortgage offerings by lender, interest rate, repayment type, 1st monthly payment, total borrowings, total amount payable and product name. You can sort the list by total amount payable, interest rate, repayment type and 1st monthly payment.

 Click on any of the mortgage offers in the table and you get a full product illustration, showing your monthly payments (within and beyond any special offer term), fees and notices (fees added to mortgage, early redemption penalties, basis of interest calculation etc.)

At this point, new customers will have to register in order to be able to apply for a mortgage. This entails selecting a password that you have to remember – normally a right pain in the 'Online Glossary'. The purpose, however, is to allow you to store information entered for future use, so that you don't have to keep re-entering your data from scratch whenever you return to the site.

EXISTING CLIENTS

For registered users, applying online is the familiar ritual of form filling. The process starts out just like the Mortgage Calculator stage for unregistered users, except that when you select your favourite offer from the list generated it is for doing the business and not for window shopping.

The application form is predictably tedious, but the good news is that you don't have to complete it at one sitting. You can log out at any stage to search for some missing item of information or for some less noble purpose. The data you have entered is saved, so that you can recommence at the point where you left off.

When you eventually submit your completed application form online, the programme will prompt you for any submission/valuation fee, which you can pay by debit or credit card.

Your chosen lender will send you the application form for signature by snail mail. You can subsequently track the progress of your online application until the process is complete.

One irritating aspect of the system is that can't register straight away when you log on to the service for the first time. You have to go through the Mortgage Calculator (How much?) process first. However, once you have registered and applied, you have to enter some of the original information again. It would surely be better to have an icon on the home page for optional registration so that you can get down to business from the off.

Overall, emfinance is an attractive and efficient site, though not nearly as thorough as E-LOAN.

www.flexemortgage.com

Flexemortgage

Overall rating: ★ ★ ★ ☆

Classification:	Intermediary	**Readability:**	★ ★ ★ ☆
Updating:	Regularly	**Reliability:**	★ ★ ★ ☆
Navigation:	★ ★ ★ ☆	**Speed:**	★ ★ ★ ☆

UK   R

The ongoing debate about unfair and restrictive mortgage terms and practices has thrown the spotlight onto so-called 'flexible mortgages' which allow you to vary regular payments, pay in lump sums at will, and take repayment holidays.

Flexemortgage is a site for transacting in flexible mortgages. It is the brainchild of Frank Eve, formerly business development director at First Active. The site is aimed at financially aware borrowers, with an emphasis on remortgaging.

Getting acquainted with flexible mortgages The site demo is very instructive. Click the yellow Try it now! icon on the home page. This links you to an animated exposition of the principles of flexible mortgages, illustrating how you can save money and shorten your mortgage term (vis-à-vis a standard 25-year mortgage) by increasing regular payments by £50 p.m., or paying in a lump sum of £50k (and even borrowing it back again five years later).

Click on the 'how' button and see how the annualised calculation of mortgage interest can leave you paying interest on capital that you have already repaid. Then learn how to use a flexible mortgage facility like a bank or savings account, and confine your interest payments to capital that you owe.

Getting a quotation Click on the Deals on Offer icon on the home page and progress to the quotation stage. A reasonably short questionnaire asks for personal details, loan requirements, employment status and whether you want an interest-only or Capital-and-Interest (Repayment) quotation.

Submit your completed questionnaire and you are taken to a table displaying flexible mortgage offerings from six lenders (Scottish Widows, The Royal Bank of Scotland, Legal and General, Standard Life Bank, Stroud and Swindon Building Society and First Active). The table displays rates of interest and whether the lender permits overpayments, underpayments, payment holidays and drawdowns.

Check the box against your lenders of choice. Your details are dispatched, and your flexible mortgage application process is launched.

Flexemortgage is a bit of a niche site. By definition, the range of lenders is likely to remain quite narrow, unless everyone starts offering them. Flexible mortgages do not suit everyone and this site may lose out against the likes of E-Loan with its wider array of lenders. Still, it is always worth a visit.

www.moneysupermarket.co.uk
Money Supermarket

Overall rating: ★ ★ ★ ☆

Classification:	Intermediary	**Readability:**	★ ★ ★
Updating:	Regularly	**Reliability:**	★ ★ ★ ☆
Navigation:	★ ★ ★ ☆	**Speed:**	★ ★ ★ ☆

UK R

Money Supermarket is primarily a search tool for seeking out and transacting in the most competitive mortgages, personal loans, and credit cards. The service is the creation of Mortgage 2000, a leading provider of online mortgage and loan comparison software to Independent Financial Advisers.

The current site also lists conveyancing, savings accounts, ISAs, building and contents insurance and life assurance. This should be taken more as a statement of intent, because none of these pages were functioning at the time of writing. Readers are asked to register for these services, with the promise that they will be advised as soon as they became operational.

Navigation is pretty straightforward. There is a single panel down the left hand side of the homepage and a highly visible shop key for launching power searches. The simplicity of this site is its greatest strength. It is refreshingly uncluttered and the tables are easy to read. The data appears to be encyclopaedic, with a database of some 4,000 mortgage products and 300 card providers.

Although the site can be used purely for informational purposes, it has a distinctly transactional feel to it, unlike a site like MoneyNet where you can window shop at relative leisure.

Mortgages Application is a lengthy eight-step process. The final table lists available mortgage offers by true cost (total cost including arrangement and valuation fees less cashbacks, and interest and capital payments over a selected period), mortgage type, initial interest rate, duration of offer term, base rate, first payment and cashback.

The search can be refined further by restricting the mortgage offers in the table to cashback only, flexible only, no redemption (penalties) and 'no overhang' (that is, no redemption period after the fixed/capped/discount term has finished).

Clicking on the details button unveils the nitty gritty of the offer. In some cases you can apply online by clicking on a red, flashing apply button. This takes you through to an online application form that you eventually e-mail off to the provider of your choice. If you complete the mortgage online, you get an additional £50 cashback.

Personal Loans After undergoing a stern examination of your disposable income and credit history, you arrive at a table showing APR, monthly payment, total repaid, total Interest and details for each listed lender. When you have found a suitable personal loan, you may be able to apply online by clicking on the apply button.

Cards You can search for a credit, donations, store, charge or business card. Select the range of features that you want, enter your average monthly balance and generate a table of providers by annual fee, standard APR, introductory APR and interest-free period. Click on any one of these headings and the providers are relisted in descending order of merit by that criterion. Click on details for the minutiae. If you want to apply, complete a 'decision-in-principle' form and e-mail it off. The lender performs a credit check and e-mails you back with a decision.

Alternatively, you can calculate the potential savings generated by switching to another card. Select the name of your existing card from a drop-down list and enter your average monthly balance and the number of years over which the calculation is to be performed. The programme generates a table listing rival cards by standard APR, transfer APR (i.e. APR for transferred balances), transfer term (i.e. the period of time over which the transfer APR applies), annual fee, cashback, interest-free period and savings. If you are sufficiently impressed, you can apply online.

There are also helpful calculators for finding the best electricity, gas, telephones and mobiles deals.

The site is clearly still under construction, so criticism may be premature. The main quibble concerns the inflexibility of the data gathering process. The eight-step mortgage questionnaire does not seem to permit you to go back and amend details entered in a previous step, except by starting the process from scratch. The personal loan questionnaire appears to be equally rigid. There are comparatively few offerings that can be applied for online at present and some of the terminology used may be a bit obscure . A glossary or a more detailed Help section would be a great advance.

This could develop into a very useful hard data site when the non-loan sections come on stream. However, the site does not yet live up to its billing as a supermarket.

www.ipromise.co.uk
Promise

Overall rating: ★ ★ ★			
Classification:	Intermediary	Readability:	★ ★ ★ ★
Updating:	Regularly	Reliability:	★ ★ ★
Navigation:	★ ★ ★ ★	Speed:	★ ★ ★ ★

UK R

Promise is the trading name of Winterthur Direct UK Ltd, part of the Credit Suisse, the international asset management, investment banking, insurance and fund management group.

Promise is a mortgage intermediary offering information on different types of homeloans, for remortgage purposes only. The current product range includes three base rate trackers (including a flexi), a 2-year discounted deal and a fixed-rate mortgage that reverts to a base rate tracker in 2003. The mortgage business is placed with The Royal Bank of Scotland and The Woolwich.

Promise claims to offer you a fairer deal by cutting out branches, commission-earning salesmen, interest bearing savings accounts and, crucially, first-time buyers. It caters for 'secure mortgage holders only, who have equity in their home.' So there!

Mortgages are free of any arrangement, legal or valuation fees. Redemption penalties apply to fixed rate and discounted mortgages, but there is no lock-in period after the term has expired. Promise receives no fees from its lenders. It makes its money by adding a margin to the interest rate.

The site itself is agreeably laid out. Each page is adorned by a comely young lady who does suggestive things with spectacles (each to his own!). A quick quote facility enables you to compare outgoings on your present mortgage with those on a 2-year 1% discounted deal and a flexible base rate tracker, and to decide whether it is worthwhile going through the application process.

The application process has been simplified by doing away with the requirement for an employer's reference and a surveyor's report.

The menu of suitable mortgage offerings depends on your reason for remortgaging (lower repayments, flexible, increase borrowing or cashback). The appropriate portfolio appears on a drop-down list during the application process.

The service eventually makes an offer in principle, and invites you to submit to an online credit check. If successful, you can agree a time for a Promise consultant to call you and take things further.

This is a fairly user-friendly site, but the range of mortgage providers is too narrow for it to challenge the likes of E-LOAN.

www.ins-site.co.uk
Ins-site

Overall rating: ★ ★ ★			
Classification:	IFA	Readability:	★ ★ ★ ☆
Updating:	Regularly	Reliability:	★ ★ ☆
Navigation:	★ ★ ★ ★	Speed:	★ ★ ★ ★

UK R

Ins-site is the life assurance and re-mortgaging website of IFA First Global Insurance Services. It is an unfussy, no-frills site for obtaining mortgage quotes from a panel of lenders, currently comprising Yorkshire Building Society, Market Harborough Building Society, The Woolwich and Scottish Widows. There are 25 re-mortgage offerings, including variable, fixed, capped, discounted, flexible and cashback schemes.

The main virtue of this site is its speed. The Quick Quote is the snappiest that you will find anywhere. Answer five simple questions and you receive a list of recommended mortgage offers that meet your criteria. Click on any mortgage offer to view the key features. Hit the Apply button to start the application process.

Ins-site is not as easy going as Promise where you don't need an employer's reference or survey, but there is a handy checklist of the information required that appears before you get into the application questionnaire. One useful feature is the Save Application button on the side navigation bar. This means that you don't have to complete it all in one sitting. If you need Mortgage Protection, you can click on the life assurance Quick Quote.

The narrow range of panel lenders belie the claims of true independence, but with new lenders expected to come on board, this could be a good site to bookmark.

Chapter 8

Insurance

'Future, n. That period of time in which our affairs prosper, our friends are true, and our happiness is assured.'
Ambrose Bierce: The Cynic's Word Book (1906)

'You will never find a widow whose husband had too much life assurance.'
Traditional, amongst life assurance salesmen

'Streets flooded. Please advise.'
Robert Benchley (American humourist): Telegraph message on arriving in Venice

General Insurance Sites

There is nothing particularly glamorous about online general insurance sites. These are practical, transactional platforms for protecting our possessions; motor vehicles, homes and contents, holidays and pets.

There is little more to this than displaying comparative quotes and policy features. The best feature of these sites is that you can generally save your quotations for up to 30 days. This allows you to shop around on other sites and eventually retrieve all your quotes for comparison.

The dominant online general insurance brokers are **Screentrade**, which seems to be the default link on virtually every infomation site. Its nearest challenger is **InsureWide.**

www.screentrade.co.uk			
Screentrade			
Overall rating: ★ ★ ★ ☆			
Classification:	Insurance	**Readability:**	★ ★ ★
Updating:	Regularly	**Reliability:**	★ ★ ★ ★
Navigation:	★ ★ ★ ☆	**Speed:**	★ ★ ☆

UK

Screentrade is wholly owned by Mysis Interactive Trading, the leading supplier of electronic trading and administration systems for healthcare, insurance and banking in the UK. Screentrade brings Mysis' general insurance quotation engine online for the benefit of consumers, with broking facilities provided by Shaws Insurance Brokers Ltd.

Screentrade is the chosen general insurance link for most information sites (see p. 16).They offer quotations for motor, household and travel insurance and you can buy policies online from a panel of insurers in each category, in a five-stage process.

First, you choose the type of insurance. Then you complete the necessary online questionnaire so that the panel insurers can prepare quotes.

The programme then displays the quotes and key features of the policies so you can make comparisons. Next you buy your policy by clicking on the **Buy This Policy** button. Finally, you pay by credit or debit card in full or by instalments. Confirmation of cover is made by e-mail or by telephone within 30 minutes.

SPECIAL FEATURES

Motor Insurance The current panel of insurers is Avon, AXA Insurance, Bishopsgate, CGU, Cornhill Insurance, Drake

Insurance, Folgate Insurance, Gan, HW, Irontrades, Legal & General, Link Insurance, Norwich Union, Royal & Sun Alliance, Sabre, Zenith Insurance and Zurich. By clicking on the **Insurance Advisor** in the side panel within Motor Insurance you'll find a guide covering types of insurance, factors affecting premiums, no claims bonuses and other discounts and excesses.

Household The current panel of insurers is made up of AXA Insurance, CGU, Independent Insurance, Ecclesiastical, Legal & General and Zurich. You can buy cover for any combination of contents, buildings and possession away from home. The procedure is much the same as motor insurance. **Insurance Advisor** in this section explains the rudiments of household insurance and saving money on home insurance. It includes a rebuilding cost and house contents calculator to use when entering sums assured on your application forms.

Travel The panel of insurers is currently made up of Bishopsgate, Folgate Insurance, Norman Insurance and Primary Direct Travel Insurance. You can buy cover for a single journey lasting up to a year, or for multiple journeys within a year. Cover is only available to UK residents starting and ending their journeys in the UK. **Insurance Advisor** gives the low down on **basic cover** (medical, personal liability, legal expenses, cancellation or curtailment and personal belongings); **extended cover** (winter sports, high risk sports, motoring holidays and recovery and breakdown); **duration** (single trip, long stay and annual multi-trip insurance) and driving abroad (checking your existing policy, the Green Card, driving in Spain and breakdown insurance)

Each insurance category has its own guide for making claims, although these amount to little more than lists of the panel members' telephone numbers.

This site is strong on content, but it isn't fast.

www.1stquote.co.uk
1st Quote

Overall rating: ★ ★ ★ ☆

Classification:	Insurance	Readability:	★ ★ ★
Updating:	Regularly	Reliability:	★ ★ ★ ☆
Navigation:	★ ★ ★ ☆	Speed:	★ ★ ★ ☆

UK

This is a nice no-frills general insurance site. You can buy insurance cover for your car, motorcycle, van, vehicle breakdown, home, travel and pet. The main virtue of this site is that it is quick. 1st Quote is a quotation and application service, pure and simple. It carries no guides or words of wisdom at all.

Car, Motorcycle and Van Insurance Applications are segmented into: single or multiple drivers; 'clean' applications, or previous claims and convictions; convictions only; and claims only. Although you ultimately have to tender the same information as with any other brokerage, this early classification makes the process seem shorter.

Buildings and Contents Insurance: A mercifully brief questionnaire enquires about the number of bedrooms in your home, whether you require accidental cover, the level of cover on possessions taken outside your home (£0, £2000 or £5000 only), and any accumulated no-claims bonuses. Insert the sum assured for the building and you can have a quote in seconds.

Travel Insurance is provided by TraveLine. You can insure for single trips, annual multi-trips or business trips and arrange special long-term cover. Optional extras include cover for winter sports, golf, scuba driving; excess waiver and Euro breakdown vehicle cover. There are five levels of benefit: bronze, silver, bronze plus, gold and platinum, in ascending order of cost.

Vehicle Breakdown Cover is provided by Green Flag. You enter the age of your vehicle (D Reg or younger; E Reg or older), accept or decline Homecall and say whether you are paying annually or monthly. The program displays a table listing the premiums of Roadside Assistance, Comprehensive and Total Protection. You simply click on the version you want and proceed to the formal application form

Pet Insurance You can insure your cat, dog or horse through PetLine. All you have to do is say whether you are paying monthly or annually, and whether you want Bronze, Silver or Gold class cover for your schnooks. What kind of a question is that?

The level of choice on the site does not seem to be the widest available. However, if you want to make a quick decision, this site is one to bookmark.

www.insurancewide.co.uk
InsuranceWide

Overall rating: ★ ★ ★			
Classification:	Insurance	**Readability:**	★ ★ ★
Updating:	Regularly	**Reliability:**	★ ★ ★ ★
Navigation:	★ ★ ★ ★	**Speed:**	★ ★ ★ ★

UK R

This is a general insurance site, for motor, household and travel cover and car rescue. The site offers quotations, applications and claims online, plus a legal advice and claims helpline.

SPECIAL FEATURES
Motor Quote Policies are selected from a panel of insurers including Equity Red Star at Lloyds, Zurich, Cornhill and AXA, amongst others. Policies offer a good range of benefits including travel within the EU, no-claims bonus protection, unlimited windscreen cover (subject to a £50 excess), and 100% of purchase price cover for total write-offs in the vehicle's first year of registration.

Legal Expenses Cover provides up to £50,000 for non-fault claims where the other party's insurers can be traced.

Home Quote Choose from building and contents insurance.

Travel Quote standard cover includes medical and additional expenses.

Car Rescue A comprehensive package covering Roadside Rescue, National Recovery, Home Rescue and Caravans and Trailers. Discounts are available for second and third vehicles kept at the same address.

The main virtue of this site is its speed. A helpful feature is the quotation reference number, so that you can retrieve a quote later without having to enter your details from scratch.

Life Insurance

Life Insurance sites are universally disappointing. They are normally confined to term assurance policies for two main reasons: firstly, term assurance is perceived as a 'simple' product to be sold on the basis of price on an execution-only basis, without advice. Secondly, term assurance policies are unregulated products as they usually do not contain any investment element. This means that they are not subject to the rigours of the regulatory procedures and so are attractive to sell.

The result is that the online market for protection products is highly restricted and there is considerable scope for misbuying. To start with, term assurance is not the only fish in the sea. There are three broad categories of life assurance contracts, with different applications.

Term Assurance is a 'temporary' form of cover, where benefits are paid on death, terminal and critical illness, within the term. These policies are useful for covering a specific risk over a known period of time: such as the duration of a mortgage or the financial dependency of children.

Endowment Assurance is a protection and investment package designed to meet a specific target (such as an interest-only mortgage) at a future date, or in the event of prior death and critical illness.

Whole Life Assurance pays benefits on death and critical illness, at any time. These policies are useful for covering a risk period of indeterminate length. They are often written in trust for Inheritance Tax planning, where the timing of the tax bill cannot be predicted.

Endowment policies are currently out of favour, and you will be hard pressed to find any site that will provide quotes for whole life cover.

In any event, Term Assurance is not a simple product. Cover may be level, escalating or decreasing ; paid out as a lump sum or in instalments; renewable at the end of the term or convertible within the term to another type like whole life; stand-alone or as part of a pension scheme.

Then there is the question of calculating the right sum assured. Life assurance is a complicated subject and there must be some doubt as to the wisdom of buying without advice. On a bad day you could end up paying the right price for the wrong policy with the wrong sum assured.

Of course, personal protection does not begin and end with life assurance. Other areas where advice should be taken are:

Permanent Health Insurance (PHI) for covering loss of earnings due to illness or disability, with a percentage paid after an agreed 'waiting' or deferment period.

Private Medical Insurance (PMI) for meeting medical expenses. MoneyNet (www.moneynet.co.uk) has teamed up with brokers HIFAC PMI Ltd to offer an execution-only PMI service where you can compare quotes compiled by the major insurers and apply online.

For an elegant exposition of personal protection policies, visit Financial Planning Horizons (www.financial-planning.uk.com). For assistance with calculating the correct sum assured on a life assurance policy, try out MoneyeXtra's life assurance calculator (www.moneyextra.co.uk). And If you want pure advice without sales visit Sort Limited (www.sort.co.uk).

www.ins-site.co.uk
Ins-site

Overall rating: ★ ★ ★ ☆

Classification:	Life Insurance	**Readability:**	★ ★ ★ ☆
Updating:	Regularly	**Reliability:**	★ ★ ☆
Navigation:	★ ★ ★ ★	**Speed:**	★ ★ ★ ★

UK R

Ins-site is the online arm of IFA First Global Securities, providing quotations and initiating applications for life assurance and re-mortgages (see Mortgages section). Ins-site deals in term assurance contracts only.

SPECIAL FEATURES

Quick Quote The main virtue of this site is its speed. Click on the Quick Quote icon and you are immediately transferred to a short questionnaire asking for personal details and basic policy details (sum assured, term, level or decreasing sum assured). The programme displays a list of the five 'top' (cheapest) quotations in ascending order of premiums for the sum assured, and asks whether the cover and premium are to be guaranteed for the whole term, or reviewable within the term. The applicant clicks on the proceed button adjacent to the quote of choice.

At this somewhat late point the **Reasons for Life Cover** drop-down menu appears and the applicant is asked to select the reason for the cover, followed by the product provider. However, although Business Protection is one of the listed reasons for taking out the life cover, there is no guide to setting up life policies for business purposes (such as key man cover, shareholder protection and partnership protection).

In order to proceed with the application, the applicant has to download and view either the product-provider's key features document or a client-specific key features document. The applicant is now able to submit the application online and to download and print off the application form for completion, and dispatch to a freepost address. The response is pretty snappy. A trial application was sent at 10.40 a.m. and First Global called back by noon.

OTHER FEATURES

The quotation and application functions of this site are supported by short guides on:

Establishing your needs A list of factors to be taken into account when calculating the sum assured. (age of self, partner and children, current income and potential earnings, mortgage outstanding, children's education and living expenses).

Products is a brief guide to different types of term assurance products such as level, convertible and renewable; guaranteed versus reviewable premiums; critical event cover; and critical illness cover. However, you can't get a quote for critical illness cover on this site.

Trusts A useful exposition of the advantages of writing a life assurance policy in trust, to avoid inheritance tax and ensure speedy payment of the benefits. You will need to look closely for this guide, as it doesn't appear on the navigation bar. It only materialises as a tiny hyperlink halfway through the application process.

Word is that this site is to be revamped shortly. If it can add a bit more rigour to its athleticism, it may be worth bookmarking.

www.lifequote.co.uk
Lifequote

Overall rating: ★ ★ ★ ☆			
Classification: Life Insurance	**Readability:**	★ ★ ★ ★	
Updating: Regularly	**Reliability:**	★ ★ ★ ☆	
Navigation: ★ ★ ★ ★	**Speed:**	★ ★ ★ ★	

UK R

Lifequote is the online arm of Independent Financial Advisers Direct Life and Pensions Limited. They provide quotations and initiate applications in the following types of life assurance: term assurance and critical illness assurance; low cost endowments; permanent health insurance; 'nil commission' personal pensions; and accident, sickness and redundancy insurance.

SPECIAL FEATURES

Term and Critical Illness Assurance The initial term assurance asks for personal and policy details. Applicants are asked to specify whether they want level term assurance or mortgage protection (with a decreasing sum assured), with or without critical illness cover.

While you are online, you can ask for quotes on alternative products, or amend your requirements. You are issued with a unique reference number so that these quotes can be retrieved on future visits to the site.

The system produces a complex quotation in about 40 seconds, complete save for the identity of the insurer. You have to await contact from one of Direct Life and Pension's consultants if you want to know more.

Permanent Health Insurance and Low Cost Endowments
The application process is similar in principle to Term and

Critical Illness assurance. The only difference is that Direct Life and Pensions will currently only quote for the Zurich Life product, on the grounds that it offers 'the most competitively priced and comprehensive products from the available options.' Likewise, the Low Cost Endowment comes exclusively from Standard Life at present.

'Nil Commission' Pensions 'Nil commission' means that you only pay a £99 'installation fee'. For this fee, you get a choice of 17 pension providers. You also get a table that shows you the effect of the provider's normal commission on the fund (assuming 7% investment growth per annum) and, ergo, the cost-effectiveness of a fee-based service.

By clicking on the name of the listed provider you go straight through to that company's pension fund performance statistics on S & P Micropal (www.micropal.co.uk).

You can hit the **Buy** button to request a key features document from your chosen company and to download an application form. The application form is accompanied by a guide on a right hand side panel, that 'translates' pensions terminology.

The main virtue of this site is the quick execution of quotations. As ever, you can' t complete a full life assurance application online with health declarations 'n all. This is done by post.

The only reservation is whether the practice of providing Permanent Health Assurance and Low Cost Endowment quotes from single providers falls within the spirit of an independent albeit execution-only service.

Chapter 9

Online Shopping and Auctions

Up to this point, the focus of this book has been on the way in which the internet facilitates the purchase of financial products. This section deals with online trading in everyday goods.

Compiling a definitive list of shopping sites is an exercise in futility, best left to others. Your best bet is to monitor the consumer directory sites that will keep you up to date with developments on the cyber high street. Try Internet Shopper (www.internetshopper.co.uk), the online version of the free Computer Shopper magazine supplement. The advantage of the hard copy version is that you can download Power Ups from the Computer Shopper CD Rom, instead of from the internet itself. On the other hand, the website enables you to browse back issues.

Internet Shopper contains a Hot Shopping section featuring online shopping sites for a range of consumer goods, compiled from reader feedback; a What's Online section; Net Tech for making your PC 'go faster'; and a URL directory.

Another site worth looking at is Shopping Unlimited (www.shoppingunlimited.co.uk), part of the Guardian newspaper's online network. The site is built around a directory of the best shopping sites compiled by Jim McClellan, author of *The Guardian Guide To Shopping On the Internet*. Hit the directory button for an alphabetical listing of shopping categories from books and magazines through to travel. Click on any of these and you get through to thumbnail sketches of the featured providers with quick links to their websites.

Online Auctions

When you shop in the high street (whether offline or online) you are essentially a 'price taker'. This means that the goods are offered to you at take-it-or-leave-it prices. Some bargaining may be permitted, but this is likely to be individual rather than collective.

On the other hand, when you bid at auction you are no longer a passive price taker. The auction is an interactive market place where the goods are sold at prices reflecting their true value to the individual bidders, forged in the white heat of competitive bidding.

The terrestrial auction is hampered by limited participation and unequal access to information. The internet auction, however, addresses these shortcomings through extensive dissemination of information, easier access and wider participation. This leads to more competitive bidding and 'truer' prices. Other blessings ascribed to online auctions include lower transactions costs and a broader range of tradeable commodities, amongst them financial services.

Types of Online Auctions

Online auctions fall into three broad categories: person-to-person (consumer-to-consumer), business-to-person (business-to-consumer) and business-to-business.

PERSON-TO-PERSON (P2P)

The person-to-person site is the most common form of internet auction site, where private individuals buy and sell goods from and to each other. eBay, Yahoo and Amazon are examples of person-to-person auction sites. eBay is the elder statesman, with a lineage going all the way back to 1995. The American sites are currently richer than their UK counterparts in terms of the range and volume of goods traded.

Amazon illustrates perfectly the difference between a conventional shopping site and an online auction site. On the one hand you can buy books and music (and a whole lot more on the US site) and buy and sell in its zShops at take-it-or-leave-it prices. Alternatively, you can try your luck in the online auction rooms where you may be able to transact at superior prices, but without the certainty of success.

BUSINESS-TO-PERSON (B2P)

Online business-to-person auctions provide cost-effective platforms for manufacturers and retailers to sell off excess capacity, surplus stock and goods on consignment. QXL, eBid and FSauctions are prominent hosts of both business-to-person and person-to-person auctions in the UK. Priceline is the doyen of business-to-person auctioning in the USA, with its patented Demand Collection System, a form of reverse auction where the bidding is done by the seller rather than the buyer. Priceline auctions off a range of goods and services including hotel accommodation, car rental, motor vehicles (purchase or leasing), airline tickets, mortgages and even groceries.

The reverse auction is the unique creation of the internet. However, there is a fine line between a true reverse auction site and a quotation or tendering service. The narrow definition of the term 'auction' implies that bidding is on the basis of price only and is interactive. With this reservation in mind and adopting a broader definition, here are some international examples of specialised business-to-person 'auction' sites for you to explore:

Real Estate Homebid.com of Arizona (www.homebid.com), the world's first online real estate auctioneer. Bamboo.com.Inc of Tennessee (www.bamboo.com) offers 360-degree virtual real-estate tours.

Mortgages A striking application of the reverse auction is where mortgage providers bid against each other to meet the buyer's terms. See BondNet (www.bondnet.co.za), a South African mortgage auctioneer, or RealEstate.com.Inc (www.realestate.com), an Atlanta-based mortgage auctioneer, with more than 250 participating lenders, bidding on the basis of APR. IMX Exchange (www.imx.com)is a California-based mortgage site where lenders bid for the business on a variety of factors, including APR.

Travel TravelBids (www.travelbids.com) auctions airline, cruise and holiday-resort packages, and claims to be the inventor of the reverse auction concept. South African Airways (www.saa.co.za) holds auctions for surplus tickets.

Hotel Accommodation Bid2Stay Online Hotel Accommodation is the site of South African hotel group City Lodge (www.citylodge.co.za; www.bid2stay.co.za). Specify your occupancy dates and enter up to five consecutive bids for the nightly rate. If you subsequently alter your arrival or departure date, you pay the standard nightly rate for the time outside your original dates.

Technology Dell Computer Corporation (www.dell.com; www.dellauction.com) allows you to bid for Dell products, and auction off any computer equipment irrespective of brand.

Wine Winebid (www.winebid.com)is a Californian-based site where you can bid for an international selection of fine wines.

BUSINESS-TO-BUSINESS (B2B)

Business-to-business online auctions facilitate the distribution of components and materials, either on consignment to independent auction hosts or through sellers' propriety auction sites.

Examples of such sites are FreeMarkets (www.freemarkets.com), which auctions custom-made components and raw materials to businesses at 'true market prices', and Industry-to-Industry (I2I) (www.itoi.com), auctioning chemicals, construction, retail merchandising and energy.

Britain's first business-to-business site is BidBusiness (www.bidbusiness.co.uk), which concentrates on construction and related industries.

Although online auctioning is still dominated by the person-to-person format, future growth is likely to be concentrated in the business-critical sector with, business-to-consumer sites expected to account for two-thirds of online auction sales by 2003.

The Anatomy of an Online Auction

The auction process differs according to the auction category and the commodity, but follows the following general pattern:

Registration The seller and potential buyers register with the auction site and supply personal or corporate details (address and e-mail addresses) and credit card details where applicable for verification and for charging any auction fees. Participants select usernames and are assigned passwords by e-mail. Usernames and passwords are retained for future auctions. Auction participants trade anonymously under cover of their usernames. Personal particulars are not disclosed until the auction is complete.

Listing The seller completes a new item form which records a description of the items (supported by photographs if necessary), the duration of the auction, payment terms, item location, proposed shipping and handling arrangements, delivery time and 'serviceable distribution area' (within North America or EU, for example).

The seller also specifies the minimum bid and the reserve price. The minimum bid is the price at which to kick off the auction. The reserve price is the minimum acceptable price to the seller and is not disclosed to bidders until it has been reached. The minimum bid is normally set below the reserve price in order to kick start the bidding.

Bidding The potential buyer uses an online bidding form and is able to view the progress of the auction. The bidder can see the highest ruling bid, examine the bidding history and even e-mail the seller (identified only by username at this stage) for more information about the items being auctioned.

Bidding can take place manually or by proxy. With manual bidding, the potential buyer bids and counter-bids personally. With proxy bidding the bidder specifies a maximum bid price, and bidding proceeds by programmed increments until the limit is exceeded.

Winning Bids In single-item auctions, the highest bid obviously wins although the process of reaching that price differs according to the nature of the auction. In traditional (English) auctions, the process starts with the minimum bid and prices are raised in set increments. In single-item Dutch auctions, however, the process starts with a high offer price, which is reduced until it draws out the first and winning bid. Such auctions are sometimes called First Bid Wins.

In multiple-item auctions, identifying the winning bid is a little more complicated. The auction lot consists of several identical items and a buyer may wish to bid for a proportion of the consignment. Under such circumstances, the winning bid is identified by the following rules:

1 The highest price bid wins
2 Where two or more bidders offer the same price, the party bidding for the larger quantity wins
3 Where two or more participants bid for the same quantity at the same price, the earliest bid wins.

Multiple-item auctions hold out the possibility that several potential buyers can enter successful bids. Under Yankee auction rules, each buyer pays the individual price bid. Under multiple-item Dutch auction rules, each buyer pays the price bid by the lowest successful bidder.

Concluding the auction Once a deal has been struck, the identities of the seller and the winning buyer are disclosed to each other by email. It is then up to the parties to negotiate over such details as the method of payment, length of the buyer's inspection period, the shipping method and the apportionment of shipping, insurance and escrow charges (see below).

Settlement The buyer sends payment to the seller. The seller dispatches the goods to the buyer who can inspect them for the duration of the agreed inspection period. If the goods are unacceptable, they are returned to the seller at the bidder's expense.

Security and Fraud Prevention

Online auctioning is vulnerable to fraudulent practice. It is estimated that half of internet fraud is committed in this context. Defenders of online auctioning downplay the incidence of fraud and argue that such risks are prevalent in offline auctions. There are three main areas of concern.

DEFAULT

Where a deal has been struck at auction, the parties are required to complete the transaction. The seller is obliged to deliver the goods and the buyer to pay. However, how can either party be sure that the other will not default?

Online auctioneers regard non-completion in a very serious light, which can lead to expulsion from future auctions and even legal action for misuse of the site. Where the parties are unknown to each other, it is sensible to employ escrow agencies to minimise the risk of default. An escrow agent is an independent third party acting as custodian of the funds and/or the merchandise until it has been confirmed that all contractual terms have been met.

Escrow services are common in the USA, but comparatively rare in the UK, where traders are usually left to their own devices post auction. The exceptions are eBid, which uses itrustyou (www.itrustyou.com), and QXL which operates its own in-house escrow-type and shipping services.

It may be wise to use an escrow agent when transacting internationally. Try Auction Escrows (www.auctionescrows.com), SafeBuyer (www.safebuyer.com), TradeSafe (www.tradesafe.com), Secure Trades (www.securetrades.com) and i-Escrow (www.iescrow.com).

CREDIT CARD SECURITY

The two leading technologies are:

Secure Socket Layer (SSL), a protocol for secure internet data transmission between the client and the server, used by Netscape Navigator and Microsoft Internet Explorer

Secure Electronic Transaction (SET) pioneered by Visa and MasterCard.

SSL is still the most widely used protocol but has been broken on several occasions. SET's creators claim that it is potentially more secure than SSL because they are building a powerful infrastructure for certification of digital signatures. However, SET may well prove to be thorough but unwieldy, and the storage of both public and private keys on millions of personal computers may be an irresistible temptation for virus writers and hackers.

SHARP BIDDING PRACTICES

Most 'disreputable' bidding strategies originate in offline auctions. These include:

Shill Bidding The illegal practice of a seller posing as a buyer, under a separate username, in order to boost prices. Anyone who manipulates an online auction in this way will be expelled from the service.

Sniping The frowned-upon (but legal) practice of delaying a bid until shortly before the end of the auction, leaving other bidders unable to counter bid. Some online auctioneers attempt to counter sniping by postponing the auction close until a 'bidless' period of time has elapsed.

Bid Shielding Two colluding parties enter separate bids, one low and the other high, under different usernames to discourage bidding by other prospective buyers. The high bid is withdrawn shortly before closing time, leaving the lower bid on the table. Since online bids are legally binding, it is unlikely that this stratagem will work. Bids can only be retracted under extraordinary circumstances.

Auction Search Engines

Tracking down particular items over a plethora of auction sites can be an almost full-time job. Inevitably, the solution lies in specialised auction search engines like Bidstream.com (www.bidstream.com), Bidfind (www.bidfind.com) and i-Track (www.itrack.com).

Bidstream and Bidfind can both search up to 250 auction sites for that elusive item. Bidstream is the acknowledged leader at present as it has direct links to the databases of all clients of OpenSite Technologies Inc., the leading provider of online-auction software.

Auction trackers are confined to US sites at present, but should eventually come on stream in the UK as the market expands.

POSTSCRIPT

The principle advantage of online auction sites is that they bring the economics of the auction room to the wider markets for goods and services, including financial services. The spirit of the auction room is already embodied in online share dealing.

The internet has already made its own original contribution to auctioning in the form of the reverse auction. It remains to be seen whether the principle will be extended to other financial products that are largely bought on price, such as term assurance.

The great unknown is how far business-to-person auctioning will extend beyond luxury goods and financial services towards the more rudimentary transactions of everyday life. In fact, the author wants nothing more than to be able to put his weekly grocery list out to tender and invite all neighbouring supermarkets to bid for the privilege of supplying him with his daily bread. Not even Priceline has attempted that yet. Now that would be truly revolutionary!

www.Amazon.co.uk
Amazon

Overall rating: ★ ★ ★ ★ ★		
Classification: P2P	**Readability:**	★ ★ ★ ★ ★
Updating: Continuously	**Reliability:**	★ ★ ★ ★ ★
Navigation: ★ ★ ★ ★ ★	**Speed:**	★ ★ ★ ★ ★

UK £ R

The Amazon site will be familiar to UK cyber shopperholics everywhere as an online retailer of books and music (and DVD and video equipment, electronics and software, toys and video games, and home-improvement products in the USA).

You can also sell off your possessions on Amazon, either by placing them in zShops at take-it-or-leave-it prices, or by taking your chance at auction.

Amazon hosts three kinds of person-to-person auctions:

Standard (or traditional) auctions for single items of a group of items to one high bidder, with or without reserve prices

Dutch auctions, where all the winners pay the lowest successful price bid

Private auctions, where the bidders are not identified during the auction and only the seller and high bidder are informed of the result

BUYING

The process is the same in principle as with other auction sites. You browse by category, use the Quicksearch tool at the top of the home page or perform an Advanced Search by a number of simultaneous filters. Featured auctions are also listed on the home page.

You will be required to register at your first auction and to supply credit-card details for verification only.

The bidding page contains important information about the state of the auction:

- The item title
- Whether it is a Dutch auction and the number of items on auction
- The item description
- The minimum bid
- The auction closing time and date
- The 'alias' of the seller
- The location of the item
- The number of bids received and the bidding history
- Whether the item is eligible for a first-bidder discount or a take-it price
- The accepted payment methods

Bidding is automated by proxy with a bid limit. Reliable 'Bid Click' keeps raising your bid by one increment at a time towards victory or oblivion. You are advised by email if you have been outbid, so that you can re-enter the fray.

There are some nice additional features: the auction is not concluded until 10 minutes of bidless time have elapsed, reducing the possibility of being sniped out by a last second bid. The seller can offer a first-bidder discount in order to attract an early bid, or may post a take-it price. You can secure the item and end the auction if you bid this price.

SELLING

The listing form requires you to provide:
- The item title
- A description and (optional) photograph
- The item category
- The minimum bid and any reserve price (discouraged)

- The auction type (Standard, Dutch, Private)
- Duration of the auction
- Accepted means of payment
- First-bidder discount and take-it price
- Display features

As a seller you can also cross-link your item to as many as nine specific products in the Amazon 'shops'. Your auction listing is advertised whenever Amazon customers look up these products in the retail catalogue. Alternatively, notice of your auction can be triggered by a key word.

CHARGES

There are no charges for registration, viewing or buying.

Sellers incur a success fee based on the value of the trade:

0 to £20 @ 5%.
£20.01 to £750 @ £1.00 plus 2.5% of the value over £20
£750.01 upwards @ £19.25 + 1.25% of the excess over £750

There is a separate tariff for optional display features:

Bold face type costs £1.50 per listing.

Category Feature Listings on the browse pages relating to the item category, sorted by auction end date so that the listing becomes more prominent as your auction nears completion. This costs £10 per listing.

Home Page Featured Listings on the Amazon.co.uk Auctions or the zShops homepages at £75 per listing.

POST AUCTION

Amazon emails the seller and victorious bidder at the end of the auctioning and introduces them to each other. You are expected to agree payment and delivery arrangements within three business days. Thereafter, apart from some vague guidelines on what to do in case of non-delivery and outright fraud, you are more or less on your own. There is no in-house or online escrow service to handle the payment.

Estimates of the cost of delivery can be obtained by links to the United Parcel Services site and its Quick Cost Calculator, the Royal Mail and Federal Express.

There is no feedback forum as such. However, you can leave a rating of a buyer or seller on the system within 60 days of the close of your auction and Amazon 'will take it seriously'.

A terrific auction site, full of innovations. It seems to have thought of just about everything, except how to prevent you from getting fleeced.

www.qxl.com
qxl

Overall rating: ★ ★ ★ ★			
Classification:	P2P/B2P	Readability:	★ ★ ★ ★ ★
Updating:	Continuously	Reliability:	★ ★ ★ ★ ★
Navigation:	★ ★ ★ ★ ★	Speed:	★ ★ ★ ★ ★

UK £ R

QXL or Quixell is a 'pan-European auction community' running person-to-person and business-to-person internet auctions in the UK, France, Germany, the Netherlands, Italy, Norway and Denmark.

QXL holds traditional, single-item auctions and multiple-item Early-Bird Yankee auctions (for items such as package holidays) where the winning bidders pay the price they have bid rather than the lowest successful bid as they would do in Dutch auctions.

The merchandise traded on QXL auction sites originates from QXL Direct (trading on its own account), Merchant Partners of QXL and individual members of the general public. Goods sold by QXL Direct and Merchant Partners are all new, but merchandise auctioned by individuals is likely to be used or second hand.

Members of the public who conduct 50 or more successful auctions and who give excellent service (respond quickly to winning bids, communicate well with auction winners) are known as Star Sellers. They get a star rating next to their auction sites, opportunities to promote their auctions on site and in the online newsletter, and get priority customer servicing.

REGISTRATION

All buyers and sellers must register to be able to trade, although anyone can browse the items listed for auction. Registration is free, mercifully brief and entails selecting a username (Member ID), password and a 'bidding alias'.

If you want to bid for merchandise auctioned by QXL Direct or Merchant Partners, you have to provide your credit-card details at registration, for immediate post-auction billing and proof of credit-worthiness.

SITE ORGANISATION

It is worthwhile exploring the overhead navigation bar in order to get to grips with this site, and to uncover detail that is either missing or obscured in the main texts.

Browse generates a list of all merchandise categories and sub-categories, and acts as one of the gateways to the auction. (The headline categories are also listed on a side panel.)

Sell shows you how to create and manage your auctions.

My QXL deals with members' ratings, affiliates programmes and pending developments (currently chat rooms and email).

Members Support holds bidder and seller guides, FAQs, registration details and security policies.

BUYING

There are 10 categories to browse (art and collectibles, cars and transport, computing, electronics, entertainment, good causes, home and garden, sports and fitness, the travel shop and 'more categories'). Each headline category fragments into numerous sub-categories. Click on any of these and you land up with a list of all auctions in the sub-category. Choose any auction that takes your fancy.

Advanced Search Alternatively, if you know what you are looking for, you can use this search feature to locate an auction by multiple criteria: location, time, subcategory, brand, seller type (QXL Direct, Merchant Partners, Star Sellers or Individuals) and seller name.

The viewing/bidding page shows the current state of the auction. The following information is displayed:

• The product description and (sometimes) a photograph of the item and whether the merchandise is new, used or second hand.
• Quantity available.
• The concluding date and time of the auction.
• The category of seller (Merchant Partner, Star Seller or individual).
• Current bids, bid increments and whether the reserve price has been met.
• Item location.
• Shipping terms, including whether the buyer pays.
• Accepted payment terms.

You can bid in two ways:

Manually in person. Bids are raised by the minimum increment by clicking on the '+' button followed by the Place Bid key. If you are outbid during the course of the auction, you are notified by email to enable you to counter bid.

BidRobot Your bid is raised by automated increments until you win or your predetermined bid limit is reached. This facility is useful when you can't stay online for the remaining duration of the auction, but you don't want to be outbid while you're not online.

WINNING BIDS

For QXL Direct auctions, your credit card is debited immediately and the goods are dispatched to you directly.

For Merchant Partner auctions, your credit-card details are sent to the Merchant Partner who charges the sale amount to your card and sends you the goods.

For Star Seller and Individual auctions, the buyer and seller's email addresses are exchanged. The buyer e-mails the seller and sends payment within four days of confirmation of terms. The seller dispatches the goods within four days of receiving payment.

SELLING

You 'create your own auction' by completing a detailed listing form with the following information:

• Your member ID and password.
• A title for your auction (for example, Blitz Laptop Computer with 'ATB').
• The primary category of the item and a product description of up to 2000 words.
• The number of identical items for sale.
• The commencement date and duration of the auction.
• The starting price (minimum bid) and reserve price.
• The allowable bidders (for example, credit-card members only) and payment terms.
• Item location.
• Shipping terms (radius from home/anywhere in home country/EU/world).

You can view the progress of your auction through the Advanced Search or by clicking on Member Services, selecting My Account and choosing My Auctions. You are informed by email whenever your auction receives a bid.

The winning buyer's particulars are emailed to you at the end of the auction. You should contact the buyer within four days to confirm your address, accepted payment method and shipping costs (if the buyer is paying). You are required to dispatch the goods within four days of receiving payment, under the rules of the auction.

CHARGES

There are no viewing or buying charges.
The seller incurs a Success Fee on the following scale:

£0 to £15.00 @ 5%
plus £15.01 to £600 @ 2.5%
plus £600.01 + @ 1.25%

You are given a credit of £5 when you first sign on. This means that your first £185 worth of auction sales are free.

POST AUCTION SERVICES

QXL SafePay is an in-house escrow-type service, which holds the payment for the full amount of the purchase plus shipping costs and a fee. The funds are released to the seller when the buyer has received the goods and is satisfied.

The QXL SafeShip service delivers door to door using approved couriers like The Royal Mail. Shipping costs depend on the delivery area, and the weight, size and handling of the item. For a small extra charge you can arrange to have the merchandise delivered between 6.00 and 9.00 p.m., Mondays to Fridays.

A businesslike site with impressive post auction services. The onscreen text is somewhat small, and the bidding form hasn't quite got the clean coherence of eBay and Amazon. The site currently lacks the joie de vivre of eBay, but things could liven up when the Category-Specific Chat Rooms are added.

www.imx.com
IMX Exchange

Overall rating: ★ ★ ★ ★			
Classification:	B2B	**Readability:**	★ ★ ★ ★ ★
Updating:	Continuously	**Reliability:**	★ ★ ★ ★ ★
Navigation:	★ ★ ★ ★ ★	**Speed:**	★ ★ ★ ★ ★

US £ R

IMX Exchange claims to be 'the world's only real-time bid/ask trading exchange between mortgage brokers and lenders.' In effect, IMX is a trading floor in cyber space, where lenders and brokers trade mortgages (rather than shares).

Industrywide Mortgage Exchange (IMX) was founded in 1995 and began trading in California in 1997 and now operates in 44 states. IMX has 1,400 mortgage brokerages and 70 mortgage lenders on its books, and has traded $1.8bn of 'wholesale mortgage assets' to date.

The IMX site is of no immediate practical use to UK borrowers at present, but it is sometimes held up as an example of the application of the principle of reverse auctioning in the mortgage market, although it does not describe itself as an auction site.

HOW IT WORKS

Unlike other mortgage services that attempt to cut out intermediaries, IMX uses the mortgage broker as the conduit between borrower and lender. The game plan is to harness the economies and the efficiency of the internet for the mutual benefit of borrowers, lenders, intermediaries and IMX itself, which takes a commission from the lender for each 'sale'.

The prospective borrower and the broker discuss a 'loan program'. The broker submits the standard loan data and a target interest rate online to the IMX Exchange database. Only the 'borrower and property-specific information' is withheld until the loan is 'locked'.

Meanwhile, the lenders are searching the IMX database for loan requests that fit their lending criteria, such as loan-to-value, property type, location, credit score, and ratio of debt to income.

The lenders place anonymous bids online for the loans that fit their criteria. A bid is not confined to the interest rate but includes other factors like fees, lock period (the period for which the interest rate is held), points (upfront fees, where each point is 1% of the loan) and 'delivery requirements'. The lender also specifies processing times for underwriting, document preparation and funding.

The broker is notified by email that a bid has been made. Bids are classified as accepted, pending or declined. When all the bids have been received, the broker selects the winning bid.

The identities of the lender and borrower are disclosed to one another. The lender requests the loan file from the broker and takes up the reins. The lender pays a fee to IMX Exchange at the close of the loan, at no cost to the broker or borrower.

IMX does not describe itself as an auction site because bids are not submitted on the basis of APR alone and there is no interactivity between the competing lenders at present. In future, lenders may be able to see the best current bid pending and hence to adjust their terms while the bidding is still open. However, this feature is still in the development stage.

www.priceline.com
Priceline

Overall rating: ★ ★ ★ ★			
Classification:	P2B	Readability:	★ ★ ★ ★ ★
Updating:	Continuously	Reliability:	★ ★ ★ ★ ★
Navigation:	★ ★ ★ ★	Speed:	★ ★ ★ ★ ★

US £ R

Priceline.com is an American auction site which operates its own patented Demand Collection System, a variant of reverse auctioning. In simple terms, Demand Collection enables consumers to name the prices that they are prepared to pay for goods and services, and matches them up with suppliers who are prepared to bid for the business and meet their terms.

In effect, Priceline acts as in intermediary between buyers and registered sellers on their database. The winning seller is the first to accept the buyer's terms. The incentive for sellers is the opportunity to dispose of excessive inventory or overcapacity. Buyers benefit from lower prices and Priceline scores by negotiating a margin for itself directly with the supplier.

Priceline holds auctions for hotel rooms, car rentals, airline tickets, new cars, home mortgages and groceries. It is also hosts a person-to-person auction site called Perfect YardSale.

One downside of the system is that the buyer does not know the identity of the supplier until the conclusion of the auction. In practical terms this could mean that you can't identify your airline or your hotel until after you have entered a binding contract. *Caveat emptor!*

HOW IT WORKS

Buyers do not need to register to use this site. The sellers are registered members of the Priceline database.

Airline tickets You tell Priceline your travel dates, the number of tickets you require, credit-card details and how much you want to pay. Priceline will respond within an hour. If Priceline finds an airline to accept your price, it will immediately purchase the tickets and charge them to your credit card. There are no additional charges for the service. Requests can only be made for round-trip travel and you can't change, transfer or cancel your tickets. You won't know with which airline you are flying until Priceline gets back to you.

Car Rental Select your location, car type and dates. Name your price for the entire period and submit your credit card details. Priceline will hawk your terms around all its registered car rental companies. If your offer is accepted, the booking will be made and your credit card will be charged immediately.

Car and Truck Purchase Furnish exact details of the vehicle you want and the price you are prepared to pay. Priceline advises you within one business day, if they find a willing supplier. If you go ahead with the deal you pay a fee of $50. If you don't show up at the dealer to complete the transaction on a vehicle that exactly matches your requirements, you pay a $200 'good faith cancellation fee', charged to your credit card.

Groceries Put your grocery list out to tender with the Priceline Webhouse Club. Pick your items from a list, nominating alternative brands for each item and naming your price. You are informed within one minute which prices have been accepted. Your credit card is charged and you print off a pre-paid grocery list. Take this down to any participating local supermarket and collect your order.

Home Mortgages You complete a request form for one of Priceline's 'home finance products', specifying the interest rate you want to pay and the terms. Your request is submitted to Priceline's registered panel of lenders. You get a decision by e-mail within 6 business hours. There is no fee payable to Priceline but a lender who agrees to your terms can ask for a $200 'good faith deposit'.

Hotel Rooms Enter the city, check-in and check-out dates and the number of rooms needed. You can specify the area of town and the quality of accommodation (1-5 star). Name the price you want to pay per night per room. If you are prepared to subscribe to a Discoverer Platinum credit card, you can have $20 per night added to your named price, at no cost to you. This will improve your chances of finding a room. The system confirms your reservation details and makes you 'initial' an acknowledgement that Priceline will charge your credit card with the total cost of your stay (including tax and a $5 processing fee) if it finds an hotel willing to accept your price. You are then required to submit your credit-card details.

Priceline undertakes to e-mail you within one hour with the result of your request. Only then will you discover the name and address of your hotel. Have a nice day!

Perfect YardSale Sellers inform Priceline of the items for sale and their minimum prices. Buyers submit their requests and name their prices. Both parties submit credit-card details for verification and billing. Priceline handles the entire transaction and offers a 7-day money back guarantee if the item is not as described. There is also a 30-day warranty against breakage or malfunction to a limit of $250 (or the final price if lower), to cover repair costs. This service is effectively a person-to-person auction facility hosted by Priceline.

The key question is whether Priceline is a true reverse auctioneer, or simply a nifty quotation service. Hal Segal of TravelBids, who claims to have invented the concept of the reverse auction and to have coined the term, has challenged the Demand Collection System in the context of air travel. The TravelBids site identifies several key differences with its own 'pure' reverse auction system, particularly the limited number of airlines supplying spare tickets to Priceline; the invisibility of bidding with the Priceline service, compared to complete bidding transparency with TravelBids; and TravelBids' 1 to 72-hour auction duration, compared with Priceline's one hour duration. Finally, unlike an authentic reverse auction, the Demand Collection System compels the customer to complete the deal if a bidder is found.

At first sight, Demand Collection seems to be a kind of reverse first-bid-wins system. The buyer kicks off with a low price, which has to be raised if it fails to draw out any sellers, and the auction winner is the first seller to accept the buyer's terms. However, the Achilles heel is the relatively narrow panel of bidders. For instance, mortgage requests are submitted to four panel lenders, and car rental requests to the five major rental companies only.

www.fsauctions.co.uk
fs auctions

Overall rating: ★ ★ ★ ★				
Classification:	P2P/B2P	-	Readability:	★ ★ ★ ★ ★
Updating:	continuously		Reliability:	★ ★ ★ ★ ★
Navigation:	★ ★ ★ ★ ★		Speed:	★ ★ ★ ★ ★

UK £ R

FSauctions is a joint venture between FreeServe, the Internet Service Provider and portal site, and auctions.com, a subsidiary of US-based internet services business, Classified Ventures.

FSauctions is a person-to-person and business-to-person online auction service, aimed at FreeServe's active customer base. The site hosts traditional auctions (with or without reserve prices) and Dutch auctions for multiple items.

Registration is free and mandatory for sellers and buyers, although anyone can browse the categories and auctions.

BUYING

Browse by clicking on the relevant category on the left-hand side panel on the home page. Alternatively, use the search tool also on the home page or go to Advanced Search. Click on the primary category and you get a list of all auctions in that category. A set of small icons next to each entry tells you whether a reserve price applies and the auction format (such as Dutch or English).

Viewing/bidding This section is nicely laid out with all the required information displayed down the left-hand side of the page. You have to log-in with your email address and password before you can bid.

Bidding is effectively automated by proxy ('RoboBid') to a bid limit. If you want to keep control of the bidding yourself, you can set your bid limit to the current price plus the smallest allowable increment. However, you may find yourself being rapidly outbid by RoboBid acting on behalf of other buyers, particularly at the early stages of the auction.

SELLING

Before you can list any item, you have to deposit at least £10 in your seller's account, payable by Visa or Mastercard.

The listing form makes the usual demands for item description, category, location, auction duration, payment terms, and shipping terms. Photographs cannot be hosted on fsauctions but can be stored on your personal website and linked by an URL on the seller's form.

The seller has the option to extend the auction for the equivalent of the original duration (Second Chance). This is a way of keeping the auction open if the reserve price has not been met. At the end of the Second Chance run, the auction is closed.

WINNING BIDS

FSauctions emails both seller and high bidder to introduce them to one another and to confirm the closing bid. It is up to the seller and high bidder to make contact and finalise payment and shipping terms.

Buyers and sellers can rate each other. Click on the **Rate a User** link to get through to the **I'm a Buyer/Seller** pages. The seller's feedback score appears next to the seller's name on the bidding page.

CHARGES

There are no charges for viewing or buying. Technically there is a listing fee of 10p, which is waived at present. The seller incurs a success fee of 3% of the final bid, provided that the item reaches its reserve price. Sellers who do not have sufficient funds in their accounts, must replenish their balances by Visa or Mastercard.

POST AUCTION SERVICES

There is no escrow service, and the only real consequence of non-delivery or misrepresentation is an adverse comment in the user ratings.

There is no resident shipping service, but you can go to the Freeserve Post Room for details of services available from Royal Mail and Parcelforce Worldwide.

A cheerful, functional service, with clear layout on the bidding page. Freeserve could make it easier for you to display photographs, and there are no serious safeguards in place against non-delivery. Freeserve has a large base of active registered accounts (1.48m in September 1999), and this site could conceivably grow into a major auction service.

www.eBay.co.uk
e-bay

Overall rating: ★ ★ ★ ★ ★			
Classification: P2P		**Readability:**	★ ★ ★ ★ ★
Updating: Continuously		**Reliability:**	★ ★ ★ ★ ★
Navigation: ★ ★ ★ ★ ★		**Speed:**	★ ★ ★ ★ ★

UK £ R

eBay.co.uk is an arm of the renowned and oldest American person-to-person auction site. It is interactive, educative and wonderfully entertaining. The heart of the site may lie in its cyber-auction rooms but the spirit resides in the Community Centre with its eBay and AOL cafés and the Category-Specific Chat Rooms.

Registration is free but somewhat protracted. You first complete and submit the initial application form. eBay confirms your application by email and issues you with an access code. Finally, you confirm acceptance of their terms and conditions by email.

SITE ORGANISATION

eBay is a complex site, so it is worthwhile taking out time to explore before you hit the auctions. The site map will give you an overview of the architecture. Thereafter, work your way through the six-section overhead navigation panel:

Browse lists featured auctions and item categories and sub-categories. Click here for a list of item categories: Antiques and Art, Automotive, Books/Movies/Music, Coins and Stamps, Computers, Collectibles, Dolls/Dolls Houses, Jewellery/ Gemstones, Photo and Electronics, Sports and Toys/Bean Bag Plush. This is your gateway to the auction itself. Each category leads to lists of sub-categories and product types so you can narrow down your search

Sell downloads the item-listing form.

Services deals with registration, buying and selling tools and monitoring past and present auctions.

Search for an auction by title, category, seller and bidder. This is useful as an alternative to Browse if you know what you are looking for in advance. For example, if you have a preference for a particular brand of laptop, you can refine your search accordingly. The search facility also enables you to participate in foreign auctions hosted by eBay.

Help introduces you to the basics of internet auctions, provides Buyer and Seller Guides, My Info (account details and passwords) and Community Standards (house rules).

Community takes you to the chat rooms, library and suggestions box.

VIEWING

As you enter an auction through Browse or Search the first thing you see is a summary of the state of the auction. You can view the current and minimum bid, the quantity of items on auction, the auction time remaining, the number of bids entered thus far (with access to the bidding history), the location of the item, acceptable payment methods and shipping details.

You can check the seller's **Feedback Profile**. If you are a frequent seller, those who have traded with you may score you positively (1 point), neutrally (0 points) or negatively (-1 point). A Feedback Rating is the sum of these points. Traders who have accumulated 10 points or more are graded by a colour-coded star system

If you have any questions about the item, you can email the (anonymous) vendor. Proceed to a description of the item which may include photographs

BIDDING

Click on the bid icon or scroll down to the bidding form. Enter a secret maximum bid. Bidding is by proxy in stated increments (such as £10 at a time) until your maximum bid is exceeded or you win. If your bid wins, the seller's particulars will be disclosed to you. You are required to make contact within three business days to make final arrangements for payment and delivery.

SELLING

Before you can sell anything, you need to file your credit card details with eBay, for payment of auction fees (listing and final value) and other charges.

LISTING

Listing entails completion of a long questionnaire requiring all the wealth of detail demanded by a typical person-to-person auction site: description of item, photograph, location, acceptable means of payment, minimum bids and reserve prices. When you submit your listing you are issued with an item number, to help you keep track of the auction. At the close of the auction, the particulars of the high bidder are disclosed, enabling you to confirm payment and delivery instructions.

CHARGES

There are no charges for viewing, bidding and buying. Sellers incur listing and final value fees.

Listing Fees for items denominated in sterling are waived until 4 July 2000. However, the seller may still incur some charges for optional non-standard displays of listed items for promotional purposes.

Final Value Fees are levied on the value of the sale at the end of the auction, with the exception of motor vehicle and

real estate. These fees are 5 per cent of the value of the highest bid up to £15.00, plus 2.5 per cent of the value between £15.01 and £600, plus 1.25 per cent of the value of the high bid over £600. For multiple-item Dutch auctions, the final value is the lowest successful bid price multiplied by the quantity sold.

OTHER FEATURES

There is no escrow service on the UK site, unlike the American sister site which hosts a link to iescrow (www.iescrow.com). Instead, eBay (UK) has an insurance scheme covering non-receipt of the items which have been paid for, or goods that differ significantly from the description in the auction. The maximum cover is £120, less an excess of £15.

If you want to read about online auctions in general this is the site to come to. Hit Help on the overhead navigation bar and select from Basics, Buyer Guide and Seller Guide for a crash course. Use the search tool for looking up specific topics.

The Category-Specific Chat Rooms are an absolute hoot. You are not allowed to discuss business but, apart from that, anything goes. Join in the banter and then click on to find out what the hell they are selling.

A serious business site that is also great fun. Beats a weekend visit to Ikea hands down!

www.bidbusiness.co.uk

Bidbusiness

Overall rating: ★ ★ ★ ★			
Classification: B2B/B2P		**Readability:**	★ ★ ★ ★ ★
Updating: Continuously		**Reliability:**	★ ★ ★ ★ ★
Navigation: ★ ★ ★ ★		**Speed:**	★ ★ ★ ★ ★

UK £ R

Bidbusiness is the UK's first business-to-business and business-to-person online auction site, specialising in the construction and related industries. Bidbusiness is the online arm of Minerals Millennium Limited, an industrial minerals trading company.

Bidbusiness hosts bid-up/bid-down auctions (see Bidding and Charges) on ten related auction sites:

constructr-auctions.com which auctions construction materials, products and services.

wheretheresmuck.com for waste disposal, waste products, scrap metal and waste product trading.

mineralbid.co.uk auctions industrial minerals, energy products, mineral extraction and site services.

propertybid.co.uk hosts commercial and domestic property auctions.

bidmachine.co.uk is the site for new and used plant, machinery and tool sales.

hirebid.co.uk for plant machinery and tool hire.

redlorryyellowlorry.com for haulage services and vehicle sales.

Yellowskips.com for skip-hire services.

agri-bid.com for agricultural products and services.

theyBIDuPVC.com for uPVC products

Products are also displayed in the Online Store at fixed prices.

Registration is free and mandatory for sellers only. The registration form asks sellers to specify all the acceptable means of payment from the buyer, to select a username ('handle') and password, and to nominate the preferred method of paying auction fees.

BUYING

Prospective buyers select the required auction site from the aforementioned list of ten Then they proceed to the product categories and to the specific item auction. Alternatively, buyers can use the power search tool to find specific commodities.

Viewing The viewing/bidding page is very similar in layout to that of any business-to-person site. There is a description of the product (with a photograph), the quantity available, the supplier username, remaining bidding time shown on a countdown clock, the current leading bid, immediate bidding history, and the minimum bidding increment. Buyers can click on the seller's handle to access the feedback ratings.

Bidding BidBusiness seems to use a terminology all of its own. Auctions operate on a bid-up or bid-down basis, depending on the time of day that the seller's listing is posted. Bid-down listings are currently posted between 4 pm and 8pm, and bid-up listings at all other times.

The bid-up basis is used when suppliers want to sell items, market-test new products or sell off inventory at best prices. The bid-down basis is used for construction tenders posted on the site, and for buyers seeking the best prices for materials and services. Bidding is either manual by set increments, or automated by proxy (AutoBid) to a unit price bid limit.

Winning Bids Winning bidders are notified by e-mail that they have won. Buyers are required to contact sellers to finalise payment and shipping within three working days. Buyers and sellers can rate each other through the AuctionRate feedback facility.

SELLING

Sellers are required to complete a listing form. Newcomers to the site can use a Wizard to guide them through the process. Experienced operators can go to the form directly. The information required is similar to that on any auction listing: title, description, whether this is to be a featured Hot Item, quantity, starting bid, reserve price, bid increment, and the start and end date of the auction.

CHARGES

There are no charges for viewing or buying. Sellers incur the following charges auction charges:

Listing Fee, which is waived until further notice.

Hot Auction Fee is an optional fee to have an item featured prominently. This service costs £25 + VAT, non-refundable even if the item attracts no bids or fails to meet its reserve price.

Final Value Fees
£0 to £249.99 @ 7% of the final value, plus
£249.99 to £2,500 @ 5%, plus
£2,500 + @ 3%

For traditional (single-item) bid-up auctions (with or without reserve price) the final value is based on the highest bid price. For bid-down auctions the final value is based on the lowest price bid. For multiple-item bid-up auctions, the final value is the highest bid price multiplied by the quantity bought. For multiple-item bid-down auctions the final value is the lowest price bid multiplied by the quantity bought.

Property auctions on propertybid.co.uk attract a seller's commission of 0.75%.

Purchases through the On-line Store incur the same charges as goods bought at auction.

POST AUCTION SERVICES

Buyers and sellers are required to negotiate their own shipping arrangements. They have no claim on Bidbusiness in respect of non-completion or misrepresentation, save for possible refund of auction fees and a negative score in the offender's AuctionRate area.

An utterly fascinating site, well laid out and easily navigable. The only reservation is some mysterious bidding terminology, which needs to be simplified or clarified. What on earth is a bid-up Dutch auction?

www.ebid.co.uk
eBid

Overall rating: ★ ★ ★ ★			
Classification: P2P/B2P		**Readability:**	★ ★ ★ ★ ★
Updating: Continuously		**Reliability:**	★ ★ ★ ★ ★
Navigation: ★ ★ ★ ★ ★		**Speed:**	★ ★ ★ ★ ★

UK £ R

eBid is a British person-to-person and business-to-person online auction site, trading in over 600 categories of merchandise.

Registration is free, and is necessary if you want to trade. However, anyone can browse the merchandise and drop in on the auctions. You do not need to submit credit-card details, but your password is emailed to you by eBid so that they can authenticate your registration.

BUYING

Select your category from drop-down list on the home page. You can refine your search by selecting new auctions which have been opened within the last 24 hours, busy auctions where at least 5 bids have been received and closing auctions which have less than 24 hours left to run. The schedule of ongoing auctions reflects whether each entry is a traditional or Dutch auction, with or without a reserve price.

The viewing/bidding section is laid out very much like any other auction site, with easy access to the bidding history and seller rating on a convenient side panel. The bidding area instructs you quite plainly what your lowest possible bid is, by adding the smallest allowable increment to the current price. If you want to engage in automated bidding by proxy, simply enter your maximum price and the system will raise your bid by the smallest increment at a time, until your limit is exceeded or you win.

SELLING

Sellers are not required to register for an auction. Credit or debit-card details are only required when the first transaction is processed. All new registrations receive £2.00 towards the charges on their future trades.

Sellers are required to fill out the detailed listing form, providing a description of the item (plus a photograph), category, starting price, reserve price (if applicable), bid increment, location, payment methods, shipping terms et al.

WINNING BIDS

The seller and winning buyer are e-mailed with the results of the auction and contact details. The parties are encouraged to leave feedback on the system for the benefit of future buyers and sellers.

CHARGES

There are no charges for viewing or bidding. Selling charges are made up of a handling fee and a closing fee which come into play when the reserve price has been met.

Handling Fee
0 to £10 of the reserve price: 15 pence
£10.01 to £75: 40 pence
£75.01+: £1.00

Closing Fee
0 to £10: 7.5% of final bid
£10.01 to £75: 5%
£75.01+ :2.5%

Fees are charged to your account and settled by credit or debit card at the end of each month.

POST AUCTION SERVICES

Buyers can avail themselves of itrustyou (www.itrustyou.com), an independent escrow service for handling payment. The buyer pays the value of the merchandise plus shipping costs to itrustyou, by credit card, cheque, money order or wire transfer. itrustyou charges 6% of the deal value plus shipping and handling charges.

The money is deposited in a client account. As soon as the funds have cleared, itrustyou instructs the seller to ship the goods, using the track and trace services of an approved carrier like Royal Mail, Parcel Force, Securicor, Fedex or UPS. The buyer and seller agree on a period of inspection, following which the funds can be sent to the seller.

If the buyer does not use the escrow service then the only sanction against non-delivery or a false item description seems to be a negative mark in the feedback section.

A functional service, with a useful (albeit pricey) escrow service. The selling charges are also a bit on the high side. The site appearance is a little dowdy and lacks the clarity of some of the more prestigious auction sites. The ubiquitous blue 'backcloth' does strain the old eyes.

www.yahoo.co.uk
Yahoo

Overall rating: ★ ★ ★ ★			
Classification: P2P		**Readability:**	★ ★ ★ ★ ★
Updating:	Continuously	**Reliability:**	★ ★ ★ ★ ★
Navigation:	★ ★ ★ ★ ★	**Speed:**	★ ★ ★ ★ ★

UK £ R

This auction site offers free buying and selling. The downside is that you are on your own if anything goes wrong. Yahoo has no involvement in the transaction and does not intervene in disputes between buyer and seller, other than to enforce the bidding/buying and listing/selling rules.

There is no escrow service and no shipping service, although useful information about the latter can be found in the resident guides.

Yahoo Auctions is essentially a person-to-person auction service. Yahoo describes the process as similar to placing and responding to classified ads. Most auctions are of the single item traditional kind, with or without reserve prices. Occasionally, you will come across a Dutch auction for a quantity of identical items. I also spotted a Firstbidwins in the undergrowth.

Registration is free and entails little more than selecting a username and a password.

BUYING

The buying process is similar to comparable auction sites. You can browse the item categories or use the search tool if you are on the home page.

The item can be viewed in the conventional way. The auction title will indicate whether this is a Dutch Auction. The bidding form tells you the current bid, time remaining, number of items, bids received and bidding history, starting price, reserve price if applicable and whether it has been met already, bid increments, location of the item and shipping terms.

The bidding system is essentially automated by proxy. You enter a maximum bid and the system increases your bids by the smallest allowable increment at a time, until you win or hit your bid limit. However, you can control the bidding in person, by setting your maximum bid at the current bid price plus one smallest increment.

SELLING

You have to register to list an item for sale, and submit your credit card details to verify your identity.

You browse through the 'auctions hierarchy' and select the category that is closest to nature of your item. The listing form requires an auction title, a description of the item with or without a photograph, shipping information, payment options, the quantity of items for sale, and starting price.

You can customise your auction further to include:

Auto-extension Prolonging the auction beyond the original termination time, as long as there is bidding activity, The alternative is known as a hard close time.

A reserve price

A sell price The first bidder to offer the sell price wins outright, and no subsequent bids are entertained.

Auto-resubmission If there is no winning bidder by the time your auction closes, the auction begins again with the same information.

International shipping Sellers who select this option have their auctions displayed on the Yahoo international sites.

POST AUCTION

At the end of the auction, Yahoo e-mails both buyer and seller. It is the seller's obligation to contact the winning bidder in order to finalise payment and shipping. This can be done by e-mailing a customisable message to the winner, downloaded from Options.

Direct links are provided to the Royal Mail, Federal Express and DHL sites for shipping. However, there are no links provided for escrow services.

The seller and the winning buyer receive an e-mail encouraging them to rate one another. They award 1 point for each positive comment, -1 for each negative comment and 0 for 'no comment'. The marks are added to those awarded at previous auctions. The seller's net score is shown against his username on the auction page.

AUCTIONEER	TYPES OF AUCTIONS	AUCTION FORMATS
Amazon (www.amazon.co.uk)	Person-to-Person	Traditional, Dutch
Bidbusiness (www.bidbusiness.co.uk)	Business-to-Person Business-to-Business	bid up/bid down English or Dutch
eBay (www.ebay.co.uk)	Person-to-Person	Traditional, Dutch
eBid (www.ebid.co.uk)	Person-to-Person Business-to-Person	Traditional, Dutch
fsauctions (www.fsauctions.co.uk)	Person-to-Person Business-to-Person	Traditional, Dutch
QXL (www.qxl.com)	Person-to-Person Business-to-Person	Traditional, Early Bird Yankee
Yahoo (www.yahoo.co.uk)	Person-to-Person	Traditional, Dutch

LISTING FEES	SUCCESS FEES			POST-AUCTION SERVICES
	£15 ITEM	£100 ITEM	£1000 ITEM	
none	£0.75	£3.00	£22.37	Insurance to £150
waived	£1.05	£7.00	£52.99	none
waived	£0.75	£2.87	£20.37	Insurance to £120 less £15 excess
none	handling* £0.40	£1.00	£1.00	*itrustyou* (escrow) @ 6% plus shipping and handling costs
	£closing* £0.75	£2.50	£25.00	
waived	£0.45	£3.00	£30.00	none
waived	£0.75	£2.87	£20.37	SafePay (escrow) SafeShip
none	nil	nil	nil	none

* assumes that the final bid is equal to the reserve price

Author's Favourite Sites

CATEGORY	WINNER	URL
Directory	Find	www.find.co.uk
Information	Interactive Investor International	www.iii.co.uk
Newspaper	FT.com	www.ft.com
Share Data	Stockpoint	www.stockpoint.com
Funds Data	S&P Micropal	www.micropal.co.uk
Financial Planning	FT Your Money	www.ftyourmoney.co.uk
Authorised Advisory	Sort	www.sort.co.uk
Share Dealing	DLJ Direct UK	www.djdirect.co.uk
Banking	Virgin One	www.virginone.co.uk
Real Estate	Home to Home	www.home2home.co.uk
Mortgages	E-LOAN	www.eloan.com/uk
Auction	Amazon	www.amazon.co.uk
General Insurance	Screentrade	www.screentrade.co.uk

REASON
Comprehensive, easy to use, directory
Great on investment data, but developing into a solid all rounder
Superb market data and news archives
Quotes. company profiles and wonderful interactive charts
Miraculous organisation of a vast database
Interactive with impressive attention to detail
A brilliant concept on a somewhat dowdy site
By a whisker from Stocktrade. Sold on the electronic ticker tape
For bringing a truly original banking idea to the net
Nicely laid out site with lots of useful links covering all aspects of property purchase
Large panel of lenders and superb presentation
Author's prerogative...
Solid and dull; all the virtues of a good general insurance site

Glossary of Financial Terms

ADR American Depository Receipt. A tradable certificate denominated in US$, issued by a US bank against a deposit of foreign shares.

AIM Alternative Investment Market. The London Stock Exchange's market for small companies without a full listing.

Annual Percentage Rate (APR) The true rate of interest payable on a loan, after allowing for all costs.

Base rate The minimum rate at which banks are prepared to lend money. Borrowers pay a premium over base rate. Changes in the base rate are triggered by changes in the rate at which the Bank of England lends to the discount houses.

Base Rate Tracker Mortgage A mortgage loan where the rate of interest tracks movements in the base rate.

Capital-and-Interest Mortgage See Repayment Mortgage

Capped Rate Mortgage A variable rate mortgage where the interest rate can lie below but not above a set level. Usually applies for the first few years of the mortgage only.

Cashback Mortgage A mortgage arrangement where the borrower receives a lump-sum payment at commencement

Closed-end fund An investment fund that issues a fixed number of shares to investors (See Investment Trust).

Collective Investment An investment fund created by pooling contributions made by numerous private investors, and administered by professional fund managers (See Unit Trusts, OEICS, Investment Trusts).

Commission A system of remuneration for financial advisers, expressed as a percentage of the sum invested or the annual regular premium on a policy.

Convertible Term Assurance A term assurance policy which can be converted to an endowment or whole life policy for the same sum assured, without having to provide fresh evidence of health and activities.

Conveyancing The legal transfer of freehold and leasehold property, conducted by solicitors or licensed conveyancers.

CREST The computerised paperless system for settlement of share purchases. Operated by CRESTco, a non-profit company formed by 70 market participants.

CREST sponsored membership Personal membership of CREST arranged by a sponsor (usually the broker). Personal members have their shares registered in their own names rather than in the name of a nominee account.

Critical Illness Insurance An insurance policy where a guaranteed sum assured is paid out on the diagnosis of any of the 'critical illnesses' specified in the policy terms.

Decreasing Term Assurance A term assurance policy where the death benefit falls at regular intervals over the term of the policy. Often used to protect Repayment Mortgages

Delayed prices Share prices displayed in arrears (See real-time prices).

Derivatives Financial instruments whose values are based on expected price movements in underlying assets (shares, currencies, and commodities).

Digital Certificate An electronic ID issued by a trusted third party known as a Certification Authority (CA)

Digital signature A message that has been 'hashed', and encrypted using the sender's private key.

Discount per share The difference between a company's net asset value per share and its share price. A characteristic of Investment Trusts.

Discounted Rate Mortgage A mortgage arrangement where the interest rate is held below the standard variable rate by a set margin for a specified period.

Dutch Auction An auction of multiple identical items, where each winning bidder pays the price bid by the lowest successful bidder (See Yankee auction).

Encryption The process of encoding or scrambling a message.

Endowment policy A life assurance policy designed to 'endow' (pay out) a lump sum at a set date or on prior death. A package of investment and life assurance often used to pay off and protect an interest-only mortgage.

Endowment mortgage An interest-only mortgage where the means of repayment is an endowment policy.

English (Traditional) auction A single item auction, where the highest bid wins.

Equities Another name for shares.

Escrow service/agency An agency that holds the money while the winner of an auction is inspecting the goods.

Execution-only No advice has been offered or sought.

Family Income Benefit A form of decreasing term assurance where the sum assured is paid in regular instalments. The death benefit is the value of the instalments due between the date of death and the end of the policy term.

Financial Services Authority The successor to the Securities and Investment Board (SIB). Currently holds the registrations of all firms authorised to conduct investment business in the UK. Will take over the functions of the Self Regulated Organisations when the Financial Services and Markets Bill becomes law.

Fixed Rate Mortgage A mortgage arrangement where the

interest rate is fixed for a set period.

Flexible Mortgage A mortgage arrangement with flexible terms permitting payment holidays, lump sum payments at any time, variations in regular repayments and interest calculated on the outstanding daily balance.

Forex Foreign exchange

FTSE Indices A series of capitalisation-weighted indices published by the Financial Times, reflecting changes in market prices of shares traded mainly on the London Stock Exchange.

General Insurance Typically motor, buildings and contents and travel insurance

Interest-only mortgage A mortgage arrangement where the sum borrowed need not be repaid until the end of the mortgage term, and only interest is paid in the interim. The loan is often repaid by the proceeds of an investment vehicle like an endowment policy, pension plan or ISA/PEP

Independent Financial Adviser (IFA) An authorised financial adviser who acts for the client rather than a product provider. An IFA may recommend and sell the financial products of any provider and is required to offer 'best advice' based on products available on the market as a whole. (See Tied Agent)

Internet Banking A system of private banking whereby customers can perform most routine banking activities from any computer linked to the Internet, rather than from one designated computer (See PC banking).

Investment Trust A closed-end public limited company (plc) that invests shareholders' funds in shares.

ISA Individual Savings Account; the successor to the PEP. A tax-free savings vehicle for holding stocks and shares, life assurance and cash. Holds a wider range of assets than the PEP but is also more complicated. The client can have one maxi-ISA with one manager per annum, or a series of mini-ISAs (shares, life assurance, cash) with three different managers.

Level Term Assurance A form of term assurance where the death benefit is a fixed sum, paid on the death of the life assured within the term of the policy.

LIBOR London Inter Bank Offer Rate; the rate of interest at which banks lend money to each other for maintaining their short–term liquidity.

LIBOR Mortgage A mortgage loan where the interest rate is linked to LIBOR.

Life assurance A contract to pay out a guaranteed sum of money on the death of the life assured, in exchange for a regular premium.

LIFFE London International Financial Futures and Options Exchange; a London-based exchange for trading in futures and options in shares, currencies, interest rates and government bonds.

London Metal Exchange (LME) An exchange for trading non-ferrous metals; copper, lead, zinc, aluminium, tin and nickel

LSE The London Stock Exchange

Mortgage A charge taken on an asset (such as residential or commercial real estate) as security for a loan. The term is commonly used to refer to the loan itself.

Mortgage Protection A life assurance policy designed to repay a mortgage if the borrower dies before the loan has been repaid.

NASDAQ National Association of Securities Dealers Automated Quotation System; A screen-based stockmarket with no trading floor, famous for listing high-tech stocks.

NASDAQ UK NASDAQ within hearing distance of Bow Bells.

Net Asset Value The value of a company's assets less its liabilities.

OEIC Open Ended Investment Company; A collective investment similar to a unit trust, but with a more transparent charging system.

OFEX An unregulated stock exchange for trading shares of smaller companies.

Online Banking A system of personal or business banking where most routine activities can be performed over the Internet.

Online Share Dealing A system of trading on the stockmarket, where buying and selling takes place over the Internet.

Open-Ended Fund A fund with no limit on the number of units in issue, and whose managers are allowed to create or cancel units (See Unit Trust and OEIC).

Order-Routing System A form of online share dealing where client orders are executed by dealers of the host stockbroker rather than directly on the Stock Exchange by the client.

Overhang A lock-in period after the fixed/capped/discount mortgage offer has finished

PC Banking A system of private banking where the customer is able to perform routine banking activities from a personal computer loaded with the bank's software.

PEP Personal Equity Plan; the predecessor of the ISA, now no longer open to new investment. PEPs are tax-free shelters for UK and European equities and equity-based corporate bond funds.

PEP transfer Capital sheltered in a PEP may be transferred to a new fund manager without dissolving the PEP shelter.

Permanent Health Insurance (PHI) An insurance policy that pays out a proportion of your income if you are unable to work due to illness or disability. The benefit is paid out after a 'deferment period', typically 1,3,6 or 12 months after the event. The deferment period is selected when the policy is taken out.

Pooled investment See Collective investment

Portfolio tracker A feature of most online information sites for tracking the value of your shares, funds and other assets throughout the day. Share valuations are usually 15 to 20 minutes in arrears, and funds are valued at previous day closing prices.

Private Key A secret key for encrypting a message, or for decrypting a message encrypted in your public key (See public key).

Private Medical Insurance (PMI) An Insurance policy for paying private medical expenses

Public Key A publicly disseminated key used for sending encrypted messages, to be decoded using the recipient's private key

Public Key Infrastructure A system for the secure transmission of messages and data based on encryption

Real-time prices The ruling share prices, displayed without delay. (See delayed prices)

Recognised Professional Body (RPB) A professional body that supervises the conduct of its members in respect of financial advice (See SROs).

Redemption penalties Financial penalties incurred when repaying a mortgage earlier than an agreed date.

Renewable Term Assurance A form of term assurance where the sum assured can be renewed for a further period at the expiry of the original policy term, without the need to submit fresh evidence of health or activities.

Repayment mortgage A property loan where a slice of the original loan is paid back with each interest payment, so that the outstanding balance reduces to zero over the mortgage term (See Capital-and-Interest mortgage.)

Reverse auction An auction where the buyers set the prices they are prepared to pay and the sellers bid for the business.

Self-Regulated Organisation (SRO) An organisation set up under the 1986 Financial Services Act to supervise the conduct of investment business of its member firms and their agents. The three current SROs are the Personal Investment Authority (PIA), the Investment Managers Regulatory Organisation (IMRO) and the Securities and Futures Authority (SFA). The SROs will be absorbed by the Financial Services Authority when the Financial Services and Markets Bill becomes law.

Standard Variable Rate Mortgage A mortgage arrangement where the interest rate is varied by the lender according to conditions in the money market.

Straight-Through-Processing An online share-dealing system where clients deal directly on the market, via the stockbroker's computer.

TechMARK index A new share index incorporating all British high-tech companies listed in the FTSE indices.

Term Assurance A form of life assurance with a fixed time limit or term. The sum assured is only paid if you die within the term.

Tied Agent An authorised financial adviser who represents a product provider rather than the client, and who may only advise on the products of one company.

Tradepoint A second London Stock Exchange where buyer and seller instructions are matched automatically by computer, without market makers.

Trust A legal device for transferring the beneficial ownership of property to others, without giving the beneficiaires control over it.

Unit Trust   A collective investment vehicle consisting of a portfolio of financial securities selected by professional fund managers. Independent trustees ensure that the fund managers invest within the terms of the trust deed. A unit trust is an 'open–ended' fund which enables the managers to create new units or cancel existing ones (See OEICS).

 Whole Life policy A life assurance policy that pays out on death or critical illness at any time (See Term Assurance)

Yankee auction   An auction of multiple identical items where the successful bidders pay the prices that they have bid (see Dutch auction)

Glossary of Internet Terms

Accelerators Add-on programs, which speed up browsing.

Acceptable Use Policy These are the terms and conditions of using the internet. They are usually set by organisations, who wish to regulate an individual's use of the internet. For example, an employer might issue a ruling on the type of email which can be sent from an office.

Access Provider A company which provides access to the internet, usually via a dial-up account. Many companies such as AOL and Dircon charge for this service, although there are an increasing number of free services such as Freeserve, Lineone and Tesco.net. Also known as an Internet Service Provider.

Account A user's internet connection, with an Access/Internet Service Provider, which usually has to be paid for.

Acrobat Reader Small freely-available program, or web browser plug-in, which lets you view a Portable Document Format (PDF) file.

Across Lite Plug-in which allows you to complete crossword puzzles online.

Address Location name for email or internet site, which is the online equivalent of a postal address. It is usually composed of a unique series of words and punctuation, such as *my.name@myhouse.co.uk*. See also URL.

America Online (AOL) World's most heavily subscribed online service provider.

Animated GIF Low-grade animation technique used on websites.

ASCII Stands for American Standard Code for Information Interchange, It is a coding standard which all computers can recognise, and ensures that if a character is entered on one part of the internet, the same character will be seen elsewhere.

ASCII Art Art made of letters and other symbols. Because it is made up of simple text, it can be recognised by different computers.

ASDL Stands for Asynchronous Digital Subscriber Line, which is a high speed copper wire which will allow rapid transfer of information. Not widely in use at moment, though the government is pushing for its early introduction.

Attachment A file included with an email, which may be composed of text, graphics and sound. Attachments are encoded for transfer across the internet, and can be viewed in their original form by the recipient. An attachment is the equivalent of putting a photograph with a letter in the post.

Bookmark A function of the Netscape Netvigator browser which allows you to save a link to your favourite web pages, so that you can return straight there at a later date, without having to re-enter the address. Favourites in internet Explorer is the same thing.

BPS Abbreviation of Bits Per Second, which is a measure of the speed at which information is transferred or downloaded.

Browse Common term for looking around the web. See also Surfing.

Browser A generic term for the software that allows users to move and look around the Web. Netscape Navigator and

Internet Explorer are the ones that most people are familiar with, and they account for 97 percent of web hits.

Bulletin Board Service A BBS is a computer with a telephone connection, which allows you direct contact to upload and download information and converse with other users, via the computer. It was the forerunner to the online services and virtual communities of today.

Cache A temporary storage space on the hard drive of your computer, which stores downloaded websites. When you return to a website, information is retrieved from the cache and displayed much more rapidly. However, this information may not be the most recent version for sites which are frequently updated and you will need to reload the Website address for these.

Chat Talking to other users on the web in real time, but with typed, instead of spoken words. Special software such as ICQ or MIRC is required before you can chat.

Chat Room An internet channel which allows several people to type in their messages, and talk to one another over the internet.

Clickstream The trail left as you 'click' your way around the web.

Content The material on a website that actually relates to the site, and is hopefully of interest or value. Things like adverts are not considered to be part of the content. The term is also used to refer to information on the internet that can be seen by users, as opposed to programming and other background information.

Cookie A cookie is a nugget of information sometimes sent by websites to your hard drive when you visit.They contain such details as what you looked at, what you ordered, and can add more information, so that the website can be customized to suit you.

Cybercafe Cafe where you can use a computer terminal to browse the net for a small fee.

Cyberspace When first coined by the sci-fi author William Gibson, it meant a shared hallucination which occured when people logged on to computer networks. Now, it refers to the virtual space you're in when on the internet.

Dial Up A temporary telephone connection to your ISP's computer and how you make contact with your ISP, each time you log onto the Internet.

Domain The part of an Internet address which identifies an individual computer, and can often be a business or person's name. For example, in the goodwebguide.com the domain name is theGoodWebGuide.

Download Transfer of information from an Internet server to your computer.

Dynamic HTML The most recent version of the HTML standard.

Ecash Electronic cash, used to make transactions on the internet.

Ecommerce The name for business which is carried out over the internet.

Email Mail which is delivered electronically over the internet. They are usually comprised of text messages, but can contain illustrations, music and animations. Mail is sent to an email address, which is the internet equivalent of a postal address.

Encryption A process whereby information is scrambled to produce a 'coded message', so that it can't be read whilst in transit on the internet. The recipient must have decryption software in order to read the message.

Expire Term referring to newsgroup postings which are automatically deleted after a fixed period of time.

Ezine Publication on the web, which is updated regularly.

FAQ Stands for frequently asked questions and is a common section on websites where the most common enquiries and their answers are archived.

Frame A method which splits web pages into several windows.

FTP/File Transfer Protocol Standard method for transporting files across the internet.

GIF/Graphics Interchange Format A format in which graphics are compressed, and a popular method of putting images onto the internet, as they take little time to download.

Gopher The gopher was the precursor of the world wide web and consisted of archives accessed through a menu, usually organised by subject.

GUI/Graphical User Interface. This is the system which turns binary information into the words and images format you can see on your computer screen. For example, instead of seeing the computer language which denotes the presence of your toolbar, you actually see a toolbar.

Hackers A term used to refer to expert programmers who used their skills to break into computer systems, just for the fun of it. Nowadays the word is more commonly associated with computer criminals, or Crackers.

Header Basic indication of what's in an email: who it's from, when it was sent, and what it's about.

Hit When a file is downloaded from a website it is referred to as a 'hit'. Measuring the number of hits is a rough method of counting how many people visit a website. Except that it's not wholly accurate as one website can contain many files, so one visit by an individual may generate several hits.

Homepage Most usually associated with a personal site, produced by an individual, but can also refer to the first page on your browser, or the first page of a website.

Host Computer on which a website is stored. A host computer may store several websites, and usually has a fast powerful connection to the internet. Also known as a Server.

HTML/Hypertext Mark-Up Language The computer code used to construct web pages.

HTTP/Hypertext Transfer Protocol The protocol for moving HTML files across the web.

Hyperlink A word or graphic formatted so that when you click on it, you move from one area to another. See also hypertext.

Hypertext Text within a document which is formatted so it acts as a link from one page to another, or from one document to another.

Image Map A graphic which contains hyperlinks.

Interface What you actually see on the computer screen.

Internet One or more computers connected to one another is an internet (lower case i). The Internet is the biggest of all the internets. and consists of a worldwide collection of interconnected computer networks.

Internet Explorer One of the most popular pieces of browser software, produced by Microsoft.

Internet Relay Chat See Chat.

Intranet A network of computers, which works in the same way as an internet, but for internal use, such as within a corporation.

ISDN/Integrated Services Digital Network Digital telephone line which facilitates very fast connections and can transfer larges amounts of data. It can carry more than one form of data at once.

ISP/Internet Service Provider See Access Provider.

 Java Programming language which can be used to create interactive multimedia effects on webpages. The language is used to create programmes known as *applets* that add features such as animations, sound and even games to websites.

Javascript A scripting language which, like Java, can be used to add extra multimedia features. However, in contrast with Java it does not consist of separate programmes. Javascript is embedded into the HTML text and can interpreted by the browser, provided that the user has a javascript enabled browser.

JPEG Stands for 'Joint Photographic Experts Group' and is the name given to a type of format which compresses photos, so that they can be seen on the web.

 Kill file A function which allows a user to block incoming information from unwanted sources. Normally used on email and newsreaders.

 LAN/Local Area Network A type of internet, but limited to a single area, such as an office.

Login The account name or password needed to access a computer system.

Link Connection between web pages, or one web document

and another, which are accessed via formatted text and graphic.

 Mailing List A discussion group which is associated with a website. Participants send their emails to the site, and it is copied and sent by the server to other individuals on the mailing list.

Modem A device for converting digital data into analogue signals for transmission along standard phone lines. The usual way for home users to connect to the internet or log into their email accounts. May be internal (built into the computer) or external (a desk-top box connected to the computer).

MP3 A compressed music file format, which has almost no loss of quality although the compression rate may be very high.

 Netscape Popular browser, now owned by AOL.

Newbie Term for someone new to the Internet. Used perjoratively of newcomers to bulletin boards or chat, who commit the sin of asking obvious questions or failing to observe the netiquette.

Newsgroup Discussion group amongst Internet users who share a mutual interest. There are thousands of newsgroups covering every possible subject.

 Offline Not connected to the internet via a telephone line.

Online Connected to the internet via a telephone line.

Offline Browsing A function of the browser software, which allows the user to download pages and read them whilst offline.

Online Service Provider Similar to an access provider, but provides addtional features such as live chat.

PDF/Portable Document Format A file format created by Adobe for offline reading of brochures, reports and other documents with complex graphic design, which can be read by anyone with Acrobat Reader.

Plug-in Piece of software which adds more functions (such as playing music or video) to another, larger software program.

POP3/Post Office Protocol An email protocol that allows you to pick up your mail from any location on the web.

Portal A website which offers many services, such as search engines, email and chat rooms, and to which people are likely to return to often . ISPs such as Yahoo and Alta Vista provide portal sites which are the first thing you see when you log on, and in theory act as gateways to the rest of the web.

Post/Posting Information sent to a usenet group, bulletin board, message board or by email.

PPP/Point to Point Protocol The agreed way of sending data over dial-up connections, so that the user's computer, the modem and the Internet Server can all recognise it. It is the protocol which allows you to get online.

Protocol Convention detailing a set of actions that computers in a network must follow so that they can understand one another.

Query Request for specific information from a database.

RAM /Random Access Memory Your computer's short term memory.

Realplayer G2 A plug-in program that allows you to view video in real-time and listen to sound and which is becoming increasingly important for web use.

Router A computer program which acts as an interface between two networks, and decides how to route information.

Searchable Database A database on a website which allows the user to search for information, usually be keyword.

Search Engine Programs which enable web users to search for pages and sites using keywords. They are usually to be found on portal sites and browser homepages. Infoseek, Alta Vista and Lycos are some of the popular search engines.

Secure Transactions Information transfers which are encrypted so that only the sender and recipient have access to the uncoded message, so that the details within remain private. The term is most commonly used to refer to credit card transactions, although other information can be sent in a secure form.

Server A powerful computer that has a permanent fast connection to the internet. Such computers are usually owned by companies and act as host computers for websites.

Sign-on To connect to the internet and start using one of its facilities.

Shareware Software that doesn't have to be paid for or test version of software that the user can access for free, as a trial before buying it.

Standard A style which the whole of the computer industry has agreed upon. Industry standards mean that hardware and software produced by the various different computer companies will work with one another.

Surfing Slang for looking around the Internet, without any particular aim, following links from site to site.

TLA/Three Letter Acronyms Netspeak for the abbreviations of net jargon, such as BPS (Bits Per Second) and ISP (Internet Service Provider).

Upload To send files from your computer to another one on the internet. When you send an email you are uploading a file.

URL/Uniform Resource Locator Jargon for an address on the internet, such as www.thegoodwebguide.co.uk.

Usenet A network of newsgroups, which form a worldwide system, on which anyone can post 'news'.

Virtual Community Name given to a congregation of regular mailing list/ newsgroup users.

VRML/Virtual Reality Modeling Language Method for creating 3D environments on the web. On a

Wallpaper Description of the sometimes hectic background patterns which appear behind the text on some websites.

Web Based Email/Webmail Email accounts such as Hotmail and Rocketmail, which are accessed via an Internet browser, rather than an email program such as Outlook Express. Webmail has to be typed whilst the user is online,

but can accessed from anywhere on the Web.

Webmaster A person responsible for a web server. May also be known as System Administrator.

Web Page Document which forms one part of a website (though some sites are a single page), usually formatted in HTML.

Web Ring Loose association of websites which are usually dedicated to the same subject and often contain links to one another.

Website A collection of related web pages which often belong to an individual or organisation and are about the same subject.

World Wide Web The part of the Internet which is easy to get around and see. The term is often mistakenly interchanged with Internet, though the two are not the same. If the Internet is a shopping mall, with shops, depots, and delivery bays, then the web is the actual shops which the customers see and use.

Index

How to use your CD

Now we've whetted your appetite for the sites reviewed in this book, we can help you to visit them quickly and easily. By registering on thegoodwebguide site, you will be able to use the hotlinks to all the sites listed, so you just click and go. You can also read the latest versions of reviews and see what we think of new sites that have been launched since the book went to press. If you wish, you can even have the updates emailed to you.

INSTALLATION INSTRUCTIONS FOR PC USERS

Insert the CD enclosed with this book into your CD drive of your PC. A welcome screen will appear with two buttons:

The goodwebguide button To register your purchase of a Good Web Guide book and to receive free updates of the reviews in the book and reviews of the latest sites, click on this button. When you've registered you can click straight through to any of the sites listed. You must have an internet connection to do this. If you are not already signed up with an internet service, you will need to install the LineOne software first.

If you click on the goodwebguide button you will be taken to a registration page where you will be asked to confirm which title in the series you have bought and to register your details. You then have free access to the updates of the website reviews in this book and to new reviews. You will also have access to the rest of the goodwebguide website.

LineOne button If you would like access to the internet you can click on this button to install LineOne's free ISP (internet service provider) software. You will need a modem to have internet access. If you already have an internet connection

(ISP) you can still install LineOne as an alternative provider.

A To join LineOne just click on the LineOne button. When the first screen appears you have a choice: If you are a new user and wish to load Internet Explorer 5 as your browser, select 'Join Now'. On the next screen, select 'Go!' and you will be taken to the Microsoft installation process.

B To join immediately, without installing a browser, click 'Join Now' and then choose 'custom' to go straight to registration.

From the 'Welcome to LineOne' screen, click 'Go' and follow the on-screen instructions.

MAC USERS

This CD is not suitable for Apple Macintosh computers. For Free LineOne Mac Software call free on 0800 111 210.

RETURNING TO THE GOOD WEB GUIDE

Once you've connected to the internet, you can either type www.thegoodwebguide.co.uk into your browser to go directly to our website, or re-insert your CD and click on the goodwebguide button.

SUPPORT

If you have any problems call the LineOne support number.
CALL 0906 30 20 100
(calls may be monitored or recorded for training purposes) 24 hours, 365 days a year. Calls charged at 50p/minute or email support@lineone.net for free support.

Other titles in thegoodwebguide series include

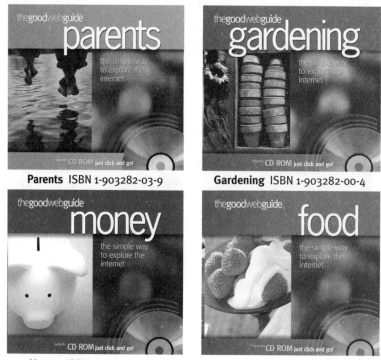

Parents ISBN 1-903282-03-9

Gardening ISBN 1-903282-00-4

Money ISBN 1-903282-02-0

Food ISBN 1-903282-01-2

Forthcoming Good Web Guide titles

The Good Web Guide to Wine
ISBN 1-903282-04-7

The Good Web Guide to Travel
ISBN 1-903282-05-5

The Good Web Guide to Genealogy
ISBN 1-903282-06-3

The Good Web Guide to Health
ISBN 1-903282-08-X

STEVEN MILLHAUSER is the author of numerous works of fiction, including *Martin Dressler*, which was awarded the Pulitzer Prize, and, most recently, *We Others: New and Selected Stories*, winner of the Story Prize and a finalist for the PEN/Faulkner Award. His work has been translated into seventeen languages, and his story "Eisenheim the Illusionist" was the basis of the 2006 film *The Illusionist*. He teaches at Skidmore College and lives in Saratoga Springs, New York.

Praise for Steven Millhauser and *Voices in the Night*

'Wondrous. Millhauser wants to startle us, and with his latest collection, the Pulitzer Prize-winning author does just that ... Millhauser's stories feel as if they'd been composed in a distant era, magically delivered from the past to mystify and delight' – *San Francisco Chronicle*

'Spellbinding, masterly, sublime . . . *Voices in the Night* abounds with marvels. Beware the uncanny magic of Millhauser: Just when you think you recognize a myth, a character, a voice, the familiar tacks toward the strange and unexpected . . . Millhauser gives us worlds upon worlds—wistful and warped, comic and chilling—that by story's end, feel as intimate as our own reflections' —*New York Times Book Review*

'Pulitzer Prize winner Millhauser imbues classic fables with a hyperrealistic sensibility in this collection of 16 stories. In his capable hands, figures like Rapunzel, Buddha, and Paul Bunyan assume new and dazzling nuances' —*Time*

'Millhauser has long excelled at the three major forms of fiction, but Voices in the Night should fix his reputation as one of the two or three best short story writers alive in America ... The stories are hilarious in the vein of Kafka, magical—that is to say not really magical at all—in the vein of Bruno Schulz, formally daring in the mode of Poe and Borges' —*Flavorwire*

'His inventiveness shows no sign of waning . . . Throughout the collection, he veers into the realm of fantasy with unsettling and mordantly funny results' —*New York Times*

Corsair presents Steven Millhauser

We Others: New and Selected Stories

Martin Dressler: The Tale of an American Dreamer

The Barnum Museum

Voices

in the

Night

Voices
in the
Night
Steven
Millhauser

corsair

CORSAIR
First published in the United States by Alfred A. Knopf, a division of Random House LLC,
New York, and in Canada by Random House of Canada Limited, Toronto.

This edition published in Great Britain in 2015 by Corsair

1 3 5 7 9 10 8 6 4 2

Copyright © 2015 by Steven Millhauser

The moral right of the author has been asserted.

Selected stories previously appeared in the following: "Home Run" (2013) in Electric Literature;
*"Mermaid Fever" (December 2009), and "A Report on Our Recent Troubles" (November 2007)
in* Harper's; *"American Tall Tale" (Summer 2012), "Phantoms" (Summer 2010), and "Rapunzel"
(Summer 2011) in* McSweeney's; *"Coming Soon" (December 2013), "Miracle Polish" (November
2011), "Thirteen Wives" (May 2013), and "A Voice in the Night" (December 2012) in* The New
Yorker; *"Arcadia" (Winter 2013), and "Sons and Mothers" (Winter 2012) in* Tin House.

A CIP catalogue record for this book
is available from the British Library.

ISBN: 978-1-4721-1431-0 [Ebook]
ISBN: 978-1-4721-1430-3 [Hardback]

Printed and bound in Great Britain by Clays Ltd, St Ives plc

TO KATE

CONTENTS

Voices
in the
Night

MIRACLE POLISH

I should have said no to the stranger at the door, with his skinny throat and his black sample case that pulled him a little to the side, so that one of his jacket cuffs was higher than the other, a polite no would have done the trick, no thanks, I'm afraid not, not today, then the closing of the door and the heavy click of the latch, but I'd seen the lines of dirt in the black shoe-creases, the worn-down heels, the shine on the jacket sleeves, the glint of desperation in his eyes. All the more reason, I said to myself, to send him on his way, as I stepped aside and watched him move into my living room. He looked quickly around before setting his case down on the small table next to the couch. I'd made up my mind to buy something from him, anything, a hairbrush, the Brooklyn Bridge, buy it and get him out of there, I had better things to do with my time, but there was no hurrying him as he slowly undid each clasp with his bony fingers and explained in a mournful voice that this was my lucky day. In the suddenly opened case I saw six rows of identical dark-brown glass bottles, each a bit smaller than a bottle of cough medicine. Two things struck me: the case must be very heavy, and he must not have sold anything in a long time. The product was called Miracle Polish. It cleaned mirrors with one easy flick of the wrist. He seemed surprised, even suspicious, when I said I'd take one, as if he had wandered the earth for years with the same case filled to bursting with unsold bottles. I tried not to imagine what would drive a man to go from house to house in a neighborhood like this one, with porches and old maples and kids playing basketball in driveways, a neighborhood where Girl Scouts sold you cookies and the woman across the street asked you to contribute to the leukemia drive but no strangers with broken-down shoes and desperate eyes came tramping from door to door lugging heavy cases full of brown bottles called Miracle Polish. The name exasperated me, a child could have done better than that, though there was something to be said for the way it sat there flaunting its fraudulence. "Don't trust me!" it shouted for all to hear. "Don't be a fool!"

When he tried to sell me a second bottle, he understood from my look that it was time to go. "You've made a wise choice," he said solemnly, glancing at me and looking abruptly away. Then he clicked his case shut and hurried out the door as if afraid I'd change my mind. Lifting a slat of the half-closed blinds, I watched him make his way along the front walk with the sample case pulling him to one side. At the sidewalk he stopped, put down his case next to the sugar maple, wiped his jacket sleeve across his forehead, and gazed up the block as if he were the new boy in school, getting ready to cross the schoolyard where faces were already turning to stare at him. For a moment he looked back at my house. When he saw me watching him, he grinned suddenly, then frowned and jerked his head away. With a sharp snap I let the blind-slat drop.

I had no interest in mirror polish. I placed the bottle in a drawer of the hutch, where I kept extra flashlight batteries, packages of lightbulbs, and an unused photograph album, and gave no more thought to it.

Early one morning, a week or so later, I stepped over to the oval mirror in the upstairs hall, as I did every morning before leaving for work. As I tugged down the sides of my suit jacket and smoothed my tie, I noticed a small smudge on the glass, near my left shoulder. It

had probably been there for years, ever since I'd brought the mirror down from my parents' attic, along with a faded armchair and
my grandmother's couch with the threadbare arms. I tried to recall
whether I had ever cleaned the oval mirror before, whether I had
ever bothered to dust the old mahogany frame carved with leaves and
flowers. I understood that I was having these thoughts only because
of the stranger with the bony fingers and the worn-down heels, and
as I went down to the hutch I felt a burst of irritation as I heard him
say: "This is your lucky day."

Upstairs I pulled a tissue from the box in the bathroom and
unscrewed the top of the brown bottle. On the dark glass, in white
capital letters, stood the words MIRACLE POLISH. The liquid was
thick, slow, and greenish white. I applied a bit to the tissue and wiped
the smudge. When I lifted my hand I was almost disappointed to see
that the spot was gone. I was aware of another thing: the rest of the
mirror looked dull or tarnished. Had I really never noticed it before?
With another dab of polish I set to work wiping the entire surface,
right up to the curves of the frame. It was done quickly; I stepped
back for a look. In the light from the overhead bulb with its old glass
shade, mixed with sunlight from the window on the nearby landing,
I saw myself reflected clearly. But it was more than that. There was
a freshness to my image, a kind of mild glow that I had never seen
before. I looked at myself with interest. This in itself was striking, for
I wasn't the kind of man who looked at himself in mirrors. I was the
kind of man who spent as little time as possible in front of mirrors, the
kind of man who had a brisk and practical relation to his reflection,
with its tired eyes, its disappointed shoulders, its look of defeat. Now
I was standing before a man who resembled my old reflection almost
exactly but who had been changed in some manner, the way a lawn
under a cloudy sky changes when the sun comes out. What I saw was
a man who had something to look forward to, a man who expected
things of life.

That afternoon when I returned from work, I went up to the oval

mirror. In the polished glass I was struck again by a sense of freshness. Had the mirror really been so deeply in need of cleaning? There
were three other mirrors in the house: the mirror over the sink in the
upstairs bathroom, the mirror over the sink in the downstairs half
bath, and the small circular mirror with a wooden handle that hung
on a hook beside the upstairs-bathroom window. None of them had
seemed to need cleaning before, but when I was through with them
I saw my new reflection glowing back at me from all three. I looked
at the brown bottle of Miracle Polish in my hand. It seemed an ordinary bottle, a bottle like any other. If the polish had made me look
younger, if it had made me handsome, if it had smoothed my skin and
fixed my teeth and changed the shape of my nose, I'd have known it
was some horrible mechanical trick and I'd have smashed those mirrors with my fists rather than allow myself to be taken in like a fool.
But the image in the mirror was unmistakably me—not young, not
good-looking, not anything in particular, a little slumped, heavy at the
waist, pouchy under the eyes, not the sort of man that anyone would
ever choose to be. And yet he looked back at me in a way I hadn't
seen for a long time, a way that made the other things all right. He
looked back at me—the thought sprang to mind—like a man who
believed in things.

The next morning I woke before my alarm and hurried over to the
oval mirror in the hall. My image shone back at me; even my rumpled
pajamas had a certain jaunty look. In the polished glass the dull walls
seemed brighter, the bedroom door a richer brown. In the bathroom
mirror I seemed to give off light; the whiteness of the sink burned in
the glass; the towels looked fuller. Downstairs, the reflected window
in the half bath showed part of a brilliant curtain, beyond which lay
the green grass of childhood summers. All day at work I thought of
nothing but those shining surfaces, like coins catching the sun, and
when I came home I went from mirror to mirror, striking poses, turning my head from side to side.

Because I prided myself on never having false hopes, on never permitting myself to imagine that things were better than they were, I
asked myself whether I might be allowing the mirrors to deceive me.
Maybe the greenish-white polish contained a chemical that, upon
contact with glass, produced an optical distortion. Maybe the words
"Miracle Polish" had caused cells in my brain to fire in a series of
associations that affected the way I saw the reflected world. Whatever
was happening, I knew that I needed another opinion, from someone
I could trust. It was Monica who would set me straight, Monica who
would know—Monica, who looked at the world through large, kind,
skeptical eyes, darkened by many disappointments.

Monica arrived, as she did twice a week after work, once on Tues-
days and once, with her overnight bag, on Fridays, and as always
when I greeted her I was careful not to look too closely at her, for
Monica was likely to draw back and say "Is something wrong?" while
raising her hand anxiously to her hair. She had a habit of assessing her
looks mercilessly: she approved of her eyes, liked the shape of her
wrists and the length of her fingers, put up with her calves, but was
unforgiving about her thighs, her chin, her biggish knees, her hips,
her upper arms. She fretted over any imperfection in her skin, like a
mosquito bite or a heat rash or a tiny pimple, and often wore a hidden Band-Aid on a shoulder or calf, holding some ointment in place.
She wore skirts that came down to her ankles, with plain blouses
over plain white bras; she liked to mix dark greens, dark browns, and
dark grays. Her shoulder-length brown hair was usually straight and
parted in the middle, though sometimes she pulled it back and gathered it in a big dark clip that looked like an enormous insect. She
inspected herself in front of any mirror, searching for flaws like a
teenage girl before a big party. In fact she was forty and worked as
an administrative assistant at the local high school. For years we had
edged toward each other without moving all the way. I liked how she
hesitated a little before easing into a smile; liked the slight heaviness

of her body, its faint awkwardness, its air of mild tiredness; liked how, when she took off her shoes and placed her feet on the hassock, she would wiggle her toes slowly and say, crinkling her eyes: "That feels really, really good." Sometimes, in a certain light, when she held her body a certain way, I would see her as a woman for whom things had not worked out as she had hoped, a woman sinking slowly into defeat. Then a burst of fellow-feeling would come over me, for I knew how difficult it was, waiting for something better, waiting for something that was never going to happen.

I took her upstairs to the oval mirror and switched on the light. "Look at that!" I said, and swept out my arm in a stagy way. It was a gesture meant to imply that what I had to show her was nothing much, really, nothing to be taken seriously. I had hoped the reflection in the polished mirror would please her in some way, but I hadn't expected what I saw—for there she was, without a touch of weariness, a fresh Monica, a vibrant Monica, a Monica with a glow of pleasure in her face. She was dressed in clothes that no longer seemed a little drab, a little elderly, but were handsomely understated, seductively restrained. Not for a moment did the mirror make her look young, or beautiful, for she was not young and she was not beautiful. But it was as if some inner constriction had dissolved, some sense of her drifting gradually into unhappiness. In the mirror she gave forth a fine resilience. Monica saw it; I saw her see it; and she began turning her body from side to side, smoothing down her long skirt over her hips, pulling her shoulders back, arranging her hair.

Now in the mornings I rose with a kind of zest and went directly to the hall mirror, where even my tumbled hair gave me a look of casual confidence, and the shadowy folds under my eyes spoke of someone in the habit of facing and overcoming obstacles. In my cubicle I worked with concentration and with an odd lightness of heart, and when I returned home in the late afternoon I looked at myself in all four mirrors. It struck me that before I could reach the oval mirror in the upstairs hall, I had to pass through the front hall, cross the dusky living room with its sagging couch, walk the length of the kitchen, and climb two sets of creaking stairs, the long one up to the landing and the short one up to the hall. One night after dinner I drove to the outskirts of town, where the old shopping center faced off against the new mall in a battle of slashed prices. In the aisle after blenders and juicers I came to them. I saw tall narrow mirrors, square mirrors framed in oak and dark walnut, round mirrors like gigantic eyeglass lenses, cheval mirrors, mirrors framed in coppered bronze, mirrors with rows of hooks along the bottom. Avoiding my reflections as well as I could, for these mirrors showed only a tired man with a look of sorrow in his eyes, I chose a rectangular mirror with a cherrywood frame. At home I opened a drawer of the hutch and took out the brown bottle. With a few careful swipes of a cloth I polished the mirror. I hung it in the front hall, across from the closet and next to the boot tray with its old slippers and gardening shoes, and stepped back. In the light of the ceiling bulb I saw my reflection, standing with a cloth over his shoulder and looking out at me as if ready to hurl himself into whatever the day might bring. The sight of him standing there with his sleeves pushed up and his cloth over his shoulder and his look of readiness—all this made me smile; and the smile that came back to me seemed to stream out of the glass and into my arms, my chest, my face, my blood.

The next day after work I stopped at a furniture store and bought another mirror. At home I polished it and hung it in the kitchen, facing the table. As I ate my dinner I was able to look up whenever I liked and see the oak table, the gleaming plate with its chicken leg and baked potato, the silverware quivering with light, and my reflection looking up alertly, like someone whose attention has been called to an important matter.

On Friday, Monica entered the front hall and stopped sharply when she saw the mirror. She glanced at me and seemed about to say something, then turned her face away. In front of the mirror she stared at herself thoughtfully for a long while. Without turning back to me, she said she supposed it wouldn't be such a bad idea to be able to check her hair and blouse before entering the living room, especially when it was pouring down rain, or when the wind was blowing. I said nothing as I watched her reflection push her hair boldly from her cheek. Together she and Monica moved toward the edge of the mirror and disappeared into the living room.

In the kitchen I saw Monica's lips pull into a little tight circle. It was an expression I'd never cared for, with its combination of petulance and stubborn severity, but in the new mirror I saw only a flirtatious pout. "It's just an experiment," I said. "If you really don't like it—" "But it's your house," she said. "But that isn't the point," I said. She threw me a look and lowered her eyes; it was a way she had of protesting silently. She sat with her back to the mirror as I brewed her a pot of herb tea. Seated across from her, I was able to look beyond her strained face to the back of her head, the back of her blouse-collar showing through her hair, the tops of her shoulder blades. They all seemed to be enjoying themselves as she talked to me about her troubles with the lawn man. Once, when she turned to look out the window, I saw in the mirror the curved line of her forehead, the upward slant of the bottom of her nose, the little slope between her nostrils and her upper lip, and I was struck by the fine liveliness of her profile.

I let a day pass, but the next day I bought a large dark-framed mirror for the living room and hung it across from the couch. I took out my brown bottle and polished the mirror well, and when I stepped back I admired the new room that sprang into view in the polished depths. Monica would of course push her lips together, but she would come to see it was all for the best. The mirrors of my house filled me with such a sense of gladness that a room without one struck me as a dark cell. I brought home a full-length mirror for the TV room, a rectangular mirror with a simple frame for the upstairs bedroom, an identical one for the guest room down the hall. At a yard sale I bought an old shield-shaped mirror that I hung in the cellar, behind the washer and dryer. One evening when I entered the kitchen a restlessness seized me, and when I returned from the mall I hung a second mirror in the kitchen, between the two windows.

Monica said nothing; I could feel her opposition hardening in her like a muscle. I wasn't unaware that I was behaving oddly, like a man in the grip of an obsession. At the same time, what I was doing felt entirely natural and necessary. Some people added windows to brighten their homes—I bought mirrors. Was it such a bad thing? I kept seeing them at yard sales, leaning against rickety tables piled with pink dishes, or hanging in hallways and bedrooms at estate sales at the fancy end of town. I added a second one to the living room, a third to the upstairs bath. In the front hall, on the back of the front door, I hung a mirror framed in a dark wood that matched the color of the umbrella stand. When I passed by my mirrors, when I caught even a glimpse of myself as I walked into a room, I felt a surge of well-being. What was the harm? Now and then Monica tried to be playful about it all. "What?" she would say. "Only one mirror on the landing?" Then her expression would change as she saw me sinking into thought. Once she said, "You know, sometimes I think you like me better there"—she pointed to a mirror—"than here"—she pointed to herself. She said it teasingly, with a little laugh, but in her look was an anxious question. As if to prove her wrong, I turned my full attention to her. Before me I saw a woman with a worried forehead and unhappy eyes. I imagined her gazing out at me from all the mirrors of my house, with eyes serene and full of hope; and an impatience came over me as I looked at her dark brown sweater, at the hand nervously smoothing her dark green skirt, at the lines of tension in her mouth.

In order to demonstrate to Monica that all was well between us, that nothing had changed, that I was no slave to mirrors, I proposed a

Saturday picnic. We packed a lunch in a basket and took a long drive out to the lake. Monica had put on a big-brimmed straw hat I had never seen before, and a new light-green blouse with a little shimmer in it; in the car she took off her hat and placed it on her lap as she sat back with half-closed eyes and let the sunlight ripple over her face. A tiny green jewel sparkled on her earlobe. At the picnic grounds we sat at one of the sunny-and-shady tables scattered under the high pines that grew at the edge of a small beach. It was a hot, drowsy day; the smoke of grills rose into the branches; a man stood with one foot on his picnic-table bench, an arm resting on his thigh as he held a can of beer and stared out at the beach and the water; kids ran among the tables; on the beach, three boys in knee-length bathing trunks were playing catch with enormous baseball gloves and a lime-green tennis ball; a plump mother and her gaunt teenage son were hitting a vol-leyball back and forth; young women in bikinis and men with white hair on their chests strolled on the sand; in the water, a few people were splashing and laughing; a black dog with tall ears was swimming toward shore with a wet stick in its mouth; farther out, you could see canoes moving and oars lifting with sun-flashes of spray; and when I turned to Monica I saw the whole afternoon flowing into her face and eyes. After the picnic we walked along a trail that led partway around the lake. Here and there, on narrow strips of sand at the lake's edge, people lay on their backs on towels in the sun. We made our way down to the shore, through prickly bushes; on the sand Monica pulled off her sandals, and lifting up her long skirt she stepped into the water and threw back her head to take in the sun with closed eyes. At that moment it seemed to me that everything was possible for Monica and me; and going up to her I said, "I've never seen you like this!" With her eyes still closed she said, "I'm not myself today!" She began to laugh. Then I began to laugh, because of what we had both said, and because of her laughter and the sun and the sky and the lake.

On the ride home she fell asleep with her head against my shoulder. The long outing had tired me, too, though not in the same way. In the course of the afternoon an uneasiness had begun to creep into me. The glare of the sun on the water hurt my eyes; the heat pressed down on me; there was a slowness in things, a sluggishness; Monica seemed to walk with more effort, as if the air were a hot heaviness she was pushing her way through. The two of us, she in her straw hat and I in my cargo shorts, seemed to me actors playing the parts of ordinary people, enjoying a day at the lake. In fact I was a man weighed down with disappointment, a man for whom things had not worked out the way he had once imagined, a quiet man, cautious in his life, timid when you came right down to it, though content enough to drift along through the little rituals of his day. And Monica? I glanced over at her. The back of her hand lay on her leg. The four fingers were leaning to one side, the thumb hung in front of them—and something about those fingers and that thumb seemed to me the shape of despair.

But when I opened my front door and stepped into the hall behind Monica, then the good feeling returned. In the mirror we stood there, she in her shimmering green blouse and I with a glow of sunburn on my face. Deep in the shine of the polished glass, her hand rose in a graceful arc to remove her straw hat.

In the living room I snatched glimpses of her in both mirrors as she walked buoyantly toward the kitchen. In the sunny kitchen her cheerful reflection picked up a pitcher of water that caught the light. I looked at the second mirror, where she began to raise her glass of shining water, paused suddenly, and opened her mouth in a lusty yawn. "I'd like to lie down," Monica said. I turned my head and saw her tight lips and tired eyelids. I followed her as she made her way slowly up the stairs and past the new mirror on the landing. For a moment her hair flamed at me from the glass. At the top of the stairs she walked sternly and without a glance past the oval mirror and into the bedroom, where I watched her bright reflection lie down on the bed and close her eyes. I too was tired, I was more than tired, but the sheer pleasure of being home filled me with a restless energy that drove me to stride through all the rooms of the house. From time to time I stopped before a polished mirror to turn my head this way and that. It was as if my house, with its many mirrors, drew all the old heaviness and weariness from my body; and in a sudden burst of inspiration I took out the bottle of Miracle Polish, which was still two thirds full, and went down to the cellar, where I applied it to a new mirror that had been leaning against the side of the washing machine, waiting for me to decide where to hang it.

Later that evening, as we sat in the living room, Monica still seemed tired, and a little moody. I had led her to the couch and tried to position her so that she could see her good-humored reflection, but she refused to look at herself. I could feel resistance coming out of her like the push of a hand. In the mirror I admired a shoulder of her blouse. Then I glanced over at the other Monica, the one sitting stiffly and very quietly on the couch. I had the sense of a sky darkening before a storm. "Can't," I thought I heard her say, so softly that I wondered if she had spoken at all; or perhaps she had said "Can."

"What did you—" I breathed out, barely able to hear my own words.

"I can't," she said, and now there was no mistaking it. "Such a perfect day. And now—this." She raised her arm in a weary sweeping motion that seemed to include the entire room, the entire universe. In the mirror her reflection playfully swept out her arm. "I can't. I tried, but I can't. I can't. You'll have to—you'll have to choose."

"Choose?"

Her answer was so hushed that it seemed barely more than an exhalation of air. "Between me and—her."

"You mean . . . her?"

"I hate her," she whispered, and burst into tears. She immediately stopped, took a deep breath, and burst into tears again. "You don't look at me," she said. "But that's not—" I said. "I have to go," she said, and stood up. She was no longer crying. She took another deep breath and rubbed her nostrils with the back of a bent finger. She reached into a pocket of her skirt and pulled out a tissue that crumbled into fuzz. "Here," I said, holding out my handkerchief. She hesitated, took it from me, and dabbed at her nostrils. She handed back the handkerchief. She looked at me and turned to leave. "Don't," I said. "Me or her," she whispered, and was out the door.

During the next week I flung myself into my work, which was just complicated enough to require my full attention, without interesting me in the least. At 5:00 I came directly home, where I felt soothed in every room. But I was no child, no naïve self-deceiver intent on evading a predicament. I wanted to understand things, I wanted to make up my mind. From the beginning there had been a deep kinship between Monica and me. She was wary, trained to expect little of life, grateful for small pleasures, on her guard against promises, accustomed to making the best of things, in the habit of both wanting and not daring to want something more. Now Miracle Polish had come along, with its air of swagger and its taunting little whisper. Why not? it seemed to say. Why on earth not? But the mirrors that strengthened me, that filled me with new life, made Monica bristle. Did she feel that I preferred a false version of her, a glittering version, to the flesh-and-blood Monica with her Band-Aids and big knees and her burden of sorrows? What drew me was exactly the opposite. In the shining mirrors I saw the true Monica, the hidden Monica, the Monica buried beneath years of discouragement. Far from escaping into a world of polished illusions, I was able to see, in the depths of those mirrors, the world no longer darkened by diminishing hopes and fading dreams. There, all was clear, all was possible. Monica, I understood perfectly, would never see things as I did. When she looked in the mirrors, she saw only a place that kept pulling me away from her, and in that place a rival of whom she was desperately jealous.

I felt myself moving slowly in the direction of a dangerous decision

I did not wish to make, like someone swerving on an icy road toward an embankment.

It wasn't until another week had passed that I knew what I was going to do. Summer was in its fullness; on front porches, neighbors fanned themselves with folded newspapers; sprinklers sent arcs of spray onto patches of lawn and strips of driveway, which shone in the sun like black licorice; at the top of a ladder, a man in a baseball cap moved a paintbrush lazily back and forth. It was Saturday afternoon. I had called Monica that morning and told her I had something important to show her. She was to meet me on the front porch. We sat there drinking lemonade, like an old married couple, watching the kids passing on bicycles, a squirrel scampering along a telephone wire. A robin was pecking furiously at the roadside grass. After a while I said, "Let's go inside." She looked at me then, as if she were about to ask a question. "If that's what you want," she finally said, and turned both hands palm up.

When we stepped into the front hall, Monica stopped. She stopped so abruptly that it was as if someone had put a heavy hand on her shoulder. I watched her stare at the place where the mirror had hung. She looked at me, and looked again at the wall. Then she turned and looked at the back of the front door. Its dark panels shone dully under the hall light. Monica reached out and touched her fingers to my arm.

I took her through every room of the house, stopping before familiar walls. In the living room a photograph of my parents looked out at us from the wall where one mirror had hung. The other place was bare except for two small holes in the faded wallpaper, with its pattern of tall vases filled with pale flowers. In the kitchen a new poster showed many kinds of tea. In place of the oval mirror in the upstairs hall, there was a framed painting of an old mill beside a brown pond with two ducks. New bathroom cabinets with beveled-edge mirrors hung over the upstairs and downstairs sinks. I could see the gratitude rushing into Monica's cheeks. When the tour was over, I led her to the drawer in the hutch and removed the brown bottle. In the kitchen she watched me pour the thick greenish-white liquid into the sink. I washed out the empty bottle and dropped it into the garbage pail next to the stove. She turned to me and said, "This is the most wonderful gift that you—"

"We're not done yet," I said, with a touch of excitement in my voice, and led her through the kitchen door and down the four wooden steps into the backyard.

Against the back of the house all the mirrors stood lined up, slanted at different angles. There it was, the oval mirror from the upstairs hall, leaning over a cellar window. There they were, the two front-hall mirrors, the kitchen mirrors in their wooden frames, the shield-shaped mirror from the cellar, the living room mirrors, the bedroom mirrors, the full-length mirror from the TV room, a pair of guest-room mirrors, the upstairs-bathroom mirror removed from its cabinet, the downstairs-bathroom mirror, the mirror from the landing, and other mirrors that I had bought and polished and stored in closets, ready to be hung: square mirrors and round mirrors, swivel mirrors on wooden stands, a mirror shaped like a four-leaf clover. In the bright sun the polished mirrors gleamed like jewels.

"Here they are!" I said, throwing out my hand. I began walking along in front of them, from one end to the other. As I passed from mirror to mirror slanted against the house, I could see different parts of me: my shoes and pant cuffs, my belt and the bottom of my shirt, my sudden whole shape in the tall mirror, my swinging hand. Now and then I caught pieces of Monica's rival, standing back on the green, green grass. "And now," I said, as if I were addressing a crowd—and I paused for dramatic effect. I glanced at Monica, who stood there with a look that was difficult to fathom, a worried look, it seemed to me, and I wanted to assure her that there was nothing to worry about, I was doing it all for her, everything would soon be fine. I bent over behind a broad mirror at the end of the row and withdrew a hammer. And raising the hammer high, I swung it against the glass. Then I walked back along that row of mirrors, swinging the hammer and sending bright spikes of glass into the summer air. "There!" I cried, and smashed another. "See!" I shouted. I swung, I smashed. Lines of wetness ran along my face. Bits of mirror clung to my shirt.

It was over faster than I'd thought possible. All along the back of the house, broken mirror-glass lay glittering on the grass. Here and there an empty frame showed triangles of glass still clinging to the wood. I looked at the hammer in my hand. Suddenly I threw it across the yard, hurled it high into the row of spruces at the back. I could hear the hammer falling slowly through the needly branches.

"There!" I said to Monica. I made a wiping gesture with both hands, the way you do when you're done with something. Then I began walking up and down in front of her. A terrible excitement burned in me. I could feel my blood beating in my neck. I imagined it bursting through the skin in brilliant gushes of red. "She's gone! That's what you wanted! Isn't it? Isn't it? All gone! Bye bye! Are you happy now? Are you?" I stopped in front of her. "Are you? Are you?" I bent close. "Are you? Are you? Are you?" I bent closer still. I bent so close that I couldn't see her anymore. "Are you? Are you? Are you? Are you? Are you?"

Monica did the only thing she could do: she fled. But first she stood there as if she were about to speak. She stared at me with the look of a woman who has been struck repeatedly across the face. There was hurt in that look, and tiredness, and a sort of pained tenderness. And along with it all came a quiet sureness, as of someone who has made up her mind. Then she turned and walked away.

There is a restlessness so terrible that you can no longer bear to sit still in your house. You walk from room to room like someone visiting a deserted town. Every day I mourned for my mirrors with their gleam of Miracle Polish. Where they'd once hung I saw only patterns in wallpaper, framed paintings, door panels, lines of dust. One day I drove out to the mall and came home with an oval mirror in a plain dark frame, which I hung in the upstairs hall; I used it strictly for checking my suit jacket. Once, when the doorbell rang, I rushed downstairs to the front door, but it was only a boy with a jar collecting money for a new scout troop. I could feel grayness sifting down on me like dust. A bottle of Miracle Polish—was it so much to ask? One of these days the stranger is bound to come again. He'll walk toward my house with his heavy case tugging him to one side. In my living room he'll snap open the clasps and show me the brown bottles, row on row. Mournfully he'll tell me that it's my lucky day. In a voice that is calm, but decisive and self-assured, I'll tell him that I want every bottle, every last one. When I close my eyes, I can see the look of suspicion on his face, along with a touch of slyness, a shadow of contempt, and the beginnings of unbearable hope.

PHANTOMS

The Phenomenon

The phantoms of our town do not, as some think, appear only in the dark. Often we come upon them in full sunlight, when shadows lie sharp on the lawns and streets. The encounters take place for very short periods, ranging from two or three seconds to perhaps half a minute, though longer episodes are sometimes reported. So many of us have seen them that it's uncommon to meet someone who has not; of this minority, only a small number deny that phantoms exist. Sometimes an encounter occurs more than once in the course of a single day; sometimes six months pass, or a year. The phantoms, which some call Presences, are not easy to distinguish from ordinary citizens: they are not translucent, or smoke-like, or hazy, they do not ripple like heat waves, nor are they in any way unusual in figure or dress. Indeed they are so much like us that it sometimes happens we mistake them for someone we know. Such errors are rare, and never last for more than a moment. They themselves appear to be uneasy during an encounter and swiftly withdraw. They always look at us before turning away. They never speak. They are wary, elusive, secre- tive, haughty, unfriendly, remote.

Explanation #1

One explanation has it that our phantoms are the auras, or visible traces, of earlier inhabitants of our town, which was settled in 1636. Our atmosphere, saturated with the energy of all those who have preceded us, preserves them and permits them, under certain conditions, to become visible to us. This explanation, often fitted out with a pseudoscientific vocabulary, strikes most of us as unconvincing. The phantoms always appear in contemporary dress, they never behave in ways that suggest earlier eras, and there is no evidence whatever to support the claim that the dead leave visible traces in the air.

History

As children we are told about the phantoms by our fathers and mothers. They in turn have been told by their own fathers and mothers, who can remember being told by their parents—our great-grandparents—when they were children. Thus the phantoms of our town are not new; they don't represent a sudden eruption into our lives, a recent change in our sense of things. We have no formal records that confirm the presence of phantoms throughout the diverse periods of our history, no scientific reports or transcripts of legal proceedings, but some of us are familiar with the second-floor Archive Room of our library, where in nineteenth-century diaries we find occasional references to "the others" or "them," without further details. Church records of the seventeenth century include several mentions of "the devil's children," which some view as evidence for the lineage of our phantoms; others argue that the phrase is so general that it cannot be cited as proof of anything. The official town history, published in 1936 on the three hundredth anniversary of our incorporation, revised in 1986, and updated in 2006, makes no mention of the phantoms. An editorial note states that "the authors have confined themselves to ascertainable fact."

How We Know

We know by a ripple along the skin of our forearms, accompanied by a tension of the inner body. We know because they look at us and withdraw immediately. We know because when we try to follow them, we find that they have vanished. We know because we know.

Case Study #1

Richard Moore rises from beside the bed, where he has just finished the forty-second installment of a never-ending story that he tells each night to his four-year-old daughter, bends over her for a good-night kiss, and walks quietly from the room. He loves having a daughter; he loves having a wife, a family; though he married late, at thirty-nine, he knows he wasn't ready when he was younger, not in his doped-up twenties, not in his stupid, wasted thirties, when he was still acting like some angry teenager who hated the grown-ups; and now he's grateful for it all, like someone who can hardly believe that he's allowed to live in his own house. He walks along the hall to the den, where his wife is sitting at one end of the couch, reading a book in the light of the table lamp, while the TV is on mute during an ad for vinyl siding. He loves that she won't watch the ads, that she refuses to waste those minutes, that she reads books, that she's sitting there, waiting for him, that the light from the TV is flickering on her hand and upper arm. Something has begun to bother him, though he isn't sure what it is, but as he steps into the den he's got it, he's got it: the table in the side yard, the two folding chairs, the sunglasses on the tabletop. He was sitting out there with her after dinner, and he left his sunglasses. "Back in a sec," he says, and turns away, enters the kitchen, opens the door to the small screened porch at the back of the house, and walks from the porch down the steps to the backyard, a narrow strip between the house and the cedar fence. It's nine thirty on a summer night. The sky is dark blue, the fence lit by the light from the kitchen window, the grass black here and green over there. He turns the corner of the house and comes to the private place. It's the part of the yard bounded by the fence, the side-yard hedge, and the row of three Scotch pines, where he's set up two folding chairs and a white ironwork table with a glass top. On the table lie the sunglasses. The sight pleases him: the two chairs, turned a little toward each other, the forgotten glasses, the enclosed place set off from the rest of the world. He steps over to the table and picks up the glasses: a good pair, expensive lenses, nothing flashy, stylish in a quiet way. As he lifts them from the table he senses something in the skin of his arms and sees a figure standing beside the third Scotch pine. It's darker here than at the back of the house and he can't see her all that well: a tall, erect woman, fortyish, long face, dark dress. Her expression, which he can barely make out, seems stern. She looks at him for a moment and turns away—not hastily, as if she were frightened, but decisively, like someone who wants to be alone. Behind the Scotch pine she's no longer visible. He hesitates, steps over to the tree, sees nothing. His first impulse is to scream at her, to tell her that he'll kill her if she comes near his daughter. Immediately he forces himself to calm down. Everything will be all right. There's no danger. He's seen them before. Even so, he returns quickly to the house, locks the porch door behind him, locks the kitchen door behind him, fastens the chain, and strides to the den, where on the TV a man in a dinner jacket is staring across the room at a woman with pulled-back hair who is seated at a piano. His wife is watching. As he steps toward her, he notices a pair of sunglasses in his hand.

The Look

Most of us are familiar with the look they cast in our direction before they withdraw. The look has been variously described as proud, hostile, suspicious, mocking, disdainful, uncertain; never is it seen as welcoming. Some witnesses say that the phantoms show slight movements in our direction, before the decisive turning away. Others, disputing such claims, argue that we cannot bear to imagine their rejection of us and misread their movements in a way flattering to our self-esteem.

Highly Questionable

Now and then we hear reports of a more questionable kind. The phantoms, we are told, have grayish wings folded along their backs; the phantoms have swirling smoke for eyes; at the ends of their feet, claws curl against the grass. Such descriptions, though rare, are persistent, perhaps inevitable, and impossible to refute. They strike most of us as childish and irresponsible, the results of careless observation, hasty inference, and heightened imagination corrupted by conventional images drawn from movies and television. Whenever we hear such descriptions, we're quick to question them and to make the case for the accumulated evidence of trustworthy witnesses. A paradoxical effect of our vigilance is that the phantoms, rescued from the fantastic, for a moment seem to us normal, commonplace, as familiar as squirrels or dandelions.

Case Study #2

Years ago, as a child of eight or nine, Karen Carsten experienced a single encounter. Her memory of the moment is both vivid and vague: she can't recall how many of them there were, or exactly what they looked like, but she recalls the precise moment at which she came upon them, one summer afternoon, as she stepped around to the back of the garage in search of a soccer ball and saw them sitting quietly in the grass. She still remembers her feeling of wonder as they turned to look at her, before they rose and went away. Now, at age fifty-six, Karen Carsten lives alone with her cat in a house filled with framed photographs of her parents, her nieces, and her late husband, who died in a car accident seventeen years ago. Karen is a high school librarian with many set routines: the TV programs, the weekend housecleaning, the twice-yearly visits in August and December to her sister's family in Youngstown, Ohio, the choir on Sunday, dinner every two weeks at the same restaurant with a friend who never calls to ask how she is. One Saturday afternoon she finishes organizing the linen closet on the second floor and starts up the attic stairs. She plans to sort through boxes of old clothes, some of which she'll give to Goodwill and some of which she'll save for her nieces, who will think of the collared blouses and floral-print dresses as hopelessly old-fashioned but who might come around to appreciating them someday, maybe. As she reaches the top of the stairs she stops so suddenly and completely that she has the sense of her own body as an object standing in her path. Ten feet away, two children are seated on the old couch near the dollhouse. A third child is sitting in the armchair with the loose leg. In the brownish light of the attic, with its one small window, she can see them clearly: two barefoot girls of about ten, in jeans and T-shirts, and a boy, slightly older, maybe twelve, blond-haired, in a dress shirt and khakis, who sits low in the chair with his neck bent up against the back. The three turn to look at her and at once rise and walk into the darker part of the attic, where they are no longer visible. Karen stands motionless at the top of the stairs, her hand clutching the rail. Her lips are dry and she is filled with an excitement so intense that she thinks she might burst into tears. She does not follow the children into the shadows, partly because she doesn't want to upset them, and partly because she knows they are no longer there. She turns and walks back down the stairs. In the living room she sits in the armchair until nightfall. Joy fills her heart. She can feel it shining from her face. That night she returns to the attic, straightens the pillows on the couch, smooths out the doilies on the chair arms, brings over a small wicker table, sets out three saucers and three teacups. She moves away some bulging boxes that sit beside the couch, carries off an old typewriter, sweeps the floor. Downstairs in the living room she turns on the TV, but she keeps the volume low; she's listening for sounds in the attic, even though she knows that her visitors don't make sounds. She imagines them up there, sitting silently together, enjoying the table, the teacups, and the orderly surroundings. Now each day she climbs the stairs to the attic, where she sees the empty couch, the empty chair, the wicker table with the three teacups. Despite the pang of disappointment, she is happy. She is happy because she knows they come to visit her every day, she knows they like to be up there, sitting in the old furniture, around the wicker table; she knows; she knows.

Explanation #2

One explanation is that the phantoms *are not there,* that those of us who see them are experiencing delusions or hallucinations brought about by beliefs instilled in us as young children. A small movement, an unexpected sound, is immediately converted into a visual presence that exists only in the mind of the perceiver. The flaws in this explanation are threefold. First, it assumes that the population of an entire town will interpret ambiguous signs in precisely the same way. Second, it ignores the fact that most of us, as we grow to adulthood, discard the stories and false beliefs of childhood but continue to see the phantoms. Third, it fails to account for innumerable instances in which multiple witnesses have seen the same phantom. Even if we were to agree that these objections are not decisive and that our phantoms are in fact not there, the explanation would tell us only that we are mad, without revealing the meaning of our madness.

Our Children

What shall we say to our children? If, like most parents in our town, we decide to tell them at an early age about the phantoms, we worry that we have filled their nights with terror or perhaps have created in them a hope, a longing, for an encounter that might never take place. Those of us who conceal the existence of phantoms are no less worried, for we fear either that our children will be informed unreliably by other children or that they will be dangerously unprepared for an encounter should one occur. Even those of us who have prepared our children are worried about the first encounter, which sometimes disturbs a child in ways that some of us remember only too well. Although we assure our children that there's nothing to fear from the phantoms, who wish only to be left alone, we ourselves are fearful: we wonder whether the phantoms are as harmless as we say they are, we wonder whether they behave differently in the presence of an unaccompanied child, we wonder whether, under certain circumstances, they might become bolder than we know. Some say that a phantom, encountering an adult and a child, will look only at the child, will let its gaze linger in a way that never happens with an adult. When we put our children to sleep, leaning close to them and answering their questions about phantoms in gentle, soothing tones, until their eyes close in peace, we understand that we have been preparing in ourselves an anxiety that will grow stronger and more aggressive as the night advances.

Crossing Over

The question of "crossing over" refuses to disappear, despite a history of testimony that many of us feel ought to put it to rest. By "crossing over" we mean, in general, any form of intermingling between us and them; specifically, it refers to supposed instances in which one of them, or one of us, leaves the native community and joins the other. Now, not only is there no evidence of any such regrouping, of any such transference of loyalty, but the overwhelming testimony of witnesses shows that no phantom has ever remained for more than a few moments in the presence of an outsider or given any sign whatever of greeting or encouragement. Claims to the contrary have always been suspect: the insistence of an alcoholic husband that he saw his wife in bed with *one of them,* the assertion of a teenager suspended from high school that a group of phantoms had threatened to harm him if he failed to obey their commands. Apart from statements that purport to be factual, fantasies of crossing over persist in the form of phantom-tales that flourish among our children and are half-believed by naïve adults. It is not difficult to make the case that stories of this kind reveal a secret desire for contact, though no reliable record of contact exists. Those of us who try to maintain a strict objectivity in such matters are forced to admit that a crossing of the line isn't impossible, however unlikely, so that even as we challenge dubious claims and smile at fairy tales we find ourselves imagining the sudden encounter at night, the heads turning toward us, the moment of hesitation, the arms rising gravely in welcome.

Case Study #3

James Levin, twenty-six years old, has reached an impasse in his life. After college he took a year off, holding odd jobs and traveling all over the country before returning home to apply to grad school. He completed his coursework in two years, during which he taught one introductory section of American History, and then surprised everyone by taking a leave of absence in order to read for his dissertation (*The Influence of Popular Culture on High Culture in Post–Civil War America, 1865–1900*) and think more carefully about the direction of his life. He lives with his parents in his old room, dense with memories of grade school and high school. He worries that he's losing interest in his dissertation; he feels he should rethink his life, maybe go the med-school route and do something useful in the world instead of wasting his time wallowing in abstract speculations of no value to anyone; he speaks less and less to his girlfriend, a law student at the University of Michigan, nearly a thousand miles away. Where, he wonders, has he taken a wrong turn? What should he do with his life? What is the meaning of it all? These, he believes, are questions eminently suitable for an intelligent adolescent of sixteen, questions that he himself discussed passionately ten years ago with friends who are now married and paying mortgages. Because he's stalled in his life, because he is eaten up with guilt, and because he is unhappy, he has taken to getting up late and going for long walks all over town, first in the afternoon and again at night. One of his daytime walks leads to the picnic grounds of his childhood. Pine trees and scattered tables stand by the stream where he used to sail a little wooden tugboat—he's always bumping into his past like that—and across the stream is where he sees her, one afternoon in late September. She's standing alone, between two oak trees, looking down at the water. The sun shines on the lower part of her body, but her face and neck are in shadow. She becomes aware of him almost immediately, raises her eyes, and withdraws into the shade, where he can no longer see her. He has shattered her solitude. Each instant of the encounter enters him so sharply that his memory of her breaks into three parts, like a medieval triptych in a museum: the moment of awareness, the look, the turning away. In the first panel of the triptych, her shoulders are tense, her whole body unnaturally still, like someone who has heard a sound in the dark. Second panel: her eyes are raised and staring directly at him. It can't have lasted for more than a second. What stays with him is something severe in that look, as if he's disturbed her in a way that requires forgiveness. Third panel: the body is half turned away, not timidly but with a kind of dignity of withdrawal, which seems to rebuke him for an intrusion. James feels a sharp desire to cross the stream and find her, but two thoughts hold him back: his fear that the crossing will be unwelcome to her, and his knowledge that she has disappeared. He returns home but continues to see her standing by the stream. He has the sense that she's becoming more vivid in her absence, as if she's gaining life within him. The unnatural stillness, the dark look, the turning away—he feels he owes her an immense apology. He understands that the desire to apologize is only a mask for his desire to see her again. After two days of futile brooding he returns to the stream, to the exact place where he stood when he saw her the first time; four hours later he returns home, discouraged, restless, and irritable. He understands that something has happened to him, something that is probably harmful. He doesn't care. He returns to the stream day after day, without hope, without pleasure. What's he doing there, in that desolate place? He's twenty-six, but already he's an old man. The leaves have begun to turn; the air is growing cold. One day, on his way back from the stream, James takes a different way home. He passes his old high school, with its double row of tall windows, and comes to the hill where he used to go sledding. He needs to get away from this town, where his childhood and adolescence spring up to meet him at every turn; he ought to go somewhere, do something; his long, pur-

poseless walks seem to him the outward expressions of an inner confusion. He climbs the hill, passing through the bare oaks and beeches
and the dark firs, and at the top looks down at the stand of pine at
the back of Cullen's Auto Body. He walks down the slope, feeling the
sled's steering bar in his hands, the red runners biting into the snow,
and when he comes to the pines he sees her sitting on the trunk of a
fallen tree. She turns her head to look at him, rises, and walks out of
sight. This time he doesn't hesitate. He runs into the thicket, beyond
which he can see the whitewashed back of the body shop, a brilliant
blue front fender lying up against a tire, and, farther away, a pickup
truck driving along the street; pale sunlight slants through the pine
branches. He searches for her but finds only a tangle of ferns, a beer
can, the top of a pint of ice cream. At home he throws himself down
on his boyhood bed, where he used to spend long afternoons reading stories about boys who grew up to become famous scientists and
explorers. He summons her stare. The sternness devastates him, but
draws him, too, since he feels it as a strength he himself lacks. He
understands that he's in a bad way; that he's got to stop thinking about
her; that he'll never stop thinking about her; that nothing can ever
come of it; that his life will be harmed; that harm is attractive to him;
that he'll never return to school; that he will disappoint his parents
and lose his girlfriend; that none of this matters to him; that what
matters is the hope of seeing once more the phantom lady who will
look harshly at him and turn away; that he is weak, foolish, frivolous;
that such words have no meaning for him; that he has entered a world
of dark love, from which there is no way out.

Missing Children

Once in a long while, a child goes missing. It happens in other
towns, it happens in yours: the missing child who is discovered six
hours later lost in the woods, the missing child who never returns,

who disappears forever, perhaps in the company of a stranger in a baseball cap who was last seen parked in a van across from the elementary school. In our town there are always those who blame the phantoms. They steal our children, it is said, in order to bring them into the fold; they're always waiting for the right moment, when we have been careless, when our attention has relaxed. Those of us who defend the phantoms point out patiently that they always withdraw from us, that there is no evidence they can make physical contact with the things of our world, that no human child has ever been seen in their company. Such arguments never persuade an accuser. Even when the missing child is discovered in the woods, where he has wandered after a squirrel, even when the missing child is found buried in the yard of a troubled loner in a town two hundred miles away, the suspicion remains that the phantoms have had something to do with it. We who defend our phantoms against false accusations and wild inventions are forced to admit that we do not know what they may be thinking, alone among themselves, or in the moment when they turn to look at us, before moving away.

Disruption

Sometimes a disruption comes: the phantom in the supermarket, the phantom in the bedroom. Then our sense of the behavior of phantoms suffers a shock: we cannot understand why creatures who withdraw from us should appear in places where encounters are unavoidable. Have we misunderstood something about our phantoms? It's true enough that when we encounter them in the aisle of a supermarket or clothing store, when we find them sitting on the edges of our beds or lying against a bed-pillow, they behave as they always do: they look at us and quickly withdraw. Even so, we feel that they have come too close, that they want something from us that we

cannot understand, and only when we encounter them in a less fre-
quented place, at the back of the shut-down railroad station or on the
far side of a field, do we relax a little.

Explanation #3

One explanation asserts that we and the phantoms were once a
single race, which at some point in the remote history of our town
divided into two societies. According to a psychological offshoot of
this explanation, the phantoms are the unwanted or unacknowledged
portions of ourselves, which we try to evade but continually encounter. They make us uneasy because we know them: they are ourselves.

Fear

Many of us, at one time or another, have felt the fear. For say you
are coming home with your wife from an evening with friends. The
porch light is on, the living room windows are dimly glowing before
the closed blinds. As you walk across the front lawn from the driveway to the porch steps, you become aware of something, over there
by the wild cherry tree. Then you half-see one of them, for an instant,
withdrawing behind the dark branches, which catch only a little of
the light from the porch. That is when the fear comes. You can feel it
deep within you, like an infection that's about to spread. You can feel
it in your wife's hand tightening on your arm. It's at that moment you
turn to her and say, with a shrug of one shoulder and a little laugh that
fools no one: "Oh, it's just one of them!"

Photographic Evidence

Evidence from digital cameras, camcorders, iPhones, and old-fashioned film cameras divides into two categories: the fraudulent and the dubious. Fraudulent evidence always reveals signs of tampering. Methods of digital-imaging manipulation permit a wide range of effects, from computer-generated figures to digital clones; sometimes a slight blur is sought, to suggest the uncanny. Often the artist goes too far, and creates a hackneyed monster-phantom inspired by third-rate movies; more clever manipulators stay closer to the ordinary, but tend to give themselves away by an exaggeration of some feature, usually the ears or nose. In such matters, the temptation of the grotesque appears to be irresistible. Celluloid fraud assumes well-known forms that reach back to the era of fairy photographs: double exposures, chemical tampering with negatives, the insertion of gauze between the printing paper and the enlarger lens. The category of the dubious is harder to disprove. Here we find vague shadowy shapes, wavering lines resembling ripples of heated air above a radiator, half-hidden forms concealed by branches or by windows filled with reflections. Most of these images can be explained as natural effects of light that have deceived the credulous person recording them. For those who crave visual proof of phantoms, evidence that a photograph is fraudulent or dubious is never entirely convincing.

Case Study #4

One afternoon in late spring, Evelyn Wells, nine years old, is playing alone in her backyard. It's a sunny day; school is out, dinner's a long way off, and the warm afternoon has the feel of summer. Her best friend is sick with a sore throat and fever, but that's all right:

Evvy likes to play alone in her yard, especially on a sunny day like this one, with time stretching out on all sides of her. What she's been practicing lately is roof-ball, a game she learned from a boy down the block. Her yard is bordered by the neighbor's garage and by thick spruces running along the back and side; the lowest spruce branches bend down to the grass and form a kind of wall. The idea is to throw the tennis ball, which is the color of lime Kool-Aid, onto the slanted garage roof and catch it when it comes down. If Evvy throws too hard, the ball will go over the roof and land in the yard next door, possibly in the vegetable garden surrounded by chicken wire. If she doesn't throw hard enough, it will come right back to her, with no speed. The thing to do is make the ball go almost to the top, so that it comes down faster and faster; then she's got to catch it before it hits the ground, though a one-bouncer isn't terrible. Evvy is pretty good at roof-ball—she can make the ball go way up the slope, and she can figure out where she needs to stand as it comes rushing or bouncing down. Her record is eight catches in a row, but now she's caught nine and is hoping for ten. The ball stops near the peak of the roof and begins coming down at a wide angle; she moves more and more to the right as it bounces lightly along and leaps into the air. This time she's made a mistake—the ball goes over her head. It rolls across the lawn toward the back and disappears under the low-hanging spruce branches not far from the garage. Evvy sometimes likes to play under there, where it's cool and dim. She pushes aside a branch and looks for the ball, which she sees beside a root. At the same time she sees two figures, a man and a woman, standing under the tree. They stare down at her, then turn their faces away and step out of sight. Evvy feels a ripple in her arms. Their eyes were like shadows on a lawn. She backs out into the sun. The yard does not comfort her. The blades of grass seem to be holding their breath. The white wooden shingles on the side of the garage are staring at her. Evvy walks across the strange lawn and up the back steps into the kitchen. Inside, it is very still. A faucet handle blazes with light. She hears her mother in the living room. Evvy does not want to speak to her mother. She does not want to speak to anyone. Upstairs, in her room, she draws the blinds and gets into bed. The windows are above the backyard and look down on the rows of spruce trees. At dinner she is silent. "Cat got your tongue?" her father says. His teeth are laughing. Her mother gives her a wrinkled look. At night she lies with her eyes open. She sees the man and woman standing under the tree, staring down at her. They turn their faces away. The next day, Saturday, Evvy refuses to go outside. Her mother brings orange juice, feels her forehead, takes her temperature. Outside, her father is mowing the lawn. That night she doesn't sleep. They are standing under the tree, looking at her with their shadow-eyes. She can't see their faces. She doesn't remember their clothes. On Sunday she stays in her room. Sounds startle her: a clank in the yard, a shout. At night she watches with closed eyes: the ball rolling under the branches, the two figures standing there, looking down at her. On Monday her mother takes her to the doctor. He presses the silver circle against her chest. The next day she returns to school, but after the last bell she comes straight home and goes to her room. Through the slats of the blinds she can see the garage, the roof, the dark green spruce branches bending to the grass. One afternoon Evvy is sitting at the piano in the living room. She's practicing her scales. The bell rings and her mother goes to the door. When Evvy turns to look, she sees a woman and a man. She leaves the piano and goes upstairs to her room. She sits on the throw rug next to her bed and stares at the door. After a while she hears her mother's footsteps on the stairs. Evvy stands up and goes into the closet. She crawls next to a box filled with old dolls and bears and elephants. She can hear her mother's footsteps in the room. Her mother is knocking on the closet door. "Please come out of there, Evvy. I know you're in there." She does not come out.

Captors

Despite widespread disapproval, now and then an attempt is made to capture a phantom. The desire arises most often among groups of idle teenagers, especially during the warm nights of summer, but is also known among adults, usually but not invariably male, who feel menaced by the phantoms or who cannot tolerate the unknown. Traps are set, pits dug, cages built, all to no avail. The nonphysical nature of phantoms does not seem to discourage such efforts, which sometimes display great ingenuity. Walter Hendricks, a mechanical engineer, lived for many years in a neighborhood of split-level ranch houses with backyard swing sets and barbecues; one day he began to transform his yard into a dense thicket of pine trees, in order to invite the visits of phantoms. Each tree was equipped with a mechanism that was able to release from the branches a series of closely woven steel-mesh nets, which dropped swiftly when anything passed below. In another part of town, Charles Reese rented an excavator and dug a basement-sized cavity in his yard. He covered the pit, which became known as the Dungeon, with a sliding steel ceiling concealed by a layer of sod. One night, when a phantom appeared on his lawn, Reese pressed a switch that caused the false lawn to slide away; when he climbed down into the Dungeon with a high-beam flashlight, he discovered a frightened chipmunk. Others have used chemical sprays that cause temporary paralysis, empty sheds with sliding doors that automatically shut when a motion sensor is triggered, even a machine that produces flashes of lightning. People who dream of becoming captors fail to understand that the phantoms cannot be caught; to capture them would be to banish them from their own nature, to turn them into us.

Explanation #4

One explanation is that the phantoms have always been here, long before the arrival of the Indians. We ourselves are the intruders. We seized their land, drove them into hiding, and have been careful ever since to maintain our advantage and force them into postures of submission. This explanation accounts for the hostility that many of us detect in the phantoms, as well as the fear they sometimes inspire in us. Its weakness, which some dismiss as negligible, is the absence of any evidence in support of it.

The Phantom Lorraine

As children we all hear the tale of the Phantom Lorraine, told to us by an aunt, or a babysitter, or someone on the playground, or perhaps by a careless parent desperate for a bedtime story. Lorraine is a phantom child. One day she comes to a tall hedge at the back of a yard where a boy and girl are playing. The children are running through a sprinkler, or throwing a ball, or practicing with a hula hoop. Nearby, their mother is kneeling on a cushion before a row of hollyhock bushes, digging up weeds. The Phantom Lorraine is moved by this picture, in a way she doesn't understand. Day after day she returns to the hedge, to watch the children playing. One day, when the children are alone, she steps shyly out of her hiding place. The children invite her to join them. Even though she is different, even though she can't pick things up or hold them, the children invent running games that all three can play. Now every day the Phantom Lorraine joins them in the backyard, where she is happy. One afternoon the children invite her into their house. She stares in wonder at the sunny kitchen, at the carpeted stairway leading to the second floor, at the children's room with the two windows looking out over the backyard. The mother and father are kind to the Phantom Lorraine. One day they invite her to a sleepover. The little phantom girl spends more and more time with the human family, who love her as their own. At last the parents adopt her. They all live happily ever after.

Analysis

As adults we look more skeptically at this tale, which once gave us so much pleasure. We understand that its purpose is to overcome a child's fear of the phantoms, by showing that what the phantoms really desire is to become one of us. This of course is wildly inaccurate, since the actual phantoms betray no signs of curiosity and rigorously withdraw from contact of any kind. But the tale seems to many of us to hold a deeper meaning. The story, we believe, reveals our own desire: to know the phantoms, to strip them of mystery. Fearful of their difference, unable to bear their otherness, we imagine, in the person of the Phantom Lorraine, their secret sameness. Some go further. The tale of the Phantom Lorraine, they say, is a thinly disguised story about our hatred of the phantoms, our wish to bring about their destruction. By joining a family, the Phantom Lorraine in effect ceases to be a phantom; she casts off her nature and is reborn as a human child. In this way, the story expresses our longing to annihilate the phantoms, to devour them, to turn them into us. Beneath its sentimental exterior, the tale of the Phantom Lorraine is a dream-tale of invasion and murder.

Other Towns

When we visit other towns, which have no phantoms, often we feel that a burden has lifted. Some of us make plans to move to such a town, a place that reminds us of tall picture-books from childhood.

There, you can walk at peace along the streets and in the public parks, without having to wonder whether a ripple will course through the skin of your forearms. We think of our children playing happily in green backyards, where sunflowers and honeysuckle bloom against white fences. But soon a restlessness comes. A town without phantoms seems to us a town without history, a town without shadows. The yards are empty, the streets stretch bleakly away. Back in our town, we wait impatiently for the ripple in our arms, we fear that our phantoms may no longer be there. When, sometimes after many weeks, we encounter one of them at last, in a corner of the yard or at the side of the car-wash, where a look is flung at us before the phantom turns away, we think: Now things are as they should be, now we can rest awhile. It's a feeling almost like gratitude.

Explanation #5

Some argue that all towns have phantoms, but that only we are able to see them. This way of thinking is especially attractive to those who cannot understand why our town should have phantoms and other towns none; why our town, in short, should be an exception. An objection to this explanation is that it accomplishes nothing but a shift of attention from the town itself to the people of our town: it's our ability to perceive phantoms that is now the riddle, instead of the phantoms themselves. A second objection, which some find decisive, is that the explanation relies entirely on an assumed world of invisible beings, whose existence can be neither proved nor disproved.

Case Study #5

Every afternoon after lunch, before I return to work in the upstairs study, I like to take a stroll along the familiar sidewalks of my neighborhood. Thoughts rise up in me, take odd turns, vanish like bits of smoke. At the same time I'm wide open to striking impressions—that ladder leaning against the side of a house, with its shadow hard and clean against the white shingles, which project a little, so that the shingle-bottoms break the straight shadow-lines into slight zigzags; that brilliant red umbrella lying at an angle in the recycling container on a front porch next to the door; that jogger with shaved head, black nylon shorts, and an orange sweatshirt that reads, in three lines of black capital letters: EAT WELL/ KEEP FIT/ DIE ANYWAY. A single blade of grass sticks up from a crack in a driveway. I come to a sprawling old house at the corner, not far from the sidewalk. Its dark red paint could use a little touching up. Under the high front porch, on both sides of the steps, are those crisscross lattice panels, painted white. Through the diamond-shaped openings come pricker branches and the tips of ferns. From the sidewalk I can see the handle of an old hand mower, back there among the dark weeds. I can see something else: a slight movement. I step up to the porch, bend to peer through the lattice. Three of them are seated on the ground. They turn their heads toward me, look away, and begin to rise. In an instant they're gone. My arms are rippling as I return to the sidewalk and continue on my way. They interest me, these creatures who are always vanishing. This time I was able to glimpse a man of about fifty and two younger women. One woman wore her hair up; the other had a sprig of small blue wildflowers in her hair. The man had a long straight nose and a long mouth. They rose slowly but without hesitation and stepped back into the dark. Even as a child I accepted phantoms as part of things, like spiders and rainbows. I saw them in the vacant lot on the other side of the backyard hedge, or behind garages and toolsheds. Once I saw one in the kitchen. I observe them carefully whenever I can, I try to see their faces. I want nothing from them. It's a sunny day in early September. As I continue my walk, I look about me with interest. At the side of a driveway, next to a stucco house, the yellow nozzle of a hose rests on top of a dark green garbage can.

Farther back, I can see part of a swing set. A cushion is sitting on the grass beside a three-pronged weeder with a red handle.

The Disbelievers

The disbelievers insist that every encounter is false. When I bend over and peer through the openings in the lattice, I see a slight movement, caused by a chipmunk or mouse in the dark weeds, and instantly my imagination is set in motion: I seem to see a man and two women, a long nose, the rising, the disappearance. The few details are suspiciously precise. How is it that the faces are difficult to remember, while the sprig of wildflowers stands out clearly? Such criticisms, even when delivered with a touch of disdain, never offend me. The reasoning is sound, the intention commendable: to establish the truth, to distinguish the real from the unreal. I try to experience it their way: the movement of a chipmunk behind the sunlit lattice, the dim figures conjured from the dark leaves. It isn't impossible. I exercise my full powers of imagination: I take their side against me. There is nothing there, behind the lattice. It's all an illusion. Excellent! I defeat myself. I abolish myself. I rejoice in such exercise.

You

You who have no phantoms in your town, you who mock or scorn our reports: are you not deluding yourselves? For say you are driving out to the mall, some pleasant afternoon. All of a sudden—it's always sudden—you remember your dead father, sitting in the living room in the house of your childhood. He's reading a newspaper in the armchair next to the lamp table. You can see his frown of concentration, the fold of the paper, the moccasin slipper half-hanging from his foot.

The steering wheel is warm in the sun. Tomorrow you're going to dinner at a friend's house—you should bring a bottle of wine. You see your friend laughing at the table, his wife lifting something from the stove. The shadows of telephone wires lie in long curves on the street. Your mother lies in the nursing home, her eyes always closed. Her photograph on your bookcase: a young woman smiling under a tree. You are lying in bed with a cold, and she's reading to you from a book you know by heart. Now she herself is a child and you read to her while she lies there. Your sister will be coming up for a visit in two weeks. Your daughter playing in the backyard, your wife at the window. Phantoms of memory, phantoms of desire. You pass through a world so thick with phantoms that there is barely enough room for anything else. The sun shines on a hydrant, casting a long shadow.

Explanation #6

One explanation says that we ourselves are phantoms. Arguments drawn from cognitive science claim that our bodies are nothing but artificial constructs of our brains: we are the dream-creations of electrically charged neurons. The world itself is a great seeming. One virtue of this explanation is that it accounts for the behavior of our phantoms: they turn from us because they cannot bear to witness our self-delusion.

Forgetfulness

There are times when we forget our phantoms. On summer afternoons, the telephone wires glow in the sun like fire. Shadows of tree branches lie against our white shingles. Children shout in the street. The air is warm, the grass is green, we will never die. Then an uneasiness comes, in the blue air. Between shouts, we hear a silence. It's as though something is about to happen, which we ought to know, if only we could remember.

How Things Are

For most of us, the phantoms are simply there. We don't think about them continually, at times we forget them entirely, but when we encounter them we feel that something momentous has taken place, before we drift back into forgetfulness. Someone once said that our phantoms are like thoughts of death: they are always there, but appear only now and then. It's difficult to know exactly what we feel about our phantoms, but I think it is fair to say that in the moment we see them, before we're seized by a familiar emotion like fear, or anger, or curiosity, we are struck by a sense of strangeness, as if we've suddenly entered a room we have never seen before, a room that nevertheless feels familiar. Then the world shifts back into place and we continue on our way. For though we have our phantoms, our town is like your town: sun shines on the house fronts, we wake in the night with troubled hearts, cars back out of driveways and turn up the street. It's true that a question runs through our town, because of the phantoms, but we don't believe we are the only ones who live with unanswered questions. Most of us would say we're no different from anyone else. When you come to think about us, from time to time, you'll see we really are just like you.

SONS AND MOTHERS

I

I had not seen my mother in a while, a fairly long while, all things considered, so long a while, to be perfectly frank, that it was difficult to remember when I'd last been out that way. And this was strange, really, since we had always been close, my mother and I. I was therefore pleased, though a little anxious, to find myself in a nearby town, during a business trip to that part of the country. My schedule was full, meetings all day, impossible to catch my breath, but I was determined to drive out there, if only for a short visit, it's the least you can do, I said to myself, after all this time.

The old neighborhood unsettled me. Things had changed everywhere, it was only to be expected, yet everything had remained the same, as though change were nothing but a new way of revealing sameness. An old maple had vanished and been replaced by a sapling. The trees I remembered had become taller and thicker, on the vacant lot where I'd once played King of the Mountain stood a yellow house with a green-shingled roof, in one yard the vegetable garden with its string-bean poles was now a lawn where you could see white wicker chairs and a birdbath with a stone bird on the rim. But there was the old willow tree on the corner, there the black roof followed by the red roof, there the creosoted telephone poles with the numbers screwed into the wood, there the stucco house with the glider on the porch followed by the brown house with the two mailboxes and the two front doors. My mother's house, the house that kept appearing in my dreams, was still where it had always been, tucked between two larger houses near the end of the block, and I was shaken for a moment, not because I was approaching my old house, after all this time, but because it was there at all, as if I'd come to believe that it could no longer have a physical existence, out there in the undreamed world.

Even before I turned in to the drive I saw that the grass was high, the shingles dingy, the front walk partly hidden by overhanging lawn. Untrimmed bushes threw up branches higher than the windowsills. My mother had always taken good care of the place, and for a moment I had the sensation that the house had not been lived in for a long time. One of the small front steps was crumbling at the side, the glass shade of the porch light was dark with dust. I pressed the familiar bell, a yellowish button in a brown oval, and heard the two-note ring. It hadn't occurred to me, until I heard that sound, that my mother might be out, on this pleasant afternoon, when the sun was shining and the sky was blue, the sort of summer day when a person might go to the beach, if she were so inclined, or drive into town, for one reason or another. It seemed to me that if my mother was out, as she appeared to be, it would be the best thing for both of us, for it had been a longish while, had it not, since I'd last come home, too long a while, really, for the kind of visit I was prepared to make. I pressed the bell again, jiggled the change in my pocket, looked over the side rail at an azalea bush. No one was home, it was just as well. I turned away, then swung back and opened the screen door, tried the wooden door. It pushed open easily. I hesitated, with my hand on the knob, before stepping inside.

In the front hall I stopped. There was the mahogany bookcase with the glass bowl on top. There was the old red dictionary I had used in high school, there the bookends carved like rearing horses, the ivory whale with its missing eye. On one shelf a book stood a little pulled out. I tried to remember whether it had always been that way.

From the hall I stepped into the dusky living room. Between the heavy curtains the shades were drawn. The old couch was still there, the old armchair where my father had liked to sit, the piano where I'd once learned to play Mozart sonatas and boogie-woogie blues. On one side of the piano was a space where a tall vase had stood, between the piano bench and the rocking chair. My mother was standing near that space, at the back of the room. I could not understand why she was standing there, in this darkened room, in the middle of a sunny day. Then I saw that she was moving very slowly in my direction. She was advancing over the flowered rug as though she were walking along the bottom of a lake. She wore a crisp dress, with sleeves that ended partway down her forearms, and she made no sound as she came stiffly forward through the twilight.

I stepped quickly up to her. "It's—me," I said, holding out my arms, but her head was bowed, evidently the effort of walking absorbed her full attention, and I stood awkwardly there, with my arms held out as if in supplication.

Slowly my mother raised her head and looked up at me. It was like someone gazing up at a building. In the shadows her face bore an expression that struck me as severe. I could feel my arms falling to my sides like folding wings.

"I know you," she said. She stared hard at me, as if she were trying to penetrate a disguise.

"That's a relief," I made myself say.

"I know who you are," she said. She smiled playfully, as if we were in the midst of a game. "Oh, I know who you are."

"I hope so!" I said, with a light little laugh. My laughter disturbed me, like the laughter of a man alone in a theater. Quietly I said, "It's been a long time." And though I had spoken truthfully, I disliked the sound of the words in my mouth, as if I were trying to deceive her in some way.

My mother continued to stare at me. "I heard the bell."

"I didn't mean to frighten you."

She seemed to consider this. "Someone rang the bell. I was coming to the door." She glanced toward the hall, then looked again at me. "When would you like dinner?"

"Dinner? Oh, no no no, I can't stay, not this time. I just—I just—"

"I'm sorry," my mother said, raising a hand and touching it to her face. "You know, I keep forgetting."

When she lowered her hand she said, "What do you want?"

The words were spoken quietly, in a tone of puzzled curiosity. It wasn't a question I knew how to answer. What did I want? I wanted everything to be the way it once was, I wanted family outings and birthday candles, a cool hand on my warm forehead, I wanted not to be a polite middle-aged man standing in a dark living room, trying to see his mother's face.

"I wanted to see you," I said.

She studied me. I studied her. She was paler than I remembered. Her grayish hair, shot through with a violent white I had never seen before, was combed back in soft, neat waves. A tissue stuck out from the top of her dress. She wore no watch.

"Would you like a cup of tea?" she suddenly asked, raising her eyebrows in a way I knew well, a way that pulled her eyelids up and widened her eyes. I recalled how, whenever I came home from college, and in the years afterward, when I came back less and less, my mother would always say, looking up at me with eyebrows raised high and eyes shining with pleasure: "Would you like a cup of tea?"

"That's just what I'd like!" I said, immediately disliking my tone, and taking my mother by the arm, which had grown so thin that I was afraid of leaving purple bruises on her skin, I led her slowly to the swinging door beside the carved cabinet with the marble top.

The kitchen was so bright that for an instant I had to close my eyes. When I opened them I saw that my mother, too, had closed her eyes. I thought of the two of us, standing there with closed eyes, in the sunny kitchen, like children playing a game. But no one had told me the rules of the game, maybe it was a mistake to have entered the kitchen, and as I stood in the brightness beside my silent mother, whose eyes remained tightly shut, I wondered what I was supposed to do. I thought of our infrequent telephone conversations, composed of threads of speech woven among lengthening silences. On the refrigerator hung a faded drawing of a tree. I had made it in the third grade. The counters looked clean enough, only a few crumbs here and there, the stove-top unstained except for a brownish rim around a single burner. When I turned back to my mother, she was standing exactly as before. Her eyes were open.

"Is everything all right?" I asked, irritated by my words, because everything was not all right, but at the sound of my voice my mother turned to look at me.

"Where did you come from?" she said gently, with a touch of wonder in her voice.

I opened my mouth to reply. The question, which at first had seemed straightforward enough, began to feel less simple as I considered it more closely, and I hesitated, wondering what the correct answer might be.

"Oh now I remember," my mother said. Her face was so filled with happiness that she looked young and hopeful, like a girl who has just been invited to a dance. Although I was moved to see my mother's face filled with happiness, as if she had just been invited to a dance, still I could not be certain whether what she remembered was that her son was standing before her, in the bright kitchen, after all this time, or whether she was remembering some other thing.

She moved slowly to the stove, lifted the small red teakettle, and began to carry it toward the sink. She frowned with the effort, as if she were lifting a great weight.

"Here, let me help with that," I said, and reached for the teakettle. My hand struck her hand, and I snatched my hand away, as though I had cut her with a knife.

At the sink my mother stood still, looked down at the teakettle in her hand, and frowned at it for a few moments. She began struggling with the top, which came off suddenly. She placed the kettle in the sink and turned on the cold water, which rushed loudly into the empty pot. She turned off the water, pushed the top back on, and carried the teakettle to the stove, where she set it carefully on a burner. She stood looking at the kettle on the burner, then began making her way to the kitchen table. I pulled out a chair and she sat down stiffly. She remained very erect, with her shoulders back and her hands folded in her lap.

I stepped over to the stove and gave a turn to the silver knob. It felt familiar to my fingers, with its circle of ridges and the word HIGH in worn-away black letters.

When I sat down at the table, my mother, who had been staring off in the direction of the washing machine, slowly looked over at me. "I don't know how long it will be," she said. It might have been the state of my nerves, or the rigidity of her posture, or the solemnity of her tone, but I could not tell whether she was talking about the water in the teakettle, or about how much time she had left on earth.

"You look younger than ever!" I said, in that false voice of mine.

She smiled tenderly at me then, as she had always smiled at me. And I was grateful, for if she smiled at me in that way, after all this time, then things must be all right between us, in one way or another, after all this time.

"Would you like to sit on the porch?" she said, looking over toward the door with the four-paned window in it. Then I remembered how, in summer, she always liked to sit on the porch. She would sit on the porch with a book from the library and a glass of iced tea with two ice cubes and a slice of lemon.

I turned off the stove and led my mother to the windowed kitchen door. The dark red paint on the strips between the panes had begun to flake away, and I recalled taking a chisel long ago and scraping off the new paint that had gotten onto the glass.

˙ I removed the chain from the door and led her down the two steps onto the hot porch. Under the partially rolled-up bamboo blinds, through which lines of sunlight fell, the windows were glittery with dust.

"You ought to let me lower the screens," I said.

"You know," she said, "there was something I was going to say. It's on the tip of my tongue." She touched her face with curved fingers. "I'm getting so forgetful!"

On the chaise longue my mother lay back as I lifted her legs into place. "It's so nice out here," she said, looking around with a tired smile. "You never hear a sound." She half-closed her eyes. "I could sit here all day." She paused. "Oh now I remember."

I waited. "You remember?"

"Of course I remember." She looked at me teasingly.

"I'm not sure—"

"The room."

"I still—I don't—"

"I have to get the room ready. That's what I have to do. The room. You remember."

"Oh, the room, oh no no no, not tonight, I was just passing through. Let's just—if we could just sit here and talk."

"That would be very nice," my mother said, placing one hand over the other, on her lap. She looked at me as if she were waiting for me to say the next thing. "If you see anything you like," she said, raising a hand lightly and motioning at the furniture, the bamboo blinds, the framed grade-school drawings on the wall. "Anything at all." Her hand returned to her lap. Slowly she closed her eyes.

I sat on the hot porch with its dusty windows, beside the old wicker table with the two cork coasters rimmed with wood. I felt that I wanted to say something to my mother, something that would make her understand, though what it was that I wanted her to understand wasn't entirely clear to me. And we didn't have all day, time was passing, I was here for just a short visit. "Mom," I heard myself say, in a low voice. The clear sound of that word, on the quiet porch, troubled me, as though a hand had been laid on my face. "Can you hear me?" In her chair my mother stirred slightly. "I know I haven't been here for a while, things kept coming up, you know how it is, but you know—" It was really too warm on the porch, with the sun coming in and the windows closed. I considered opening one of the windows and lowering the screen, but I didn't want to disturb my mother, who appeared to have fallen asleep. In a vivid slash of light, her forearm looked so fiercely pale that a vagueness or mistiness had come over it, as though it were evaporating in the heat. I glanced at my gleaming watch. The afternoon was getting on. Yet I couldn't very well leave my mother asleep on the porch, like an abandoned child, I couldn't simply tiptoe away, could I, without saying goodbye. And there were things I wanted to say to my mother, things I had always meant to say to her, before it was too late. In the heavy sunlight, which pressed against me like warm sand, I leaned back and closed my eyes.

II

Often I dreamed of walking through the rooms of my old house, looking for my mother, only to wake up and find myself in a distant city. Now as I woke up in my old house, on the familiar porch, I had the confused sensation of entering a dream. For how likely was it, after all, that I was sitting on the porch of my childhood house, on a summer's day, like a boy with nothing to do? I saw at once that the light had changed. Though sunlight still came through the dusty windows, a brightness had seeped from the air. Heavy-looking branches pressed against the glass. I saw one other thing: my mother was not there. Ropes of cobweb stretched from the top of a window to the back of the chaise longue. How had I not noticed them before? I felt ripples of anxiety, as if I'd been careless in some way that could never be forgiven, and flinging myself up from the chair, so that the legs scraped on the wooden floor, I threw a glance at the dusty branches and hurried into the kitchen.

She was not there. On the stove a dented teakettle, reddish black, sat on its unlit burner. In the changed light I saw thick streaks of grime on the stove, cobwebs in corners, a yellowish stain on the table. A square of linoleum curled back at the base of the refrigerator. Outside the dirty window, big leaves moved against the glass. The pane had a crack shaped like a river on a map.

I pushed open the creaking door and entered the living room. It was much darker than before. I imagined the sunlight pushing against the front of the house, feeling for a way in. My mother was standing with her back to me, in the middle of the room, like someone lost in a forest.

"Oh there you are!" I said, in a tone of hearty cheerfulness. She continued to stand there with her back to me. In the darkening room she seemed unable to move, as if the air were a cobwebby thickness tightening about her. I walked up to my mother, stepped around her as one might walk around a lamppost, and turned to face her.

"I was worried about you," I said.

She raised her head slowly, in order to look up into my face. It seemed to take her a long time. When she was done, she frowned in perplexity. "I'm sorry," she said, squinting up at me as if into a harsh brightness. "It's hard for me to remember faces."

I bent my face toward hers, thumped a finger against my chest. "It's me! Me! How can you—listen, I know I haven't been out here for a while, it's hard to explain, there was always something, but I'm here now and I—"

"That's all right," she said, reaching out and patting my arm, as if to comfort me.

I stood before her, uncertain what to do. It may have been an effect of the darkening light, in that room of heavy curtains and closed shades, but her hair looked thinner than before, a few strands came straggling down, one of her eyelids was nearly closed. A white gash of slip hung below her crooked dress. Her face now struck me as gaunt and sharp-edged, as though the bones of her nose and cheeks were pressing through her skin. I looked around the room. The edges of the fireplace seemed to be crumbling away, the couch was sinking down under the weight of the heavy afternoon, the piano keys were the yellow of October leaves.

"Would you like to sit down?" I asked.

My mother looked at me with a puzzled frown. Her eyes seemed dim and vague. "That would be a very nice thing to do," she said. She reached out and touched my hand. "You know, I'm not as young as we used to be." She laughed lightly and lowered her hand. She looked at me again. "It's so nice of you to come." She glanced down, as if she were searching for something on the rug. I followed her gaze, wondering whether she had dropped a ring or a coin. In the room's darker dusk, the pattern of swirling flowers had melted away.

When I raised my eyes, she was looking at me. "Such a nice boy," she said, and touched the back of my hand with two fingers.

Again I took her upper arm, so thin that it was like grasping a wrist, and began directing her slowly toward the armchair beside the lamp table. She advanced with such difficulty that it was as if she weren't moving her feet at all, but allowing me to push her along the surface of the rug. My hand, heavy with veins, reminded me of an ugly face. As we drew closer to the chair, my mother began to move so slowly that I could no longer tell whether we were making our way forward, inch by inch, or just standing there, like people trying to advance against a gale. I urged her on with gentle tugs, but I could feel her pulling back against my fingers. Then I noticed that her mouth was taut, her arm tense, her eyebrows close together. "It's all right," I whispered, "we can just—" "No!" she shouted, in a voice so fierce that I dropped my hand and stepped back in alarm. "Is there something—" I began, and at once it came back to me, her refusal to sit in my father's chair ever again, all those years ago, after the funeral. Once more I took her arm, this time turning her in the direction of the couch. As we came up to the shadowy coffee table I saw a shape that I remembered, and I bent down to look at the blue man with the blue bundle on his back. Dust lay on his blue hair. One of his blue shoulders was chipped. "Look at that!" I said, picking up the statue and turning him from side to side. "Old Man Blue. Remember how I used to think he was the oldest man in the world?"

"Older and older," my mother said.

At the corner of the couch she sat down rigidly, as though she could no longer bend in the right places. Though the room was warm, I drew the red-and-gray afghan over my mother's legs. "Here," I said, turning on the table lamp. The dim bulb flickered but did not go out. On the lampshade I saw a faded woman with a faded parasol, bending over a faded bridge. "Now we can sit and have a nice talk."

"You can't do that," she said faintly. Her eyes had begun to close. I tried to understand why we could not sit and talk for a while, there were things I needed to say to my mother, even though I didn't know what they were, and if we talked I would perhaps find what I was looking for. Then I saw my mother slowly raising a hand, as if she were reaching for something, though her eyes were closed. The hand rose to the level of her shoulder and continued higher, until it stopped between her face and the lamp. Her hand was so thin that the light seemed to shine through it.

"Do you want—" I said, and with sudden understanding I bent forward and turned off the lamp. Slowly my mother's hand descended to her lap and was still.

I returned to my father's sagging chair, in the silent living room, and sat looking at my mother as she remained upright and unmoving in her corner of the couch. Despite the change I sensed in her, since our time on the porch, she seemed calm, in her way, sitting there with the afghan on her lap. It was like the old days, when I would come home from wherever I was and my mother would take up her position exactly there, in the corner of the couch, with a book and her reading glasses, while my father graded papers in his study and I sat in the armchair with a book of my own. I had liked coming home, liked sitting in that chair with the sound of pages turning and children playing in the street, liked, above all, the sense of something peaceful from childhood still flowing through the house, and I wondered how it was that I had let it all slip away. And as I sat there, in the drowsy warmth, I seemed to hear a humming sound, a spectral tune, drifting up out of my childhood. It was something my mother used to sing, a song from her own girlhood. "I remember," I said, because I wanted to talk to my mother, I wanted to tell her that I remembered a tune she had once hummed, when I was a boy, but the sound of the humming crept into my words, and only then did I realize that my mother was sitting there humming that tune. And I was stirred that she was humming a tune from our two childhoods, as she sat in the darkening room with her eyes closed, a tune that ascended in three leaps and then came slowly down, like a feather falling, but at the same time I wanted her to stop humming that tune so that I could speak to her, before I was no longer there. After all, it was only a short visit. When my mother stopped humming I said, "I know I haven't been back for a while, but if we could just talk a little, a little talk, talk to me—" The words sounded louder than I had intended, as if I had shouted them in an empty house.

At the sound of my voice my mother seemed to start awake. She pushed the afghan from her lap and began struggling to get up. As if roused from a sleep of my own, I began to rise, so that I could catch her if she fell, and for a moment we were both half risen and leaning forward, as though we had both seen something dangerous in the dusky dark. Motionless in her half rising, my mother said, in a raspy whisper that seemed to come from the room itself: "Why are you here?" The question was like a rush of wind. It seemed to me that if only I could answer that question, then something in the day would be saved, and I tried to find the words that were lying deep within me, like blood. But already my mother had sat back against the couch, as if she had been pulled backward by a pair of hands. In the dissolving room a weariness came over me, like the tiredness of childhood, and I sank down for a moment into the armchair in order to gain the strength to rise.

III

When I opened my eyes the room had sunk deeper into darkness, it might have been sunset or midnight or winter or some other time, and I had the feeling that if I didn't get up at once from my father's chair and return to the outside world, I would become part of the dying room, like Old Man Blue or the faded woman on the lampshade. On the barely visible couch I could make out a crumple of afghan. My mother seemed not to be there. I pushed myself to my feet and made my way through the dark over to the couch, where I began patting the afghan as though my mother might have slipped under it, like a cat. Then I lifted it up, to make sure. Under the afghan I felt something smooth and hard. I could not understand what it was, under the afghan, my fingers kept pressing here and there, then suddenly it revealed itself to be an eyeglass case. For a moment I had the odd sensation that the eyeglass case was my mother, who had grown smaller and taken on a new form. And I felt a surge of guilty relief to think that my mother had become an eyeglass case, since then I might be able to take my leave without worry, knowing it was unlikely she would come to harm.

Even as I pursued this thought I began to look about. Maybe she

had strayed over to the piano, or maybe she was sitting quietly in
the kitchen, waiting for her water to boil. As I stepped through the
room, which seemed to be nothing but an expanse of darkness, I saw
a figure standing not far from the rocking chair. I wondered where
she was trying to go, in that all but motionless way of hers, but when I
came close to her I saw that she was facing the corner where the vase
had once stood. She was standing between the rocking chair and the
piano, as if she were considering whether to advance into the wall.

"Do you want to sit down?" I said, in a voice that might have been
a whisper or a yell, but she stood fixed and immobile there. "I really
have to be on my way," I said, angry at the impatience in my voice,
for what right did I have to be impatient, I who had not been out
this way for longer than I cared to remember. Then I reached out to
touch my mother, who was like someone lying on a couch, though she
was standing upright before me. My hand came to rest on the lower
part of her upper arm. It felt stiff as a stick. My mother seemed to be
hardening, here in the dark. In the black air, her wisps of hair seemed
pressed to her skull, the skin of her face wax-pale. "What do you want
me to do?" I said, and I heard in my voice a petulance, as if I had been
deprived of something.

"Can you hear me?" I asked. "I'm right here," I said. My mother
said nothing. I stood there like a man in a wide field, standing by
a tree. She was so still that it was as if she had come to the end of
motion. I tried to look at my watch, but most of my arm had vanished. In the dark I began to pace tensely up and down, with a kind of
ferocious wariness, fearful of crashing into an edge of furniture. The
restraint of my furious pacing made me feel that I was fighting my
way through a soft obstruction, as though the flowers in the rug had
sprung up to the height of my thighs. I imagined the bushes outside,
rising over the tops of the windows, bursting through the glass. In the
cracked streets, weed-spears were springing up. Bony cats roamed
the deserted houses. It seemed to me that if only I could get my

mother to settle in one place, instead of drifting through the house like someone driven by a terrible restlessness, if only I could know that she was calm and still, then I might be able to take my leave with some measure of peace. For though I had not said to her all that I was hoping to say, during this visit, though I had said almost nothing to her, in the course of the afternoon, still we had sat together on the porch, as we used to do, we had sat together in the living room, just the two of us, and that was something, surely.

It occurred to me that she might be better off on the sunlit porch, lying on the chaise beside a glass of iced tea on the wicker table, rather than standing here in the dark living room, and with that idea in mind I stopped pacing and began to make my way toward her. She was still motionless, but I had the impression that her position had changed in some way. As I drew closer, it appeared to me that she was leaning slightly to one side. I tried to make sense of her enigmatic posture, which might have been that of someone starting to turn around. Then I began to realize, in a slow and confused way, that my mother was falling. I sprang toward her but it was too late. She fell with a sharp knock against the arm of the rocking chair. I seized her with both hands. Her arms felt hard as stone. Something rattled as I lifted her up. The empty rocking chair swung back and forth.

"Are you all right?" I cried, but she was locked away in a dream. The side of her hand, where it had struck the chair, seemed hollowed out, as if a piece had chipped off. I looked desperately about. In her rigid condition I could not place her in a chair. For a wild moment I considered laying her across the piano bench.

I lifted my mother in my arms as if she were a young wife or a rolled-up rug and pushed open the door to the kitchen with my foot. The light had drained away. Gigantic leaves pushed up against the windows like hands. With my foot I dragged two chairs from the kitchen table and arranged them side by side. I laid my mother across the seats so that she was pushed up safely against the backs, then rushed over to the old phone on the counter. The line was dead. Dusty cobwebs stretched across the dial.

I understood that it was imperative to remain calm, that a solution would present itself, but I found it difficult to concentrate my attention. My mother's position on the chairs seemed perilous. When I bent over to make certain she was safe, I saw that her dress was twisted and the top buttons had come undone. A knob of collarbone thrust up like a knuckle.

Carefully, tenderly, I lifted her in my arms. Her face was smooth and calm. In her hardened state, she seemed to be content. I looked about the kitchen, which was sinking out of sight. I had the sense of a forest springing up outside.

Holding my mother tightly in my curled arms, I returned to the blackness of the living room. I could see nothing. Her bed lay far away. I thought of the couch, which stood hidden across immense stretches of dark. Even if I could find my way there, even if I could lay her gently down, I imagined her rolling slowly off the cushions and cracking against the edge of the coffee table. Maybe I wasn't thinking clearly, maybe I wasn't thinking at all, but as I gazed frantically around the dark I found myself calling to mind the corner near the piano, where the tall vase had once stood. She had always loved that vase.

Still holding my mother sideways in my arms, as if I were carrying her across a stream, I made my way along the rug to the space between the piano and the rocking chair. They rose up darker than the dark. "Are you all right?" I whispered. My mother said nothing. I tipped my arms to one side until I felt her foot touch the rug. Carefully I stood her upright. Gently I leaned her at an angle against the side of the piano. "There," I said. I drew up the rocking chair so that it rested against the edge of her tilted foot, then stepped away.

In the stillness of the living room my mother stood leaning against the piano, as though she were listening intently to someone playing the slow movement of a sonata. She seemed at peace, there in her favorite room, lounging against the old piano, as she used to do. It was she who had taught me to play the piano, when I was seven, and she often liked to stay quiet like that, listening to me play. She was safer here, it seemed to me, than anywhere else, I said to myself, at least for the time being, I thought. For a while I stood in the dark, watching my mother at rest in her corner. Then I came forward and kissed her stony shoulder. "It was good seeing you again," I said. I would make the necessary calls, I would see to it that she was looked after properly. I stepped back and gave a little wave.

When I reached the front hall I turned to look at the living room, which was no longer there. My visit had had its ups and downs, not everything had gone as smoothly as I might have liked, but we had talked a little, my mother and I, we had sat in the old places. Now she was resting at a safe angle against the side of the piano. She would be all right, I felt, in her way. I cast a farewell glance in her direction, giving a final wave into the dark, and as I turned toward whatever was left of the day or night I took what consolation I could in knowing that we'd had a good visit, taken all in all, and that I was bound to be out that way, once again, in a while.

MERMAID FEVER

The mermaid washed up on our public beach in the early morning of June 19, at approximately 4:30 a.m., according to the most reliable estimates. At 5:06 a.m. the body was discovered by George Caldwell, a forty-year-old postal worker who lived two blocks from the water and was fond of his early-morning swim. Caldwell found her lying just below the tide line; he thought she was a teenager who had drowned. The body lay on its side among strings of seaweed and scattered mussel shells. Caldwell stepped back. He did not want trouble. He immediately called 911 on his cell and stood waiting in the near-dark some ten feet from the drowned girl until two police cars and an ambulance pulled up in the beach parking lot. The sun had not yet come up but a band of sky over the water was turning pearly gray. "I thought she was a high school girl," Caldwell later told a reporter; we read it in the *Listener.* "It was still dark out there. I thought she was wearing some sort of a dress with the top torn off. I could tell she didn't look right. I didn't want to get too close." The body was taken to the Vanderhorn Funeral Home on Broadbridge Avenue and examined by the coroner and three local doctors. The initial report stated that the body "had the appearance of a mermaid" but that further tests would have to be conducted before a definitive statement could be issued. Two marine biologists from a nearby university arrived a few hours later and confirmed the accuracy of the initial examination, stating in their confidential report that there could be no doubt the mermaid was authentic.

From the beginning our town was torn between the impulse to disclose everything and the desire to protect our streets from media invasion. Officials cooperated as fully as possible with outside investigators but refused to allow photographs of our mermaid. They also refused to relinquish ownership of the body, which was claimed as town property. A special committee, appointed to handle mermaid affairs, voted to permit the release of the body for twenty-four hours into the care of a hospital in Hartford, where further tests were performed and tissue samples collected.

The mermaid was said to be sixteen years old and in excellent health. The cause of death was blood loss from a large wound in the lower fishbody, which appeared to have been attacked by a shark. We learned that she had human lungs, a human heart, a human stomach, and part of a human intestinal tract; below the waist, where the skin grew seamlessly into scales, the inner organs, including the reproductive system, were those of a large saltwater fish. She had green eyes, a small straight nose, small ears lying flat against the head, and well-formed teeth. Her hair was abundant and lustrous, a mixture of straw and blond, and fell in long undulations to her waist. The scales were gray-green, with brown and black markings. They were spread across the back of the fishbody and came around to the front, leaving on the belly a strip of whiteness about ten inches wide that tapered to four inches at the tail. The forked tail fin grew parallel to the human shoulders; such an arrangement suggested that the mermaid swam on her stomach, with the fin held horizontally, in the manner of a dolphin or whale, although one scientist stated emphatically that they were only making the best possible guess, since nothing at all was known about the habits of mermaids and she might sometimes have swum on her side, with the fin in a vertical position.

An immediate question arose: What should be done with our mermaid? The body was being held at the funeral home, where experts were invited to find ways of preventing decomposition. The Committee, in an emergency session, voted unanimously that a discovery of this kind was too important to be kept away from the residents of our town, who deserved to see the natural wonder for themselves. The issue was urgent; already there was talk of a disturbing odor. A team of biologists from a research lab in New Haven proposed a method of arterial injection with a newly developed non-formaldehyde solution that preserved organs and prevented shrinkage; in this way the mermaid might be kept on display for several weeks or more. A debate ensued about a suitable location for such an exhibit. Some suggested the town hall, others the library, but quite apart from questions of space it wasn't difficult to find persuasive arguments against the display of a half-naked sixteen-year-old girl in public institutions intended for business or study. It was finally decided to house the display at the Historical Society, which had a small room for temporary exhibits. Objections were raised by those who felt that the body of a mermaid washed up on a beach had no place in a building dedicated to the history of our town, but they were outnumbered by those who argued that the Historical Society was the closest thing we had to a museum.

A custom manufacturer of museum display cases was hired to construct a tempered glass case, eight feet high, in which the body of the mermaid was to be kept in a clear liquid preservative intended to prevent desiccation and permit easy viewing. Inside the glass case the designer placed a large boulder, closely resembling one of the black basalt rocks on our jetty; on it the mermaid was seated. Her torso was upright and her fishbody lay stretched across the rock, where it was held down by concealed grips. At the bottom of the case grew several water plants with long, spiky leaves.

The exhibit opened on June 26 at 9:00 in the morning. Within days it proved to be the largest attraction in the eighty-four-year history of our Historical Society. Cars with out-of-state plates lined the sycamore-shaded street, with its shuttered eighteenth-century houses and its new steel-and-glass recreational facility. Mothers and daughters, groups of wisecracking high school boys, visiting Girl Scout troops, and grandparents stooped over canes waited in line for nearly an hour before they found themselves face-to-face with the mermaid in her glass case. So many people reached out to touch the glass that one morning a blue velvet rope appeared, suspended between brass posts two feet from the display.

She sat on her rock with one hand resting by her side and one arm partly raised, the forearm lying on a bit of green netting stretched over small steel uprights driven into the stone. Her long hair was carefully draped over each breast so that it concealed the nipple and most of the breast itself, though there was only so much that could be hidden, and complaints were regularly made that the exhibit was unsuitable for public viewing. Her green eyes were open, her lips closed in what some thought was a faint smile. Her cheekbones were high, her air reflective; she might have been a local girl sitting in the ice-cream parlor, except for something vaguely foreign in her look, perhaps a slight narrowness in the ears, or something about the forehead, it was difficult to tell. Children pointed and whispered, older boys made coarse jokes—all this was to be expected. What no one had foreseen was the way she stayed in our minds long afterward. Day after day we returned to stand before the glass case and stare at our mermaid. She looked just to the right or left of us, or a little above, as if she were gazing off at a place we could never see.

It wasn't long after her appearance among us that Rick Halsey, captain of the high school swim team, told a reporter standing near the display case that the mermaid was the best thing that had ever happened to our town and that he was going to throw a pool party in her honor. At the back of his parents' house was a large in-ground swimming pool where he and his teammates liked to practice at night.

Halsey was an easygoing young man with a wide circle of friends; the party was well attended. Girls arrived in mermaid bathing suits composed of bikini tops and long skirt-like bottoms that tightened at the ankles. Many of the lower halves glittered with sewn-on scales made of sequins. It was later said that a few female guests dispensed with tops and covered their breasts with nothing but their long hair. The party was reported in the "Friends and Neighbors" section of the *Listener*, with a color photograph of two laughing mermaids stretched out in lounge chairs by the poolside. The idea caught on quickly; mermaid parties sprang up all over town. Diana Barone, a local seamstress, created for her daughter the first bottom that concealed the feet and spread out in the shape of a tail fin. The wearer had to walk with her feet pointed to the sides. The new constriction in walking, which resulted in little mincing steps, proved surprisingly popular among high school and college girls.

It was only a matter of days before mermaid suits began appearing at our beach. You would see girls taking off their T-shirts and jeans to reveal the triangle tops and string bikinis of last season, only to reach into their beach bags and remove the new fishtail bottoms, styled in glittering scales of many colors. A local store offered an array of new suits, of which the most poplar was the Mermaidini: a skintight scaly bottom with zip-off tail fin and a bold bikini top with a realistic breast and nipple printed on each cup. Even bolder was the cheveux top, or Mermette, which consisted of easy-to-attach clip-in hair extensions designed to cover the bare chest. All over the beach you could see them, the mermaids of our town: lying on their stomachs on beach towels, with their lower scales glistening in the sun; sitting on the rocks of the jetty and combing their long hair; laughing wildly as boys scooped them up and carried them wriggling down to the low waves, where they threw the mermaids high out over the water—for a moment you could see them hovering there, in the blue air, the shining sea-girls of summer.

Such changes in public fashion do not pass unnoticed in our town. From the first day, protests had arisen against the creature in the display case, who, whatever else she might be, was also a naked teen-ager indecently exposing her breasts in public. The protests intensi-fied as the new styles erupted on our beach. Mermaid suits, it was said, encouraged women to display their breasts for the delectation of male voyeurs; the constriction of fish-bottoms at the ankles caused women to walk in a new, provocative manner, more suitable for the bedroom than the beach. The tight-ankled style, moreover, disabled women in a backward-looking way reminiscent of the corset and the hobble skirt. Defenders of the new costumes pointed out that the scaly bottoms covered the lower body entirely and were far more modest than the string and thong bikinis they replaced; the painted breasts, which some found so disturbing, concealed the real breasts far more completely than the skimpy tops of recent fashion. Even the much-criticized cheveux tops were broad and thick and protected the breasts from view, at least when the women were out of the water. As for the issue of constriction, the defenders yielded no ground: the tight fishtails, they claimed, were worn in a spirit of play, of sheer fun, even of bravado, which narrow-minded ideologues bound by crip-pling dogmas were incapable of comprehending.

As charges and countercharges burst forth at town meetings and in the local paper, young mothers with toddlers began appearing at the beach in the new costumes; children emerged from cars in gaudy fish-tail suits; and even older women were soon wearing modified, looser versions, which, whatever their drawbacks when it came to ambula-tion, were welcomed as a convenient method of protecting the lower body from the sun's malignant rays and, in some cases, of concealing varicose veins or fatty accumulations on the hips and thighs.

But the new beach fashions, however striking, were only the most visible sign of a fascination that struck much deeper. We knew that a mermaid had washed up on our beach. Wasn't it likely, wasn't it more than likely, that others should be nearby? From the first announcement of her appearance among us, mermaid sightings were reported daily. Each claim was immediately and scrupulously investigated. A second-grade math teacher, Martha Lloyd, was sitting on a blanket on the beach at dusk when she saw a mermaid rise from the water not far from shore. The mermaid looked directly at her before diving under. What struck Mrs. Lloyd was the uncanny resemblance of the young mermaid to the one in our display case—the face was older, but the cheekbones and eyebrows looked so familiar that Mrs. Lloyd was certain she had seen the girl's mother. The next night two witnesses reported seeing a mermaid sitting on the last rock of the jetty. In the moonlight they could see her slightly bowed head, her darkly gleaming scales. There were more unusual sightings: a mermaid seated on the rim of the rotunda in the duck pond in the public park at nightfall, a mermaid under a backyard spruce tree. Joseph Ernst, a retired building contractor, saw a mermaid in his bedroom one night, but she disappeared when he approached. Eight-year-old Jenny Wheeler ran screaming from her bubble bath when she saw a child mermaid rising from the far end of the tub, but when she returned to the bathroom with her mother, the mer-child was no longer there.

Partly in order to verify reports of mermaid sightings, and partly in order to record evidence more accurately, an association of concerned citizens was formed, which became known as Watchers in the Night. Members, who ranged from waitresses and yard workers to doctors and financial advisers, divided their time between visiting locations where mermaids had been sighted and patrolling the beach at all hours of the night. Wearing binoculars around their necks, and carrying notebooks and ballpoint pens, they walked along the shore, sat far out on the jetty, climbed onto tall lifeguard chairs and watched the waters of the Sound. From the public beach and the adjacent private beach they gathered long hairs, fish scales, broken mirrors, barrettes, fragments of comb, bits of bone, and turned them over to the Historical Society, which sent them off to a laboratory for testing. The specimens were invariably identified as familiar seashore debris, except for two of the bones, which came from a dead cat. One branch of the Watchers made it their business to set nets a few hundred yards out in the water, in order to catch mermaids who might stray toward shore.

Along with the sightings, which produced belief and skepticism in equal measure, came reports of a more elusive kind. These accounts were little more than rumors or stories, which drifted through the air like odors of exotic flowers. It was said that staring into the eyes of our mermaid could make you see things that weren't there. It was said that Richie Gorham, a college junior who had spent many hours before the glass display case, left his house one night to wander down to the beach. At the end of the jetty he saw a mermaid, who lured him onto the rocks and then into the middle of the Sound, where she pulled him down to an underwater grotto. Gorham was found the next day lying facedown in the north woods, where he was suffering from a raging migraine and unable to remember anything about the last day and night. One woman, swimming alone in the last light of dusk, said that a mermaid had swum up against her and tried to drag her off; she fought violently and escaped to the beach with a bloody scratch along the length of her forearm. People who lived near the beach reported that they could hear mermaids singing at night—it was a high, haunting, deeply sad melody, like nothing on this earth. The singing filled the listener with restlessness, yearning, and a kind of heavy, weary ecstasy. One young man, glimpsing a mermaid at night, was so filled with longing that he went to bed and would not eat for days; his joints ached, his heart was heavy, he kept hearing sighs and whispers. Now and then a girl or grown woman would be struck: the victim would hear a mermaid call to her in the middle of the night, and she would rise from her bed and walk down to the water, where she stood looking for a long time as small waves broke at her feet.

One of the stranger episodes of that summer was the case of Melanie Lautenbach, whose story we partly had to reconstruct. Melanie
was sixteen years old; in the fall she would be a senior at William
Warren High. She was quiet, dark-haired, a bit on the short side, a
little shy, with a vaguely sullen look that changed to an appreciative
openness whenever anyone spoke to her. She seemed tense and a
little wary, as if anticipating a rejection that never came. She wore
jeans and tight stretch-tops that gave shadowy glimpses of her bras,
with their smooth white cups that seemed designed to press down
and conceal her low breasts. From the very first day, Melanie had
gone to look at the mermaid in the display case at the Historical
Society. There she stared for a long time at the girl with the green
eyes and the perfect hair, the perfect body, who gazed at her and
through her and beyond her from her perch on the rock. Each day
after school Melanie walked the two miles to the Historical Society,
where she gazed at the girl in the glass case, the girl who never had
to worry about walking down the hall past shrewd-eyed boys and tall,
high-breasted girls who swung their hips and laughed and showed
their white teeth that gleamed like little clean dishes. She could feel
the mermaid looking into her, knowing her; she knew the mermaid
back. A great calm came over her at these meetings, a peacefulness
tinged with quiet excitement. At home she would sit on her bed for a
long time, thinking of the mermaid, feeling the water against her own
skin. In front of the mirror she stood in a long skirt and no top, pulling her hair over the front of her shoulders, staring at her too-white
breasts with their nipples like purple wounds.

Her plan grew slowly. One day she bought a cheveux top in a mermaid shop; a week later she returned and bought the bottom half
of the suit. One night at two in the morning she left her house and
walked the mile and a half to the beach. By the side of an overturned
rowboat not far from a lifeguard chair she changed into her cheveux
top and fishtail. The heavy hair fell over the skin of her breasts like

hands. Down at the water, low waves broke and washed up onto the wet sand. She stood for a moment before walking straight in up to her rib cage. She paused again, did not look back, and began to swim. She swam straight out into the deep, rocking water, now on her side, now on her stomach. In the note she left for her parents, she said she had gone to be with her sisters. For she was one of them, and they were calling to her, far out over the water; she was going out to join them, in that peaceful place where every gaze was clear. Melanie was reported missing the next day. That night, she washed up on the beach of a neighboring town, where at first there was a great deal of excitement about the new mermaid, before the truth came out.

The case of Melanie Lautenbach brought home to us the danger of visiting our mermaid, but hadn't we always known that? The naked girl on her rock in the glass fortress, the visitor from another world who stared off at something just over our shoulders—what else was she if not dangerous? In fact the death of Melanie, far from giving us pause, seemed to spur us to deeper reckonings. Of course there were those who deplored our passion, who wagged their fingers and warned of trouble, but on the whole we ignored them, for we knew that we needed to feel our way toward wherever it was our mermaid was taking us.

We now began to hear of more extreme instances of mermaid infatuation. In a new tattoo parlor on a side street off Main, girls laid themselves down on a bright white table, removed their pants and underwear, and under the fierce eyes and sharp needle of a little old man who was said to be a master artist from Tokyo, received, slowly and painfully, over every inch of their lower bodies, beginning just beneath the navel and moving down along the thighs, the buttocks, the knees, the calves, the ankles, and the full length of the soles, a series of perfectly replicated overlapping fish scales. We began to hear rumors of sexual practices so bizarre that they must have been real. We heard of frenzied, unconsummated couplings, initiated by husbands and lovers who said they were no longer stimulated by female legs, which struck them as gangly and spidery, and who required their women to wrap up their lower bodies tightly before lovemaking. One recently married woman, recovering from minor surgery, begged her surgeon to stitch her legs together so that she would be beautiful.

In truth, legs were disappearing from the women of our town. At the beach there were fishtails as far as you could see; on our streets and in our yards, women of all ages wore long tapered skirts that concealed the legs and feet. In the bedrooms of every neighborhood, mermaid lingerie was all the rage. It so happened that a number of women, angered by male demands that they resemble mermaids, but at the same time stirred by feelings of kinship with the visitor they obsessively imagined, took a stand of their own: the male lower body was declared to be inferior to the lower fishbody, smooth and powerful and lithe. Men resisted, then began to embrace the new fashion; and all along our beach, and on the rocks of our jetty, we saw the new mermen, shimmering in the summer light.

It was at this period that the second mermaid washed up on our shore. The *Listener* reported the full story: the excited phone call, the arrival of the police at four in the morning, the body half buried in sand and seaweed, the thick yellow hair, the long-lashed blue eyes, the graceful neck, the discovery of the hoax. Three college students confessed it. They had ordered a blow-up doll from an online company, covered the lower half of the body in a mermaid tail, and left her partially buried on the beach at half-past three in the morning.

The deception enraged us, but fevered us too—it was as if the hoax revealed to us the deeper truth of our unappeased yearning. Over the next few days a rash of new sightings was reported. It was said that a school of mermaids had taken up residence in our waters, just beyond the jetty. They were seen swimming below the waves within ten feet of the beach. As rumors blossomed, and children woke in the night from green ocean dreams, we felt that something more was waiting for us, something that would fill us with the thing we lacked.

Meanwhile, in her display case, our mermaid was changing. Her skin had become mottled, her fish-scales dull; the whiteness of her fishbelly looked faintly yellow. Even her hair seemed somewhat different, a little lanker and less vibrant. One of her eyelids had begun to droop; her gaze had grown vacant. We wondered whether we had looked at her so often that she was being worn away by the intensity of our stares. The very liquid in which she was immersed seemed hazier than before. We knew her days were numbered.

Perhaps it was the sense that she was leaving us, perhaps it was the knowledge that we had failed her in some way, but as the summer moved toward its end we surrendered extravagantly to our mermaid dreams, as if we knew it was already too late. We were tired of human things, we wanted more. You could feel a kind of violence in the air. At a dance party on Linden Lane, a group of high-school girls stripped the clothes off fourteen-year-old Mindy Nelson, painted her naked hips and buttocks and legs bright green, bound her ankles with duct tape, and carried her writhing and screaming out of the house into the back woods, where they tossed her into a shallow stream; her hysterical shouts attracted the attention of a neighbor. At an adult mermaid party in a ranch-house neighborhood, a costume variation resulted in complaints to the police: through uncurtained windows, in darkened rooms lit only by candles, people in neighboring houses saw men and women dressed in scaly fish-tops that covered their faces and descended to the waist; from the hips down they were entirely naked. In the blue nights of August, groups of boys, wearing no shirts, roamed the backyards of quiet neighborhoods, looking up at second-story bedroom windows, where now and then a mermaid would appear, sitting with her tail over the sill as she combed her hair slowly in the dim red light of her room.

Even the children of our town could not escape the general unease. At Norman Sugarman's seventh birthday party, Mrs. Sugarman went upstairs to fetch a comb in her bedroom. There she found two six-year-olds, a girl and a boy, sitting naked on the bed. They had each thrust their legs into a black nylon stocking; the stocking-ends snaked out beyond their feet. Their eyelids were green, their cheeks were rouged, and on their chests they had drawn brilliant crimson circles for breasts, with bright green nipples.

Such distortions and corruptions, unsavory though they were, struck many of us as representing a desperate striving, for we knew in our bones that the season of mermaids was running out. What was it we were looking for? Sometimes we felt a little impatient with our mermaid for just sitting there, for not doing anything. What did she want from us? Couldn't she see we were pushing ourselves to the limit? It was a time of exaggerated rumors, of impossible stories, which we ourselves invented in order to see how much we could bear. We said that if you touched the scales of a mermaid, you would be struck blind. We said that certain women of our town were mermaids, who disguised themselves as human beings in order to lure men away from safe middle-class lives into under-sea realms of danger and madness. We spoke of the secret births of mermaids to the wives and daughters of our town. We whispered that if a mermaid chose you, and took you out into the ocean, you would become as a god. We created in ourselves new visions, new gullibilities—we wanted to become children or seers. We could feel ourselves straining at the confines of the possible. We wanted to believe that the time of mermaids was at hand, that our lives were about to change forever. It was as if we were waiting for something from our mermaid, who had come to us from out there, but we did not know what it was.

In the warm summer nights, when the sea-smell hung in the air, you could see us at our open windows, staring out in the direction of the water.

In this tense atmosphere of impossible expectation, our mermaid did something at last, something that made us look at her in a new way: she disappeared. One morning the glass case was gone. A sign on a stand told us that the Historical Society was no longer able to preserve her properly. We learned that she had been sent to a marine laboratory in New Haven and from there to Washington, D.C., where she was to be examined by a team of scientists before being turned over to the Smithsonian for further study. Even as the facts were reported to us, even as we agreed that it was probably all for the best, a skepticism penetrated our belief, as if words were being used to deflect us from the thing we wanted to know. Before our eyes we had only the sign where the glass case had been. Soon there was not even that.

In the midst of our disappointment we detected the presence of another feeling, one that surprised us, though not entirely. It was a lightening of spirit, almost a gaiety. We understood that our mermaid's departure was somehow pleasing to us. Had we secretly resented her? Her absence gave rise to our exuberant farewells. Some said that she had been spirited away in the night by others of her kind, who had vowed to return her to the ocean. Others claimed they had noticed small movements in her eyelids and lips; after a long sleep, our mermaid had gradually awakened. Whether she had smashed the glass and escaped alone to the water, or been aided by unknown forces in the night, who could say? The important thing was that she was out of human hands, she was back in her true element. Disappearance improved her. As the old parties ended, and the costumes were tossed into drawers and boxes, never to be looked at again, as legs reappeared and breasts retreated, as we returned to the normal course of things, our lost mermaid underwent a sea-change: her mottled skin grew fresh and lovely, her scales glistened, her gold hair caught the light, and like an exiled queen restored to her throne, she assumed again her rightful place in her own land, far in the distance, forever out of reach, out there beyond where we can clearly see.

THE WIFE AND THE THIEF

She is the wife whose husband sleeps. She is the wife who lies awake, listening to the footsteps below. The thief is making his way steadily through the living room, stopping now and then, perhaps to bend close to objects, to hold them up and feel their weight, before he drops them into his sack. Do thieves have sacks? She knows she ought to wake her husband up, there isn't a second to lose, but she needs to be sure, very sure, before she destroys his sleep. Her husband can never fall back to sleep if you wake him up at night, next day at the office he's a wreck of a man, his day ruined, his life a living hell, and though he never complains, in a direct sort of way, that he'd rather be dead, he manages to let her see, at breakfast early in the morning, and again at dinner, the tiredness in his eyes, the sadness of a body that has been unfairly deprived of sleep, none of which would matter a damn if only she could be sure. She's sure, but is she sure she's sure? It's possible that the footsteps are not footsteps at all, but only the sounds a house makes, in the middle of the night, a creak of floorboards, a faint snap of wood in a door. But she's sure the sounds she hears are not those sounds, at least so far as she can tell. The sounds she hears are far more regular than that, they are the sounds, she swears she's sure, that footsteps make, when someone is moving through your house, threatening your very existence. But even if she's sure she's sure, or as sure she's sure as she can be, that the sounds she hears are not the sounds a house makes, but the sounds that foot-steps make, when a thief has broken into your house and is creeping around, dropping things into his sack, if thieves have sacks, how can she wake her husband up? What on earth's he supposed to do? He's a good man, a decent man, kind, intelligent, a bit of a temper, true, best to keep out of his way then, but no man of action, no fighter of thieves. He would simply lie there, as she is lying there, wondering what in god's name to do, now that a thief has entered the house, in the middle of the night, and is robbing them blind, or worse, he'd think it his duty to go downstairs and confront the thief, who would crack him in the head, tie him up, throw him into the trunk of a car, she needs to get a grip on herself. Best to do nothing, just lie there and wait it out. Let the thief take whatever he likes, the flat-screen TV, the silver dove on the mantel, be my guest, the Chinese lamp from her mother on their fifth anniversary, the cut-glass bowl in the dining room, he can have it all, every last bit of it, take it, break it, feel it, steal it, just clear out, mister, and leave us alone. Better to be alive in an empty house than dead on the floor next to tasteful furniture. It's true he's taking a long time down there. He must think they're fast asleep, safely tucked in for the night, nothing to worry about on his end, hey, take your time, steal everything, and what if he starts climb-ing the stairs in search of money, her jewelry box on the lace runner on top of the dresser, what about that? She listens for a step on the stairs, a sound in the hall, but the footsteps remain below, moving now, she's sure of it, from the living room to the dining room, or from the dining room to the living room, it's hard to tell. She should call the police, is what she ought to do, her cell phone is sitting on the night table, six inches away, but what if the thief hears her and heads upstairs, what if he's holding a knife in his hand, what if the knife is a gun, what if the police arrive and find an empty house, nobody home but a sleeping husband and a neurotic wife who's got nothing better to do than make crazy calls in the wee hours, ruining everything for everyone? Best to lie still and breathe slowly, try counting to a thousand, one Mississippi, two Mississippi, who is she kidding, she can't just lie there doing nothing like a bump on a log when a thief is moving around downstairs, in the middle of the night, stopping to put things in his sack, if thieves have sacks, before he makes off with the whole living room. And what of her own sleep, what about that? It's 3:10 by the bedside clock. She'll never get to sleep with a thief in the house, snooping around and stealing everything, tomorrow she'll have a raging headache, she'll want to die from exhaustion, from screaming shame. For she ought to've done something, while she still had the chance, ought to do something right now, this second, before it's too late, since she's the one who's lying awake, listening to the thief as he prowls through their house, in the middle of the night, in his hoodie or his ski mask.

She tells herself not to move a muscle, just lie there like a nice corpse, even as she throws the covers off and feels her bare soles on the rug. She only wants to listen, to make *sure* sure, before she wakes her husband up. A house makes many sounds, in the middle of the night, and though she's completely sure the sounds she hears are the sounds of footsteps, she will be surer when she opens the bedroom door. Over her short nightgown she slips her silk robe, pulls the belt tight as she walks with immense caution to the door. What if the thief hears the turn of the knob, the click of the latch? In the hall she stops. She listens, hears nothing, hears something, hears nothing. At the top of the stairs she hears the sounds of footsteps, she's sure now, absolutely sure, though to be perfectly honest it's hard to hear anything over the thudding in her chest.

With her hand on the banister she begins to descend, placing first her left foot and then the right on each stair. The last thing she wants is for the thief to hear her as she comes slowly down the stairs, first her left foot and then the right. At the same time the one thing she

wants more than anything in the world is for the thief to hear her, as
she comes slowly down the stairs, first her left foot and then the right,
so that he'll flee with his sack of stolen goods, if thieves have sacks,
what else would they have, and leave everybody in peace, if you can
call it peace to be awake in a house where a thief's been prowling
around at three in the morning, stealing your things and driving you
insane. It occurs to her that he might all of a sudden stop, if he hears
her footsteps on the stairs. He'll stop and wait for her, the foolish wife
in the slinky robe, coming half naked down the stairs, that's what he'll
do, and then she, and not her husband, will be the one lying on the
floor with scratchy rope tied around her wrists and ankles, in the middle of the night, duct tape over her mouth, or maybe a cord around
her neck, her nightgown up around her waist, policemen standing
over her, studying her thighs, examining the pubic ridge with its coils
of hair, before covering her with a sheet. Go back, go back, before
it's too late, go back, go back, let it all wait, but already she's at the
bottom of the stairs, facing the front hall, on her left the living room,
dining room on the right. The windows of her house have tie-back
curtains on both sides, covering the blinds and the window frames,
but a faintness of light comes through, an easing of the dark, probably
from the streetlamp next to the sugar maple. She can make out the
shapes of parts of things, an arm of the couch, a corner of the hutch.
The footsteps have stopped. The thief is waiting. Maybe he's waiting
for her to return upstairs, so that he can make his escape without having to throw a cord around her neck, if thieves have cords, and drag
her behind the couch, if that's what he's planning to do, if she enters
the room.

She eases her way into the living room, with its shapes of parts of
things, its unblack dark. She's a cat in the night, her fur alive, whis-
kers twitching. All at once she stops, with a hand raised to her open
mouth, like that poster in the lobby of the movie theater, the woman's
body stiff with fear, the long robe half open, but it's only a sound from
outside the house, a car door slamming, the Kelly kid back from a

date, or some other sound, a squirrel on a garbage pail. What if the thief is waiting for her? What if he's sitting on the couch? There's someone on the couch, she can see him there, a dark thief, waiting, or is it a throw pillow, she needs to calm down. Three o'clock in the stupid morning and she's creeping around in the dark like a madwoman with her arm outstretched and her hair plunging along her cheeks. She should've pinned her hair up, or put a clip in it, as if anybody could see her, in the practically black dark. He has to be in here somewhere, she heard the footsteps, if they were footsteps, what else could they have been. She moves from couch to armchair, from armchair to lamp table, from lamp table to six-disc CD player, peering, touching, one hand clutching the thin robe closed at her throat. The new flat-screen is still on its stand, the silver dove on the mantel, nothing missing, everything in its place. Is he still in the house? She moves quickly now, into the dark dining room, where the cut-glass bowl still sits on the table, into the kitchen, where the cabinets remain shut. The thief must have heard her on the stairs. He's fled, vamoosed, she's saved the house. She's won.

Back in the living room she checks the front door, locked tight, and turns around. She listens. He might have come in through a window. Might have come in here, there, who knows where. She moves through the downstairs rooms, checking the windows, all closed, checking the door in the kitchen, locked tight, that opens onto the porch. In the living room she throws herself down on the couch, head flung back against the top of a cushion. She has to be sure, surer than sure, before she can return to bed. What if he's hiding in a corner? What if he finds her? Finds her, binds her, whacks her, sacks her, shhh. What if he's outside, waiting? Better if she'd found a window smashed, drawers open, coasters and folded maps scattered across the floor, TV gone, cut-glass bowl gone. The muscles in her arms are clenched, as though she's struggling to lift a heavy box. Her whole body is a fist.

After a while she swings herself out of the couch and goes to the front door. Beyond the door is the front yard, the sugar maple, the night. She stands for a few moments and unlocks the bolt. She opens the door and looks through the screen at the dark walk, the lawn. Through the leaves of the maple the light from the streetlamp seems to be shaking a little. The wife closes the door and stares at the lock. She does not turn it. If he's coming he's coming. Let him get it over with. She can't stand it anymore. She climbs the stairs, slips into bed beside her sleeping husband, who has not moved. In the dark she lies awake, listening for the front door, listening for the footsteps, which might have stopped, though she can't be sure.

In the morning, after her husband leaves for work, the wife moves through the house, opening drawers, looking in cabinets, checking closets. Her husband has told her about the open front door, he must have forgotten to lock it, robberies in the neighborhood, you can't be too careful. It's possible, she thinks, that the thief was hiding in a corner and slipped out of the house when she returned to her bedroom. He's been in the living room, knows what's there, the Chinese lamp on the table, the silver dove on the mantel, he's bound to be back, bound to. It's not a big house, they're not rich, not by a long shot, but they're comfortable, as the saying goes, they own lots of things, cameras and blenders and two sets of luggage and that nice box of chocolates, she's not thinking clearly. She's sure she heard the footsteps, though how sure can you be, in the middle of the night, and if they weren't footsteps, but only the sounds a house makes, what good does that do her? If she's made up the footsteps she might as well've made up everything, the husband at work, the house, the marriage, the time in first grade when she fell out of her chair and John Connor pointed at her and shouted: "You're dead!" She touches her hand, her cheek. She's there. She's real. She is waiting for her husband to return from work. She is waiting for the night.

At night the wife lies awake beside her sleeping husband. His face is turned slightly away, and he breathes easily, peacefully. He has checked the doors, locked the windows, robberies in the neighborhood, why only the other day. Is he dreaming, her peaceful husband? Dreaming of her? In the dark she listens to the footsteps. The thief is walking carefully through the living room, stopping now and then before continuing on. He knows she's there, knows she is listening. The footsteps are not the sounds a house makes, in the middle of the night, she's sure of it this time, or as sure as anyone can be, under the circumstances. He has returned to complete what he was unable to complete the night before, because she stopped him, as he moved through the dark living room, she drove him away. She is the one who lies awake, she is the one who guards the house.

The wife throws the covers off, slips into her robe, steps across the room into the hall. How else can she be one hundred percent sure? She needs to put an end to it. She needs her sleep. She makes her way down the stairs without attempting to conceal the sounds of her bare feet on the steps. At the bottom of the staircase she whispers, "Is anybody there?" After a while she says, "I know you're there." The footsteps have stopped. She does not hesitate as she enters the living room.

She moves with sure steps through the dark, staring fiercely into corners. She touches the couch arm, the back of the armchair, the rocker, the walls. He is not there. She passes through the dining room, where the cut-glass bowl crouches like a tense animal on the table, and enters the kitchen. Through the kitchen window she can see the faint glimmer of the side of the white garage, the two dark lawn chairs on the black grass. The thief has tricked her once again, though he was here only seconds ago, listening to her footsteps on the stairs. Now he's not here. He has disappeared into the night, in his hoodie or his ski mask. Time to let him go, let it all go, time to climb the stairs and fall asleep beside her husband, who's lying there peacefully, dreaming his dreams. But how can she climb the stairs and fall asleep beside her husband, lying there peacefully, on a night like this? She is too restless for sleep. Sleep is for husbands, sleep is for the good people of this world. It's thieves and wives who walk in the night.

It is warm in the kitchen, a warm night of summer. He must have entered through the back door, which she unlocked after her husband went upstairs to bed. Did he escape the same way? She opens the door and steps onto the back porch—no porch, really, just four steps and a landing, with posts and a little roof. The air is warm, with a ripple of coolness. A warm-cool night, the dark sky bright with stars, a sliver of moon, like a tipped-back rocking chair.

She walks down the steps and feels the grass cool and sharp-soft against her bare feet. She strides past the row of spruces that separate her yard from the husband and wife next door, asleep in their bed, past the pinewood fence in back, past the side of the garage. The thief must have stood somewhere in the dark yard, studying the house, planning his way in. A safe world of yards and fences, of people asleep in the night, behind locked doors, under the tipped-back moon. The thief must be somewhere. Where is somewhere? Somewhere is nowhere. She throws herself onto one of the reclining lawn chairs and leans back with her legs on the stretched-out part, her ankles crossed, her slithery robe open at her knees. A warm night of summer, dim glow of streetlights over the roofs, a good night for prowling. He must have climbed the back steps, tried the door, surprise! She hears something in the trees. A cat? Raccoon? If the thief is hiding under the trees, he'll come out, he's got to, after a while. He's only waiting for her to go back upstairs, if he's there, so that he can complete the work she interrupted.

She glances suddenly at the lawn chair next to her. He is not there. She looks behind her. He is not there. He is not there, and he is not there, and he is not there, and he is not there. He has gone away, her thief in the night, he doesn't want to rob them anymore. She turns to look at the house. In the warm-cool air, under the tipped-back moon, she is waiting, she is watching, she is restless, she is ready. She bends and unbends her toes, squeezes the chair arms, flings back a twist of hair from her face. Something is rising in her, a tide of night sorrow, at any moment she will burst into loud tears, she will cry out with bitter laughter. Lights will go on, people will stare out of windows, the moon will tip back in its chair and fall out of the sky. Her soles itch. She's got to jump up, jolt herself loose. There's only so much waiting you can hold inside.

As she climbs the porch steps, the wife looks quickly over her shoulder. She enters the kitchen and locks the door that her husband locked before going to bed. From a box under the sink she removes a large plastic bag with tie handles. She opens a second bag and lines the first with it. She pauses, listens, then opens the cellar door. From a hook on the back of the door she removes a baseball cap and pulls the peak low on her face. She closes the door and moves through the kitchen. In the dark living room she takes the windup clock with the four glass sides and places it in the bag. From the top of the lamp table she removes the painted glass tray from Italy and the ivory statuette of a girl with a parasol and places them in the bag. She moves swiftly and surely about the room, taking the porcelain vase with the ostrich feathers, the silver dove on the mantel, the photo album of the trip to California, the spiral lightbulbs in the bottom drawer of the corner cabinet, the two TV remotes, the dictionary, the framed photograph of herself in a straw hat standing by a stream, the small painting that shows a woman reading by a haystack, letters from drawers, the wooden owl. From the dining room she takes the cut-glass bowl and a set of blue wineglasses, from the kitchen the silver napkin holder, the coffeemaker, the clock. With the aid of a flashlight she drags the heavy bag down the cellar steps and carries it past the furnace and the water heater to the pile of boxes and broken furniture in the corner. The boxes contain old dishes, folders of outdated medical records, discarded gloves and hats. She thrusts the bag of stolen goods into a space between boxes. Over the space she places an upside-down table with three legs.

At the top of the stairs she hangs the cap on its hook. She closes the cellar door. In the kitchen she returns the flashlight to the drawer. She moves through the living room, climbs the stairs, opens the bedroom door. Her husband is lying asleep on his back. He has the nose of a little boy. She removes her robe and slips under the covers. She can feel a dark peacefulness flowing in her like the water of a pebbled brook. She closes her eyes and sleeps like the dead.

A REPORT ON OUR
RECENT TROUBLES

-

We have completed our preliminary investigation and hereby submit our report to the Committee.

For nearly six months our town has suffered events that threaten its very existence. Entire families have moved away, in the hope of finding relief in other towns, only to discover that they cannot escape what some have called a curse, others a fatality; we ourselves prefer less colorful forms of speech. Those of us who remain have attempted to go about our business as if nothing has changed, while knowing that everything has changed. The very expressions on our faces have altered. Even the smiles of our children are no longer the old smiles, but betray an air of exaggeration, of willed cheerfulness. On block after block we see the empty houses, the untended lawns. Cats scratch at screen doors that never open. Large groups of townsfolk gather in vacant lots at dusk, as if for a purpose, only to drift away. Under such conditions, who can speak? We who dare to hope, we who are in the thick of things but try to stand apart, in order to grasp the ungraspable—we have taken it upon ourselves to trace the history of these aberrations and to discover their secret cause.

For as long as anyone can remember, our town has been a pleasant place to live in. Situated at the far end of the commuter line, we enjoy the sense of a vital connection to the larger world, as well as a satisfying sense of self-exclusion from that world, of communal separation for the sake of our own way of life. Here, we preserve touches of an older, more rural America. The north woods, the stream with its railed wooden bridge, the Indian burial ground—such retreats coexist peacefully with our train station, our six-lane thruway, and our new microchip plant. Here, the streets are shady, the houses in good repair, the backyards bright with swing sets, lawn chairs, and round cedar tables under broad umbrellas. In Sterling Park, our children play baseball on a diamond with real bases, a pitcher's mound with a pitcher's rubber, and a chain-link backstop, while our dogs lie down, beside slatted benches, in stripes of sun and shade. Of course, like other towns, we have our share of troubles, we're only human. But on the whole we are happy to be here, where the sky has always seemed a little bluer, the leaves a little greener, than in other towns we know.

Was there a turn, a change in the atmosphere? To single out a particular moment is to distort the record, for it suggests a clear history of cause and effect that can only betray our sense of what really happened. We can nevertheless agree that something began to reveal itself in March of this year, about six months ago. At that time three incidents occurred, apparently unrelated, which made a strong impression on the town without seeming to point in a direction. The first was the death by suicide of Richard and Suzanne Lowry, of 451 Greenwood Road. The Lowrys were in their early fifties, rich, healthy, happily married, with a wide circle of friends. They left no note. The police investigation uncovered no secret, no mistress or lover, no illness, no problem of any kind, and it was above all the absence of a motive that disturbed and finally angered a good many of us, who blamed the Lowrys not simply for throwing their lives away but for leaving us with an impenetrable mystery. There was some unpleasant talk among us that they did it in order to spite us, to show us that they needed no one and nothing. Although this explanation struck most of us as petty and malicious, we took it as a sign of the dissatisfaction we all felt, a testament to our irritable unforgiveness.

Two weeks later came the news of Carl Schneider, a seventy-four-year-old retired high-school geometry teacher who had been diagnosed with cancer of the liver. His death, by his own hand, attracted less attention than the Lowry deaths, though we were all aware of it and felt secretly thankful to Mr. Schneider for providing us with a reasonable suicide, some would say an admirable suicide, one that we could readily understand. In this sense the two incidents, which had nothing to do with each other, were connected in our minds. We also noted that in an interview in the *Town Ledger,* Schneider's forty-six-year-old daughter said that her father had read about the Lowrys and had mentioned them during a visit. In a small town, someone remarked at the time, it's difficult to kill yourself without word getting around.

Four days after the death of Carl Schneider, two high school juniors, Ryan Whittaker and Diane Grabowski, were discovered in the basement playroom of the Whittaker house, lying side by side on the daybed near the Ping-Pong table. The cause of death was bullet wounds to the head from two handguns, both owned by the boy's father. A note was found, pinned to the young man's polo shirt, written in his hand but signed by both teenagers and addressed to both sets of parents. In it they apologized for any distress their action might cause and stated that they died willingly by their own hand as a way of affirming their love and celebrating it forever in death. The note had a self-conscious, literary tone that we found exasperating and touching in equal measure, but what stuck in our throats was the fact that our town had experienced five suicides in less than a month.

It might have been left at that—a dark month, a run of bad luck—if it hadn't been for an incident that took place in early April. George

Sabol, a high school sophomore, and Nancy Martins, a ninth-grader, were found by police on a blanket in the woods behind the Sabol house. This time there was a single gun—a .38 Smith & Wesson semiautomatic—but the suicide note revealed that the plan was for Nancy Martins to fire the first shot, into her left temple, after which George Sabol would fire a shot into his own left temple. The note, printed from Sabol's computer and signed in ink by both students, spoke of their undying love and the eternal bond of death. The written statement and the weapon made it evident that Sabol and Martins had patterned their deaths after the double suicide of Whittaker and Grabowski, and it was this unmistakable connection that first sent a ripple of alarm through our town. Fathers began to lock their guns away, mothers followed their sons and daughters anxiously from room to room; the high school expanded its counseling program and urged people to come forward with any information concerning unusual behavior. In the night we began to wake suddenly, our hands tense against the sheets.

Scarcely had we had a chance to absorb the deaths of George Sabol and Nancy Martins when we were confronted with another incident, more troubling still. The morning paper reported that three groups of high school students—two, two, and three—had been found dead, in three different homes; all three groups left suicide notes modeled on the ones we knew. It was also reported that five of the seven students belonged to the Black Rose, a secret association devoted to the cause of Meaningful Death. A stapled handbook, printed on purple Xerox paper, was discovered in the bedroom of one dead boy; from it we learned that members of the Black Rose were encouraged to give meaning to their lives by choosing their own death. Suicide was praised as a celebratory act, which transformed the drift and emptiness of ordinary life into the certainty of choice: to choose death was to impose a design on randomness. What disturbed us wasn't so much the danger or incoherence of such ideas as their very existence. The next day two more deaths were reported, in different neighborhoods; a page torn from a handbook of the Black Rose was found in the pocketbook of one victim. It was now that we began to take the car keys away, to impose strict curfews, to keep our cell phones on at all times. In the houses of our town, unease drifted like smoke.

At this period we felt that if only we could put an end to the Black Rose, we could also put an end to the sickly fashion for death that had seized our sons and daughters. In this sense, though we hated and feared the Black Rose, we also clung to it, in a way were grateful to it, since it provided us with the hidden reason we desperately sought. Our teenagers were in the grip of a morbid philosophy—a decadent dogma—which had inspired a fatal game. We would fight a battle to win back the minds of our children, we would hurl ourselves against the forces of darkness with weapons of the sun. It was true that not every death could be traced to the Black Rose; there was even some evidence that membership was confined to a small circle of fanatics. But just as we felt we were getting to the heart of things, a new turn unsettled us—for it seemed that the Black Rose had already been left behind, while new seductions emerged with disquieting ease.

A passion for spectacular suicide now seized our sons and daughters. It was as if they had begun to vie with one another for the most memorable death. One group of six high school students, visiting a nearby amusement park, rode the roller coaster and were found dead at the end of the ride; all six had injected themselves on the way up the track with a solution of potassium chloride. None of the six was in any way connected with the Black Rose. Joanne Garavaglia, a popular girl with a passion for home video, went up to her attic one night and filmed herself as she raised a bone-handled hunting knife and plunged it into her throat. Lorraine Keating hanged herself at dusk from the branch of a hickory tree in front of a group of admiring friends. The fad for suicide notes had already been replaced by a taste for terse, obscure messages, such as "Never Enough" and

"Evermore," while the act of dying became an increasingly elaborate art, discussed and evaluated in high school hallways and behind the locked doors of bedrooms bathed in afternoon sunlight.

Young teenage girls were especially susceptible to the new trend for eye-catching death. It was seen as a way of drawing the right kind of attention to yourself, of making yourself stand out from the crowd. A popular girl, by means of a well-staged death, could become more popular still; an unpopular girl could break free from her isolation and loneliness in the short space of a single magnificent gesture. Jane Franklin was a quiet girl who walked the halls alone. On the night of the spring dance, she pulled on a pair of black jeans and a black hooded sweatshirt, climbed to the top of the water tower behind the chemical plant, and set herself on fire. Two days later Christine Jacobson, a blond cheerleader and co-captain of the girls' swim team, walked to the front of her English class, raised a dark object slowly with both hands, and shot herself in the center of the forehead.

Even as the epidemic of suicide raged through our high school, we noticed that its effects were being felt in two opposite directions: upward, in the colleges where our older sons and daughters were finishing their spring semester, and downward, in the William Barnes Middle School and our six elementary schools. A college junior who had graduated from our high school fastened a pair of satin-covered foam angel wings to his shoulders and leaped to his death from the top of the astronomy building; a college sophomore painted the word "luminosity" in neon-green letters on the side of her car, drove through a guardrail on the outskirts of her rural campus, and sailed into the air above a much-photographed ravine. Four seventh-graders were found in a stand of spruce between two backyards after they had swallowed rat poison dissolved in cherry Kool-Aid. Howard Dietz, a fourth-grader, pried open his father's gun cabinet one day after school and, sitting on the edge of his bed, opened his mouth, placed the barrel of a twenty-gauge shotgun between his teeth, which had recently been fitted with braces decorated with metallic-blue brackets, and pulled the trigger. One group of sixth-grade girls initiated a brief vogue: wearing jean shorts, bathing-suit tops, and bright red lipstick, they dragged a barbecue grill into a backyard toolshed, shut the door, and inhaled the fatal fumes of charcoal briquettes. We held town meetings, consulted with crisis counselors and family therapists, engaged in lengthy discussions with our children. We dreaded opening the morning paper.

What haunted us, apart from the deaths themselves, was the spirit in which the perpetrators appeared to seek their own destruction. For it was difficult to deny that a majority of deaths were chosen in a mood of adventure, of high daring, even of exhilaration. Here and there, to be sure, an adolescent boy rejected by his girlfriend swallowed a fistful of barbiturates, a depressed girl who felt unloved slipped into a tub of warm water and slit her wrists. These deaths were in some sense comforting, almost pleasing, for we could imagine ourselves, under similar circumstances, arriving at the same decision. But what were we to make of the atmosphere of excitement evident among the others, their sense of embracing the unknown with something like fervor? Death as a spirited game, death as a challenge, as an intriguing art form, an expression of originality—this death was something we knew nothing about, we who understood what it meant to wake in the night with dread in our hearts.

Excitements falter. Fads fade away. Although we were dazed with exhaustion and anxiety, we remained stubbornly hopeful, for we knew that crises of adolescence do not last. And in fact the school suicides began to diminish, without actually coming to an end. At the same time we were unable to ignore new signs of trouble. It happened here and there—a marriage suicide, the suicide of a young mother. We understood, with a kind of rage, that the same parents who listened to their sons' rock bands and imitated their daughters' styles in hip-hugger jeans and spaghetti-strap tank tops were not immune to the latest craze. As the deaths spread among the adults of our town, we began to hear talk of the Blue Iris, an association all too clearly inspired by the Black Rose but with a crucial difference. Whereas the Black Rose promoted suicide as a method of imposing a design on the randomness of life, the Blue Iris spoke of death as the culminating moment of existence—the climactic event to which every life aspired. Precisely for this reason, death should be chosen at a moment of fulfillment. We began to hear of sexual suicides, ingeniously enacted at the height of lovemaking. Couples began to look to death as an erotic stimulus, a mechanism for ultimate release, as though they were seeking, in the act of self-murder, a cosmic orgasm. Others chose different moments of heightened feeling: a wedding ceremony, a longed-for promotion, a sudden eruption of irrational happiness. We took note of these suicides with a certain disdain, for they seemed too closely modeled on a fading teenage fashion, while at the same time they made our blood tremble. The new suicides were our neighbors; they were ourselves.

Frank and Rita Sorensen were a handsome couple in their late thirties, with the sort of marriage many of us envied. He was a real estate developer who had brought a new recreational center to the west end of town, she was an interior decorator who had improved many of our kitchens and dens. They seemed a happier, more talented, more successful version of ourselves. They lived with their two young daughters, Sigrid and Belle, in a big house on Roland Terrace, where we were present at their summer barbecues and winter dinner parties. We knew the sound of their laughter, the energy of their glances, we could feel the easy flow of affection between them. Although they were happy, in a way that was impossible to doubt, it's true that we could feel in them, at times, a shadow of disappointment, a ripple of disenchantment, of a kind that struck us as familiar, for their lives, like ours, were in a certain manner complete, they could look forward to years of pleasure and success and laudable accomplishment but to nothing more—it was as if, somewhere along the way, they had misplaced a youthful sense of discovery, a sense that life is an adventure that might lead to anything on earth. Like us, they accepted their happiness without thinking much about it; like ours, their happiness was complicated by another feeling that wasn't sorrow but that closed in on them from time to time. One day they joined the Blue Iris. We noticed at once their new zest, their new seriousness. They attended meetings, invited us to lakeshore cookouts and Friday night pool parties, drank hard, laughed with their heads thrown back, passed the crab dip. One night they retired to their bedroom, lay down on their bed fully clothed, raised their matching pistols with ivory-inlaid rosewood grips, and shot themselves in the head. A typed note in a sealed envelope explained that they were fully conscious of what they were doing and, more in love than ever, chose to complete their lives on a crest of happiness. They urged others to join them in this act of fulfillment.

Some accused the Sorensens of harboring a dark secret, but for most of us the tone of the note was all too familiar. Others blamed the Blue Iris, which they attacked as a false religion, a satanic cult dedicated to the corruption of the will to live. Those of us who had laughed late into the night with the Sorensens said nothing, for we saw in their deaths still another sign that our town had lost its way.

Indeed, it's often difficult to recall a more innocent time, when we cheerfully planned birthday parties for our children and looked forward to family picnics on shady redwood tables beside the stream. We have grown accustomed to the daily suicide reports, the weekly death counts—sometimes high, sometimes low—now a lull, now a flare-up—here a bachelor in his leather recliner in front of the flat-screen TV, there a group of close-knit friends in cushioned chaises around the swimming pool. On nearly every block, a house has been struck. People approaching one another on the sidewalk shift their eyes suddenly, thinking: Will he be next? Despite it all, we manage to carry on, as if we don't know what else there might be to do. The daily paper continues to land on front porches, even of abandoned houses. Children skip rope. Hedge-trimmers buzz. Lawn mowers sound in the air of summer.

In such a world, people seek answers. Some say we're being punished for the way we live—the casual adulteries, the heavy drinking, the high divorce rate, the sexual promiscuity among our teenagers, the violent visual culture among our children. Others, while rejecting the punishment hypothesis as a throwback to moribund theological systems, nevertheless claim that our town has carried certain forms of behavior to their logical conclusion, for a culture based on material pleasures must necessarily lead to an embrace of the ultimate material fact, which is death. Still others, dismissing this argument as a secular version of the theological critique, insist that our town represents a new, healthy attitude toward the conduct of life: disdaining evasion, we bravely face the truth of our mortality.

For our part, while honoring the sincerity of these explanations, we believe the truth lies elsewhere. The behavior of our citizens, though far from perfect, is surely no worse than one finds in other suburban towns. And we take special pride in seeing to it that our town is an ideal place for raising children. Our school system is first-rate, our three parks well cared for, our neighborhoods safe. Visitors from other towns praise our shady residential streets, lined with sugar maples, lindens, and sycamores; they comment on our friendly and welcoming Main Street with its outdoor cafés, its array of ice cream shops and exotic restaurants housed in carefully preserved nineteenth-century buildings with arched windows outlined by stone moldings. Even the older houses in our blue-collar neighborhoods, south of the railroad tracks, display well-mowed lawns and fresh-painted shingles, on streets lined with broad porches. How then do we explain this eruption of wished-for death, this plague of self-annihilation?

The answer, we have concluded, lies not in our failure to live up to a high code of conduct—not in the realm of failure at all—but in the very qualities of our town that we think of as deserving praise. By this we don't mean to suggest that our town is a sham, that beneath our well-groomed surface is a hidden darkness—a rot at the heart of things. Such an explanation we find naïve, even childish. It suggests that by the simple act of tearing off a mask we can expose the hideous truth beneath—a truth that, once revealed, will no longer have the power to harm us. Such an analysis strikes us as banal and consoling. Our town, we maintain, is in fact the excellent place we've always found it to be. It is precisely the nature of this excellence that we wish to examine more closely.

Those who admire our town speak of it as pleasant, safe, comfortable, attractive, and friendly. It is all these things. But such qualities, however worthwhile, contain an element of the questionable. At their heart lies an absence. It's an absence of all that is not pleasant, all that is uncomfortable, dangerous, unknown. By its very nature, that is to say, our town represents a banishment. But the act of banishment implies an awareness of the very thing that is banished. It is this awareness, we maintain, that breeds a secret sympathy for all that is not reassuring. Surfeited with contentment, weighed down by happiness, our citizens feel, now and then, a sudden desire: for the unseen, for the forbidden. Beneath or within our town, a counter-town arises—a dark town devoted to the disruption of limits, a town in love with death.

Severe illnesses demand severe remedies. We propose that the Committee insert into our town the things we have kept out. We suggest a return to public hangings, on the hill behind the high school. We support gladiatorial contests between men and maddened pit bulls. We recommend the restoration of outlawed forms of public punishment, such as stoning and flaying. We advise a return to the stake, to fire and blood. We ask that once a year a child be chosen by lot and ritually murdered on the green before the town hall, as a reminder to our citizens that we walk on the bones of the dead.

Our town has been emptied of darkness, robbed of death. There is nothing left for us but brightness, clarity, and order. Our citizens are killing themselves because their passion for what's missing has nowhere else to go.

We urge the Committee to consider our recommendations with the utmost seriousness. Anything less than a violent response to our crisis will certainly fail. Some say that it is already too late, that our town is heading for extinction. We, on the contrary, hold out an anxious hope. But we must act. Already the disease has begun to spread to other towns—here and there, in nearby places, we read of extravagant suicides, of deaths that cannot be accounted for in the usual way.

We who have studied these matters, we who have pursued our investigations into the darkest corners of our minds, are not ourselves exempt from stray imaginings. On warm spring evenings, when dusk settles over our houses like a promise of something we dare not remember, or on blue summer nights when we step from the shadows of porches into the brightness of the moon, we feel a stirring, a restless desire, as if we were missing something we had thought would be there. Then we take firm hold of ourselves, we set our jaws and turn back, for we know where these flickers of feeling can take us. And perhaps what is happening in our town is simply this, that a familiar flicker, of no harm in itself, has been allowed to develop without impediment, that our citizens have become gifted in the dark art of not holding back. For at that moment, before we turn away, we too have seen the distant figure beckon, we too have heard the black wings beating in the brain.

Respectfully submitted to the Committee by the undersigned, this seventeenth day of September.

COMING SOON

O ne Saturday afternoon in summer, Levinson, self-proclaimed refugee from the big city, sat at his favorite sidewalk café on Main Street, sipping an iced cappuccino and admiring the view. He felt, without vanity, the satisfaction of a man who knows he has made the right choice. This was no boring backwater, as his friends had warned, no cute little village with one white steeple and two red gas pumps, but a lively, thriving town. Women in smart dresses and broad-brimmed straw hats sashayed past within reach of his arm. Over the café railing he watched husbands in baseball caps pushing baby carriages with one hand and leading dogs with the other, while wives in oversized sunglasses gripped the handles of bright-colored shopping bags stuffed with blouses and bargain jeans. There were aging bikers with black head wraps and tattooed forearms, Japanese tourists in flowered shirts taking pictures with iPhones, swaggering teenage boys in sleeveless tees and low-slung cargo shorts, a stern Hasid in a long black coat and black high-crowned hat, laughing girls with swinging hair and tight short-shorts and platform wedge sandals.

Even the shops and buildings seemed to be moving, breathing, changing shape as he watched. Across the street, two men behind a strip of yellow caution tape were lifting a plate-glass window into the renovated front wall of Mangiardi's Restaurant. Farther down, on a stretch of sidewalk cordoned off by a wooden partition, workers in hard hats were smashing crowbars into the brick facade of the Vanderheyden Hotel. And still farther away, where the stores and restaurants ended and the center of town gave way to muffler shops and motels, a tall red crane swung an I-beam slowly across the sky, in the direction of a new three-level parking garage on the site of a torn-down strip mall.

Levinson had moved here nearly a year ago, when the consulting firm he worked for opened an upstate branch. He'd never regretted it. The city was a lost cause, what with the jammed-up traffic, the filthy subways, the decaying neighborhoods and crumbling buildings. The future lay in towns—in small, well-managed towns. He'd put a down payment on a shady house on a quiet street of overarching maples, but he hadn't kissed the city goodbye in order to sit back with his hands on his belly and live a soft life. He still worked as hard as ever, often staying at the office till six or seven; on weekends he mowed his lawn, caulked his windows, cleaned his gutters, shoveled the drive. He was seeing two women—dinner and a movie, no more—while waiting for the right one to come along. He had a decent social life; the neighbors were friendly. He was forty-two years old.

On weekends and evenings, whenever he was free, Levinson liked nothing better than to explore the streets of his town. Main Street was always alive, but that wasn't the only part of town with an energy you could feel. On residential streets, houses displayed new roofs, renovated porches, bigger windows, fancier doors; in outlying neighborhoods, empty tracts of land blossomed with medical buildings, supermarkets, family restaurants. During early visits to the town he'd seen a field of bramble bushes with a sluggish stream change into a flourishing shopping plaza, where stores shaded by awnings faced a parking lot studded with tree islands and flower beds, and shortly after his move he'd watched, day after day, as a stretch of woods at

the west end of town was cut down and transformed into a community of stone-and-shingle houses on smooth streets lined with purple-
leaved Norway maples. You could always find something new in this
town—something you weren't expecting. His city friends, skeptics
and mockers all, could say what they liked about the small-town
doldrums, the backwater blues, but that didn't prevent them from
coming up for the weekend, and even they seemed surprised at the
vitality of the place, with its summer crowds, its merry-go-round in
the park, its thronged farmers' market, and, wherever you looked,
on curbsides and street corners, in vacant lots and fenced-off fields,
men and machines at work: front-end loaders lifting dirt into dump
trucks, excavators digging their toothed buckets into the earth, truck-
mounted cranes unfolding, rising, stretching higher and higher into
the sky.

After paying at the cash register and dropping a couple of quarters
into the tip jar, Levinson set off on his post-cappuccino Main Street
stroll. Though by now he knew the eight-block stretch of downtown
as well as his own backyard, he was always coming upon things that
took him by surprise. In the Chinese takeout, the tables were pushed
to one corner and a man with a power drill was boring into a wall; a
sign in the window announced the opening of a new Vietnamese restaurant. From a platform on the scaffolding that rose along the facade
of a nearby building, men in hard hats were adding scroll-shaped support brackets to an apartment balcony. A new Asian bistro, which had
taken the place of an Indian restaurant, now had a snazzy terrace
reached by a flight of granite steps; two men on ladders were installing a dark green awning.

Half a block away, a long section of sidewalk had been closed off
by an orange mesh fence, forcing Levinson to walk on a narrow strip
of street bordered by a low wall of concrete blocks. Behind the mesh
fence he saw a bucket truck, a few men in lime-green vests and white
hard hats, piles of bricks and lumber, a man in a T-shirt and safety

goggles standing on the platform of a scissor lift, and an orange safety cone with a small American flag stuck in the hole at the top.

After another block, Levinson turned left onto West Broad and walked over to one of his favorite spots: a fenced-off construction site on the corner of Maplewood. Here the foundation was being dug for an apartment building with ground-floor retail spaces, on land formerly occupied by the parking lot of a small department store. Through an open door in the wooden fence, Levinson looked down at the reddish earth, at the blue cab and silver drum of a concrete mixer, at piles of mint-green plastic sewer pipes. He watched with pleasure as a yellow backhoe lifted a jawful of earth and debris into the bed of a high-piled dump truck, which immediately started up a dirt slope that led to the street.

One thing Levinson liked about his adopted town was the way you could follow its daily evolution, chart its changes, pay close attention to every detail, without feeling, as you did in the city, that your head was about to crack open. Sleepy villages held no charm for him. His interest had quickened when the realtor told him about high-tech businesses coming to town, bidding wars being waged for prime locations, fancy condos on the way. The housing market was on the upswing. Lately he'd been noticing even more activity than usual, as shops and restaurants changed hands, apartment complexes sprang up, old buildings came crashing down. Fields of shrubs and weed-clumps sent up clouds of brown dirt under the blades of dozers.

As Levinson crossed Main and headed back toward his neighborhood, he felt the familiar sensation of downtown trickling away in two blocks of bars and restaurants, and then, as if suddenly, you found yourself in a world of tree-lined streets and two-story houses with shutters and front porches. For a moment it seemed that he'd come to another, quieter town. The impression quickly gave way to a sharper sense of things: a man stood on a ladder slapping paint onto the side of a house, workmen on a roof were laying the rafters of a new dormer, and, in yard after yard, people were planting bushes, trimming trees, scraping paint from window frames, rushing to open doors as deliverymen carried couches, refrigerators, and dining room tables along front walks and up steps.

When Levinson reached his block, he waved to old Mrs. Breyer, sitting on her wicker settee on the broad front porch. "Nice work," he said, pointing to the new ceiling, with its glistening walnut stain, and the freshly painted porch posts. She relaxed into one of her wide, girlish smiles, keeping her teeth covered by her lips. Levinson passed a freshly laid driveway that still gave off a smell of tar, stopped to examine a red flagstone walk that only a week ago had been squares of concrete, and, stepping aside to let a neighbor girl in a brilliant pink helmet ride past on her training bike, he climbed his front steps and sank into one of the two cushioned chairs beside the round iron table.

In the warm shade, Levinson half-closed his eyes. Tomorrow, Sunday, he was flying down to Miami for two weeks to stay with his sister and nephews and visit his mother in assisted living. It would be good to see the family, good to get away for a while. When you liked a place, you liked leaving it so that you could look forward to coming back. It was his town now, his home. Sometimes he wished he'd taken up another line of work, like civil engineering or town planning; he enjoyed thinking about large spaces, about putting things in them, arranging them in significant relations. Levinson felt the muscles of his neck relaxing. As he drifted toward sleep, he was aware of the sounds of his neighborhood: the clatter of skateboard wheels, the *zzzroom zzzroom* of a chain saw, the dull rumble of a closing garage door, a burst of laughter, and always the chorus of hand mowers and riding mowers, of hedge trimmers and pressure washers, of electric edgers and power pruners, and, beneath or above them all, like the beat at the hidden heart of things, the ring of hammers through the summer air.

When he opened his eyes, he was surprised to find that he was no longer sitting in the shade of his front porch. For some reason he was lying in a bed, in a room with a dark bureau slashed by a stripe of sun. As he stared at the bureau, it seemed to him that it was becoming more familiar, as if, at any moment, he might discover why it was there. Ah, he was in his bedroom—the sun was shining between the shade and the window frame. How had it happened? Levinson tried to remember. The walk along Main, the return to the front porch, the flight to Miami, his mother's frail hands—of course. He'd returned from Miami and hurled himself into a frantic week of work, staying late at the office and collapsing into bed immediately after dinner. Now it was Saturday; he'd slept later than usual. It was time for his morning routine—breakfast, the lawn, the calls to his sister, his mother, and his brother, Murray, in San Diego, the cleanup of the garage—before the walk into town for his bagel and iced cappuccino. Then dinner with a few friends at eight.

As Levinson stepped onto his front walk, he noticed with surprise that the Mazowskis' house, across the street, had grown larger. It stretched out on both sides, almost to the property lines. When he turned right and set off for town, he saw that the house of his neighbors the Sandlers was stucco instead of white shingle. It all must have happened while he was away. Walking along, he was struck by other changes: the Jorgensen house had a second porch above the first, in front of what's-his-name's place a tall hedge with a latticed entrance gate had replaced a row of forsythia bushes, and as Levinson gave a wave to Mrs. Breyer, sitting on her porch, he saw, high overhead, a third story, with an octagonal tower at one end.

On block after block, the houses were escaping their old forms, turning into something new. He passed a half-finished side porch propped up on brick piers; men in hard hats were pacing the blond floorboards. A nearby house had big bay windows and an attached garage that Levinson didn't recall seeing before. On one corner the sidewalk was closed to pedestrians; beyond a portable chain-link fence, a small white house with a red roof stood entirely enclosed by the studs, beams, and rafters of a much larger house, which was being constructed around it. Levinson tried to imagine what would happen to the original house—would it remain inside, a house within a house?—but his attention was distracted by the neighboring house, a new two-and-a-half-story mansion faced in stone, with a roof garden where a couple sat dining in the shade of an arbor.

Forcing himself to lower his eyes, because there was only so much you could take in before exhaustion struck you down, Levinson stared at the familiar sidewalk as he climbed the steep street leading to Main. When he reached the corner, he looked up and stopped in bewilderment. A five-story department store with immense display windows rose before him. It stood in the place once occupied by Jimmy's News Corner, Antique Choices, and the Main Street Marketplace. Next to the new building was a deep courtyard crowded with tables, where people sat drinking dark beer; a sign said GRAND OPENING.

Everywhere Levinson looked, he saw new shops, new buildings—an ad agency, a Moroccan restaurant, a hair boutique, a gelato parlor. There was even a roofed arcade, with a row of shops stretching back on each side. The old savings bank was still there, with its high front steps and its fluted columns, but it stood two stories taller and was connected to a new building by a walkway enclosed in glass, in a space occupied three weeks earlier by a men's clothing store and a wine shop; and though City Hall still stood across from the bank, one wall was covered by scaffolding and the front steps were concealed behind a plywood fence, through which he could hear sounds of drilling and smashing.

As Levinson made his way toward his iced cappuccino, he did his best to take it all in. The Vietnamese restaurant, which three weeks ago had replaced the Chinese takeout, was now a shop specializing in fancy chocolates. The old Vanderheyden Hotel looked like a Renaissance palazzo. The nail salon was a Swedish-furniture store. And Levinson's sidewalk café, his Saturday retreat, with its iron railing and fringed umbrellas, the place he had longed for in Miami, was now Louise's Dress Shoppe, with racks of sale dresses and silk scarves standing outside, under an awning.

Scarcely had he registered his disappointment when he noticed a new sidewalk café a few stores down, where dark red fabric stretched between iron posts. Soon he was sitting in the shade of a table umbrella, drinking an iced cappuccino and trying to get a grip on things. The changes were stunning, almost impossible to believe, but a lot could happen in three weeks, especially in a town like this. Levinson was all too familiar with the kind of person who deplored change, who swooned over old buildings and spoke vaguely but reverently of earlier times, and though he was startled and a little dizzied by the sight of the new downtown, which made him wonder whether he had fallen asleep on his front porch and was dreaming it all, he looked out at the street with sharp interest, for he was wide awake, drinking his iced cappuccino on a Saturday afternoon in town, and was not one of those people who, whenever the wrecking ball swung against the side of a building, felt that a country or a civilization was coming to an end.

Invigorated by his rest, Levinson set off on his Saturday stroll along Main, determined to let nothing escape him. He examined the displays in the windows of new stores, observed the redesigned facades of half-familiar buildings. He passed the granite steps and broad glass doors of something called XQuisiCo Enterprises, where he remembered a jeweler's and a cigar store. At the end of Main he turned onto West Broad and walked to the corner of Maplewood, to see how his construction site was coming along.

It was no longer there. Along the entire length of Maplewood, on both sides, five-story brick apartment complexes with broad balconies rose above new stores shaded by ornamental pear trees. Levinson tried to recall the earlier street—the wooden fence with the opening, an office supply store, Nagel's Dry Cleaning—but he became uncertain, maybe he was leaving out a building or two, it wasn't a street he knew particularly well. He walked along the new Maplewood, checking the shop windows, looking up at a family having lunch on a fourth-floor balcony hung with baskets of flowers; he passed an opening between buildings, which gave a glimpse of a wide courtyard where a clown with painted tears on his white face stood juggling dinner plates in a circle of seated children holding balloons.

At the next street he turned left toward Main. He had a clear view of the new sidewalk café, with its red-fabric railing; next door, workmen were replacing brick with stone, under a sign that read COMING SOON. He had a confused sense, as he crossed Main Street, that the stores were no longer the same, that everything had changed again, but surely he was mistaken, an effect of overexcitement in the oppressive afternoon heat.

Tired now, Levinson began to make his way home. When he reached the tree-lined streets at the outskirts of his neighborhood, he realized that he must have made a wrong turn somewhere, for he was passing houses he had never seen before, though some seemed dimly familiar. Maybe it was a street he knew, whose houses had all received new breezeways, gables, porches, add-ons. Or maybe the old houses had all been torn down and replaced with new ones.

He hadn't gone far when a row of orange-and-white-striped barrels blocked his way. Beyond the barrels, people stood watching something in a yard. It seemed to Levinson that between two houses with adjoining lawns, a paver fed by a dump truck was laying asphalt on a new street, leaving only narrow strips of grass on both sides. Levinson turned back. He found another street, where he spotted a porch that he thought he recognized, though he could no longer be sure. He turned right, passed a half-finished house with walls wrapped in pink insulation, and came to a line of sawhorses stretching across the road. He turned onto another street. From a porch, someone waved. It was old Mr. Gillon, who lived on Levinson's street, a block from his house.

The heat had exhausted Levinson. His temples throbbed; his forearms glistened. Under familiar branches, unknown housefronts shim-
mered in the sun. A bike helmet lay sideways on a front lawn, like a
gaping mouth. Suddenly his house rose up. Levinson climbed onto
the porch, gripping the iron rail. He sank into one of the chairs. His
head was hot. Across the street, a large backhoe stood on the front
lawn, blocking half of the Mazowskis' house. In the warm shade,
Levinson closed his eyes.

When he opened his eyes, a light rain was falling. Under the dark
gray sky, porch lights were on, windows glowed yellow. On the strip
of lawn between his sidewalk and the street, a sawhorse sat next to
a safety cone. He imagined them coming closer, advancing along his
front walk. In the dusky air, the houses across the way reminded him
of a childhood trip he'd taken with his parents, to someplace in Arizona or New Mexico. Through the window of his hotel room he had
stared out anxiously at the wrong-looking houses, with their strange
chimneys, their make-believe doors. Levinson stiffened: the dinner.
It was already 7:25. He wouldn't have time for a shower—just enough
time to towel himself down, change his clothes.

Ten minutes later, when Levinson stepped out his front door, the
rain had stopped; a crack of pale sky showed through the somber
clouds. The streetlights had come on. On his front lawn he saw a
length of gleaming steel pipe. Across the street a wire fence ran along
the curb, enclosing the front yard and the backhoe. Three men, dark
against the evening sky, stood on the roof of the Mazowskis' house.
On the side of the Sandlers' house rose a two-story scaffold tower that
Levinson hadn't noticed before. A man in a hard hat stood next to it,
with his fists on his hips, looking over at him.

Levinson backed his car out of the drive and headed down his
block in the direction of Main. The restaurant where he was meeting
his friends was on the far side of town, out by the new mall.

At the end of the second block, Levinson's street was closed off.

Men in hard hats stood bent over jackhammers as they tore up the road. Levinson turned right. Halfway down the street a large truck with two safety cones on its front bumper stood in the way. A man with an orange stripe across his jacket was waving him to the right, where a narrow lane ran between backyards. At the end of the lane, Levinson turned onto a street that felt unfamiliar, though it couldn't have been far from his house. The sun had dropped beneath the rooflines; against the darkening sky, a crane was lowering something onto a roof.

At the next corner he turned again, but he was no longer certain whether he was heading toward Main or away from it. He passed a large house where a crowd of people were laughing on a wraparound porch. Someone raised a glass, as if to him. In an orange glow of sodium vapor lamps, Levinson kept looking for a street that would lead him to the center of town, but he found himself in an unknown neighborhood, where a stretch of half-built houses gave way to a dark field. Behind a chain-link fence, a tower crane rose up beside an immense frame of steel beams.

Levinson turned around and headed back. It was 7:55. He came to a street of two-story houses with front porches. It seemed to be his own street, though it was hard to tell. At the end of the block, men with lights in their hats were excavating a front yard. Levinson lowered his window. "How do I get to Main?" he shouted. "That way!" one of the men called, waving him to the left. Levinson turned left; in the light of a flickering streetlamp he saw a half-constructed house with roof trusses in place. In the blackness of the next yard he made out a dim foundation covered by floor joists. The street came to an end; an unpaved path led into what appeared to be a forest. A metal sign leaning against a tree read MEN AT WORK. As Levinson followed the path, branches scraped sharply against the side of his car. The path widened, began to rise; guardrails appeared; he was on a ramp; all at once Levinson found himself on a six-lane highway, where ruby taillights rushed away into the distance. On the other side of the divider, yellow headlights came streaming toward him. Under a blue-black sky, Levinson entered the second lane, passed below a sign with a name and exit number he did not recognize, and rode off into the night.

RAPUNZEL

Climbing

Hand over hand, each foot lifting above the other and pressing against the rough stone, his back tense, his neck arched, the braided hair tightening in his fists: the Prince is strong, but it's no easy task to make his way up the face of the tower. The adventure excites him. He thrives on obstacles, perils, impediments of every kind. He is filled with such exhilaration that he would cry out for joy, except that his teeth are clenched and his lips stretched wide in a grimace of exertion. He remembers his first glimpse of her: the window high above, the dark figure below, the hair coming down like a shower of fire. Now he's climbing that burning hair, which, in the summer dusk, in the shadows of the high pines and firs, is not golden, as he always remembers it, but the color of a bale of hay in the shade of a stable. There is danger in the climb, since at any moment he might fall and crack his neck, break his back. And even if his hold is sure, a second danger threatens from the forest: the sudden return of the sorceress, who will see him trying to reach the forbidden place. The Prince welcomes danger, exults in it, for it's danger that makes him feel his life. In the late dusk the tower lies in darkness, but up above, where the sky is still pale, the casement window catches the last light. The Prince thinks: If only it could be this way forever!—the pull in his arms, the thrill of the ascent, the scrape of branches against his neck. An owl calls in the forest. The Prince pauses, slaps at an insect, continues climbing. From his upthrust hip, his sword hangs straight down, as if it has stopped suddenly in the act of falling.

The Mirror

As the Prince climbs the tower, the sorceress returns through the forest to her cottage at the edge of the darkening village. The cottage is surrounded by a high wall; the sorceress has no use for neighbors. Inside, she walks past the table and the cupboard and goes at once to her dressing table, where she picks up an oval mirror with an ivory handle. It is always like that: after the tower, the mirror. In the glass she sees her reflection staring at her with a familiar look of revulsion. She glares back with fascinated loathing, with a kind of eager bitterness. She detests the thick eyebrows, the small eyes set too close together, the thrusting ridge of the nose, as if drawn by a village caricaturist sketching a witch. Her lips are a knife-slash, her chin juts out like a knuckle. From a wart in her chin-cleft, three hairs stick out like tubers sprouting from an old potato. Her skin is yellow. Her black hair hangs in her face like bush-branches over a fence. Her herbs, her roots, her medicinal salves, even her spells, which can raise towers out of thin air—all useless. She thrusts the mirror aside. The cruelty is that she has always loved beautiful things. At once she thinks of Rapunzel. And her heart lifts: the golden hair, skin like the down of a swan, the graceful slope of the nose. Rapunzel is safe in the tower, asleep under her coverlet. She will visit her darling when night is done.

Hair

In the tower chamber, Rapunzel lies waiting for the Prince. Some-times she waits by the window, but this evening she is lying on her bed, on the other side of the small room. Her braided hair stretches across the coverlet and over the wooden table to the hook in the ledge. She's proud of her hair, which is much longer than she is, and comes pouring out of her like rain from the sky, though it takes up a lot of room and can be a nuisance as it drags around the floor picking up dust. Sometimes she wishes she could cut it all off with a sharp snip-snip and watch it lie there nice and dead without it slithering along after her all the time. At sunset, as soon as the sorceress let her-self down, Rapunzel drew up the thick braid, waved good night from the window, and stood watching as the sorceress disappeared into the dark trees. Not long after, the Prince appeared in the small clearing at the base of the tower. Rapunzel tied her braid again around the hook in the ledge, then let down her hair hand over hand, as if she were lowering a bucket into a well. When the last handful was over the sill, she returned to the bed and lay down. Even though her braid is tied to a hook, she can feel the tug of the Prince as he climbs. He's like a boy, her Prince, teasing her by pulling her hair. Through the window she sees the darkening sky. She knows that he loves the dif-ficult climb, but she herself does not love it; she worries every second about the return of the sorceress, she's afraid that even the slightest movement on her part will cause him to lose his grip and plunge to his death, and she dislikes the perpetual tugging at her scalp. She wishes they could find another way. But the tower has no door, there is no stairway, even the sorceress can't reach the top without climbing the rope of hair. Of course, there's the half-finished silk ladder hidden under the mattress, but the thought of it fills her with anxiety. Rapun-zel turns her mind to more pleasant things: the moment the Prince will appear in the window, the leap of her heart, his hand on her face. She can hear the squeak of her hair on the hook, the sound of his foot, far down, scraping against stone.

Beautiful Women

As the Prince climbs toward the top of the tower, he thinks suddenly of the palace, which lies on the other side of the forest. Rapunzel is so unlike the ladies of the court that he sometimes finds it difficult to account for what draws him to her, night after night. The ladies of the court are so beautiful that they are dangerous to behold. Sometimes a courtier, catching a stray glance, is stricken as by a bite in the throat; such a man sickens with love as with a wasting disease. The Prince, who has never been sick in his life, admires the ladies of the court and is by no means indifferent to their amorous glances. He has had many opportunities for clandestine adventure and, for so young a man, is already an experienced lover. But although there are many varieties of physical loveliness at court, he's aware of a note of sameness, for the ladies who surround him are remarkable above all for something high and severe in their beauty: the tightness of their pulled-back hair reveals the fine lines of their cheeks and foreheads, the narrowness of their nostrils, the exquisite modeling of their lips. Sometimes a courtier, bored by such abundance of perfection, seeks out the opposite: a coarse-featured peasant girl, a plump merchant's wife with a crooked tooth. The Prince, too, has had adventures in the country villages and farms, though he looks not for coarseness but for the unexpected burst of beauty in a gesture or a look. Always, in his love adventures, he has felt pleasure and something else: a remoteness, a lack of conviction, as though he were sitting nearby, observing the antics of the young Prince performing a seduction. It is never that way with Rapunzel. It's as though she has slipped inside him and

moves when he moves. What he sees, when he looks at her, is harder
to say. The court ladies would find her wanting in beauty. There is
nothing proud and haughty in her face, nothing lofty in the cut of
her bones. Sometimes, turning to look at her as she lies beside him,
he is startled by something childish and unformed in her features;
it's as if he has never seen her before, doesn't know what she looks
like. At other times, when the Prince is alone and tries to summon
her to mind, he can't see her with any certainty; he sees only what
she is not. What he remembers, always, is the first sight of her hair,
falling from the tower like fire. She seems to exist only in the realm
of dream. Is that why he returns to her, night after night? To assure
himself that he isn't dreaming? And suppose she finds the courage to
leave the dream-tower, as he wants her to do. Will she dissolve in the
hard light of the sun? The Prince's thoughts irritate him like gnats; he
shakes them away. Reaching up, he grips the hair, lifts a foot and slaps
it higher on the wall. He looks up at the evening sky. Somewhere up
there, an invisible woman is waiting.

Waiting

The sorceress, too, is waiting. She is waiting for the long night to
begin, so that it can come to an end. In the first light of dawn, she
will return to her Rapunzel. She can, at any moment, leave her cottage and make her way through the forest to the tower, but she resists
what she recognizes to be no longer a real temptation. After all, she
spends the entire day with Rapunzel; the night is for herself. It is better that way. She doesn't want Rapunzel to tire of her—lately there
have been troubling signs—and besides, there are things that need to
be done at home. Because she hates the sharp light of the sun, which
draws attention to her witch's face, her demon's hair, she works in the
dark. As soon as the moon is up, she will step outside and tend her

vegetable garden, cut dead twigs from her pear and plum trees, water her shrubs and flowers. Then she will carry her clothes in a basket to the stream that runs along the edge of the village. She will wash her clothes under the moon and carry them home to hang on a line to dry. She will bake bread in the oven for Rapunzel, she will fetch water from the well. Only then will she prepare for bed. In the dark she'll remove her long black dress and slip on her nightdress, which no one has ever seen. She will lie down in her bitter bed and think of Rapunzel, white and gold in her tower. Standing at her dressing table, the sorceress glances again at the mirror. She reaches for it, snatches away her hand. She begins to pace up and down with her hands behind her back, the top of her body leaning forward, as if she is walking uphill.

Helpless

As she waits for the Prince to reach the window, Rapunzel feels the sensation she always feels when he's partway up the tower: she is trapped, she can't move, she wants to cry out in anguish. She understands that her feeling of helplessness is provoked by the long climb, by her refusal to stir for fear that she'll cause the Prince to lose his grip, by the continual tugging at her scalp. What's taking so long? She reminds herself that only during the climb itself does she feel this way. The Prince's descent takes place swiftly, nothing could be easier, no sooner has he dropped below the sill than he's standing at the foot of the tower far below, looking up. The sorceress herself climbs the tower as if she's walking across a room, even though she carries a sack on her back filled with vegetables and bread. Why oh why does the Prince take so long? He must enjoy making her miserable. Or is it possible that he isn't taking as long as she imagines, that he's actually rushing up to her like a great wind, and that only the eagerness of her desire makes his progress seem so slow? Through the open window Rapunzel can see the top of the hook, the little jumps of yanked hair. Will he never arrive?

Disappointment

The window is just above his head, with another pull his face will rise over the sill, but as the Prince grips the window ledge he feels the familiar burst of disappointment. He is disappointed because the climb is about to end, the victory is within reach, already he longs for a new difficulty, a stronger danger—a beast in the forest, an assassin in the chamber. He would like to battle a dragon at the mouth of a cave night after night, as he fights his way to Rapunzel. He is happy of course at the thought that he'll soon be reunited with his beloved, whom he has imagined exhaustively during the long hours of the tedious day, but he knows that, in the instant of seeing her, he will be startled by the many small ways in which she fails to resemble his memory of her, before the living Rapunzel replaces the imaginary one. As he pulls himself up to the window ledge, he wishes that he were at the bottom of the tower, climbing fiercely toward his beloved.

Suspicion

As the Prince rises above the window ledge, the sorceress pauses in the act of pacing in the dark cottage. Rapunzel has seemed changed lately—or is she only imagining things? Sometimes, when the sorceress looks up from the table in the tower to watch Rapunzel sitting across from her, bent over her needlework, she sees the girl staring off with parted lips. If she asks her what she's thinking, Rapunzel laughs gaily and replies that she isn't thinking anything at all. Sometimes the girl sighs, in the manner of someone releasing an inward pressure. The sorceress, whose unhappiness has sharpened her alertness to signs of discontent, is alarmed by these evidences of a secret life. She speaks gently to Rapunzel, asks her if she is feeling tired, reaches into the pocket of her dress and draws forth a piece of marzipan. The sorceress is well aware that she has placed Rapunzel at the top of an inaccessible tower in the middle of a dark forest, but she also knows that her sole desire is to shield the beautiful girl from the world's harm. If Rapunzel should become dissatisfied, if she should ever grow restless and unhappy, she would begin to imagine a different life. She would ask questions, open herself up to impossible desires, dream of walking on the ground below. The tower would begin to seem a prison. It is not a prison. It is a refuge, a place of peace. The world, as the sorceress knows deep in her blood, is full of pain. She vows to be more attentive to her daughter, to satisfy Rapunzel's slightest desire, to watch for the faintest signs of unrest.

At Last!

Rapunzel watches as the Prince swings gracefully into the chamber, stares at her as if spellbound, and at once turns to unfasten her hair from the hook in the ledge. Everything about the Prince moves her heart, but she is always disappointed by the way he looks at her at the moment when he arrives. He seems bewildered in some way, as if he's surprised to find her there, at the top of the tower, or as if he can't quite figure out who exactly she is, this stranger whose hair he has just been climbing. With his back to her he begins pulling up her hair from below, setting the coils of her braid on the table, pulling faster and faster as the slippery heap of hair slides from the table and drops to the floor, where it quivers and shakes like a long animal. When the Prince turns toward her with his hands still holding her braid, as if he has come to her bearing a gift of her own hair, he no longer wears a look of bafflement but one of tender recognition, and as she rises to meet him she feels her release flowing through her like desire.

Shameless

The Prince lies back languorously on the rumpled bed, watching Rapunzel move about the chamber in her nightdress of unbound shimmering hair, and reflects again on her absence of shame. He knows many court ladies who are without shame in matters of love, but their shamelessness is aggressive and defiant: the revelation of nakedness is, for them, an invitation to enjoy the forbidden. One lady insists that he stand aside and watch as she undresses herself slowly, pausing for him to admire each part as she caresses herself with her hands; at the very end she holds before her a transparent silk scarf, which she then lets fall to the ground. In their desire to outrage modesty, to cast off the constraints of decorum, the Prince sees an allegiance to the very forces they wish to overcome. Sometimes a peasant girl in a haystack reveals a sensual frankness for which the Prince is grateful, but that same girl will carry herself primly to church on a Sunday. Rapunzel is without shame and without an overcoming of shame. She walks in her nakedness as if nakedness were a form of clothing. The innocence of her wantonness disarms the Prince. There is nothing she won't do, nothing she feels she should resist. Sometimes the Prince wishes that she would tease him with a sly look, that she would cover her breasts with an outspread fan of peacock feathers, that she would lie on her stomach and look at him mischievously over her shoulder, as if to say: Do you dare? The Prince is a fearless lover, but there are times when he feels shy before her. At such moments he longs for her to resist him violently, so that he might force her into submission. Instead he bends down, far down, and kisses, very slowly, each of her toes.

Into the Forest

Rapunzel watches from the window as the Prince descends quickly, hand over hand, and leaps to the ground. He looks up, calls her name. So far down, he seems no Prince, but a small creature of the forest, a fox or a weasel. He turns, vanishes into the trees. The dark sky is breaking up with dawn. A sudden desire comes: to leap from the tower, to fall down, down; her hair lifting above her like a column of smoke; the wind rushing up at her; the world's weight gone; lovely falling; blissful dying.

Brushing

In the brightening chamber, the sorceress sits at the table by the window, brushing Rapunzel's unbraided hair. Rapunzel sits across from her, sipping an herbal brew. Her needlework lies to one side; she looks a little tired. The sorceress fears she isn't sleeping well, or perhaps is coming down with something; the herbal remedy should restore her. Because the hair is so long, the sorceress doesn't begin at the top and brush down. Instead, she begins at the bottom, holding an armful of hair on her lap and brushing it free of tangles. The brush is of pearwood, with dark boar bristles; the sorceress received it from an old woman in the village as payment for curing an ache in the back. When she finishes with one lapful of hair she reaches down for another, gently pushing aside the brushed portion, which spills puffily over her legs to the floor. From a distance the hair is blond, but up close she can see many colors: wheat, fawn, red-gold, butter yellow, honey brown. The hair on her lap is a warm cat, asleep in the sun. When she is done brushing, the sorceress will plait the hair patiently into a single thick braid. The soft folds will gradually become heavy as rope, a sunshiny snake slithering along the floor. Again she looks at Rapunzel; she never tires of looking at Rapunzel. The girl's head is turned toward the window but she is not gazing out. Her eyes are half closed; morning light strikes her neck and lower cheek; she is not blinking; she is gazing in. A penny for your thoughts! the sorceress wants to cry, but she continues brushing the hair in her lap. Suddenly she bends forward, buries her face in the hair, breathes it in, covers it with kisses. She looks up guiltily, but Rapunzel dreams away.

The Ladder

The Prince, riding home through the forest in slants of dawn-light, reproaches himself for his weakness. Once again he hasn't asked about the ladder. Each night he brings Rapunzel a cord of silk, which she's supposed to weave into the lengthening silk ladder concealed beneath her mattress. He might easily have presented her with a fully formed ladder, when the idea first came to him, but he wants her to engage fully in the act of escape. The Prince fears that she may not be ready to leave her sheltered life for the public life of a Princess; lately, indeed, she has avoided all mention of the ladder. This ought to disturb him more than it does, but he himself is not without doubts. Instead of asking her about her progress, he hands her the silken cord in silence. She slips it under the mattress. They do not speak of it.

Secrets

As the sorceress continues to braid her hair, Rapunzel is relieved to be spared another of those piercing looks. Can the sorceress suspect something? Rapunzel understands that by concealing the existence of the Prince, she's cruelly deceiving the sorceress, who is also her godmother. The thought pains her like a splinter burning in a finger. She'd love to tell her all about the Prince, since the sorceress would be sure to like him if only she knew him; often Rapunzel imagines the three of them living together in the sunny chamber. An instinct tells her to keep it to herself. She knows that the sorceress adores her, spoils her, sees to her every need, but it's precisely the intensity of her devotion that warns Rapunzel not to speak. She is everything to the sorceress; but everything leaves room for nothing else. Sometimes, at a sudden sound, the sorceress will leap up and go to the window. Then her eyes, searching the forest, grow hard and cold; her body, bent forward, seems crooked and ancient. At such moments Rapunzel looks away and waits for the change to pass. She knows that the sorceress craves continual signs of strong affection, which for that matter Rapunzel has always felt for her; the nightly visits of the Prince can be taken only as acts of betrayal. It's also true that the Prince, while not attacking the sorceress directly, disapproves of what he calls Rapunzel's imprisonment, and wants her to escape with him from the tower to the court. There they will be married and live in happiness all the days of their lives. Rapunzel glances at the mattress, under which the latest cord of silk lies beneath the half-finished ladder, and then at the sorceress, who is bending over and pressing her face against the folds of Rapunzel's hair.

The Plan

The Prince's plan is composed of two parts, the escape and the destination. He has revealed both parts to Rapunzel up to a point, but only up to a point, since each part includes complex secondary calculations that he hasn't yet found time to discuss with her in the detail they deserve. The escape will be difficult, without a doubt. The tower is forbiddingly high—to jump is out of the question. But the Prince has thought of two ways. The first is the ladder, which requires her full participation, demonstrated over the course of many weeks. They no longer discuss the ladder, which lies hidden under the mattress like an old love letter buried in a drawer. But there's a second way, one that acknowledges the impulsive in human nature and invites Rapunzel to risk all at a moment's notice. When he judges the mood to be right, the Prince will reveal this second method. They will spring into action. He'll fasten her braid to the hook and lower himself to the bottom. Immediately Rapunzel will draw up her hair, unfasten it from the hook, and fasten it a second time, using the very end of the braid. In this manner she'll be able to descend by means of her own hair. At the bottom, the Prince will cut the braid with a pair of gold scissors borrowed from his mother's seamstress, and they will escape into the forest, where two horses will be waiting. They will ride off to—where, exactly? For the destination, like the escape, is no simple matter, and here, too, the Prince has not been entirely forthright with Rapunzel. He has told her that he wants to bring her to the court, and this is true enough. But he hasn't confessed to her his fear that she might find it difficult to live as a Princess among courtiers and ladies, all of whom have a style and manner that might seem to her impossible to emulate. They themselves, and in particular the court ladies, will observe her closely and judge her according to their code. Rapunzel is not familiar with the fashions of the court. She lacks the court wit, the court polish, the court gift for concise and allusive speech. Even her name will draw amused attention. The Prince is not ashamed of Rapunzel, but he knows that the pressure of polite disapproval is likely to make him impatient with her shortcomings. Even if she should make an initial impression of freshness and innocence, such qualities might, in the long run, come to seem wearisome to the court. It might therefore be better to avoid the court altogether and flee with Rapunzel to a royal residence in the remote countryside. Such residences, it is true, are supplied with large contingents of servants, many of whom wield great power within the household and are accustomed to highborn masters with an instinct for command. Gentle Rapunzel, who has no experience of public life, will immediately be seen as weak. Wouldn't it be better, in every way, to choose a humble cabin on a wooded mountainside, far from the haunts of man? There they can live alone, without a care in the world. They will eat wild berries plucked from the vine, drink water from clear streams, and wander hand in hand in the paradise of Nature. In his mind, the Prince hears the phrase "paradise of Nature," which pleases him, but which also makes him uneasy. The Prince knows himself; he knows that he grows restless when he's away from court for more than a few days, for he misses the repartee, the rich feasts, the continual arrival of messengers bearing reports of wars, the sense of being at the center of a vital world. Mightn't it be better, all things considered, simply to move with Rapunzel from place to place, staying no more than a few weeks in a single dwelling? The thought of a wandering life does not please him. It's as if he can never imagine a settled existence for himself and his beloved. It's as if he himself is imprisoned in the tower, and can see nothing beyond the familiar chamber, which he carries in imagination from region to region— a restless and unhappy solitude.

Night Worries

In the cottage, in the middle of the night, the sorceress walks around and around the table with her hands behind her back, the top of her body leaning forward. Ah, she is sure of it: Rapunzel is concealing something. The girl flicked her eyes away more than once during the day, as if to avoid scrutiny. At other times she sat staring off with her eyes half closed, like someone fallen into a trance. The sorceress senses danger. Has someone discovered the tower? Has Rapunzel been seen in the window? She imagines the worst: a stranger scaling the tower, entering the chamber. Rage flames in her; she must calm herself. After all, the tower is well hidden, surrounded by massive trees in the middle of an immense forest. It can't be seen at a distance, since the top does not reach above the highest branches. Even in the unlikely event that someone should discover it, there is simply no way for him to reach the top: the tower is too high, the walls are without purchase for foot or hand, and no ladder in the world is long enough to reach the window. Even if such a ladder should be fashioned in the workshop of a master craftsman, it could never be carried through the dense forest, with its irregular growth of vast, mossy trees. Even if a method should somehow be contrived to carry it through the trees, the ladder could not by any stretch of the imagination be set upright in the small space between the tower and the thick branches, which come almost to the tower walls. Even if, for the sake of argument, it should be granted that a way might be found to stand the ladder against the high tower, the sheer impossibility of drawing it up into the little chamber would immediately become apparent. Even if, by a suspension of the laws of Nature, the ladder should miraculously be drawn up into the chamber, it would leave highly visible traces of its presence in the tangle of thornbushes that grow around the tower's base. No, the turned-away looks, the half-closed eyes, the drift of attention, must have some other cause. Has Rapunzel caught an illness? It might have been transmitted by one of the crows that sometimes land on the windowsill and sit gleaming there like wet tar in sunlight. She's told the girl time and time again to stay away from that windowsill. But Rapunzel's appetite remains unchanged; in fact, she has been growing plumper of late. There must be another explanation. Something is wrong, the sorceress can feel it like a change in the weather. As she continues pacing around and around the table, she thinks of secret causes, hidden reasons, dark possibilities. In the night that does not end, in the circle of floorboards that creak like animals in pain, she pledges herself to new intensities of vigilance.

Unreal

Because the Prince knows about the sorceress, but the sorceress does not know about the Prince, Rapunzel reproaches herself for behaving dishonestly toward the sorceress; but she knows that she has been dishonest toward the Prince as well. It isn't simply that she's stopped working on the silken ladder concealed beneath the mattress. It is far worse than that. The Prince has often spoken to her of his life outside the tower. He has described the court, the jeweled ladies, the circular stairways, the unicorn tapestries, the feasts at the high table, the bed with rich hangings, and she has listened as though he were reading to her from a book of wondrous tales. But when she tries to imagine herself stepping into the story, a nervousness comes over her, an anxious shudder. The images frighten her, as if they possess a power to do harm. The ladies, in particular, fill her with a vague dread. But there is something else. The court, the King, the hand-maidens, the flagons, the hounds—she can't really grasp them, can't take hold of them with the hands of her mind. What she knows is the table, the window, the bed: only that. The Prince has burst into her world from some other realm, bringing with him a scent of far-off places; at dawn, when he vanishes, she wakes from the dream to the table, the window, the bed. And even if she were able to believe in the dream-court, she knows that she herself can be no more than an outlandish visitor there, an intruder from the land of faery. Under the stern gaze of the King, the Queen, the courtiers, the jeweled ladies, she would turn into mist, she would disappear. If only things could stay as they are! Now the sun has set. The sorceress has vanished into the forest, the Prince has not yet come. It is cool at the window. Rapunzel feels a burst of gratitude for this moment, when the calm of dusk comes dropping down like rain.

1812 and 1819

In the 1812 edition of the *Kinder- und Hausmärchen,* the discovery of Rapunzel's secret comes when she innocently reveals her pregnancy by asking the sorceress why her dresses are growing tight. In the second edition, of 1819, Wilhelm Grimm, in an effort to make the stories more suitable for children, altered this passage. The discovery now comes when Rapunzel thoughtlessly asks the sorceress why she is harder to pull up than the Prince.

Discovery

It happens suddenly, as these things do: a careless word, a moment's lapse of caution. Everything changes in an instant. Now the sorceress, hideous with rage, stands leaning over Rapunzel, who is falling backward in her chair as she lifts one forearm before her face. The sorceress holds a large pair of scissors wide open—like a beast's jaws—above Rapunzel's braid. The braid hangs over the girl's shoulder and trails along the floor. The sorceress's nose, like another dangerous instrument, thrusts violently from her face, as if she's trying to slash Rapunzel's cheek with it. From the wart on her chin, three stiff hairs spring forward like wires. Her eyes look hot to the touch. Rapunzel's eyes, above her forearm, are so wide that they look like screaming mouths. Her eyebrows are raised nearly to the hairline. An immense shadow of scissor blades is visible on the bodice of her flowing dress.

Dusk

It never palls: the feel of the hair in his fists, the sheer wall soaring, the pull of the earth, the ache in his arms, the push of his feet against stone. No palace behind him, no dream-room above him, but only the immediate fact: hardness of stone, twist of hair, thrust of knee. He is young, he is strong, he is happy, he is alive. The world is good.

Wilderness

With a crunching squeeze of the scissors the sorceress has cut off Rapunzel's hair, her treacherous hair, and has banished her to a wilderness. It is a place of rocks and brambles, of weed-grown heaths; prickly bushes and twisted trees rise from the parched earth. Sunken paths of bone-dry streambeds hold clumps of thistle. The sun is so hot that toads lie dead in the shadows of rocks. The night will be bitter cold. Rapunzel crouches in the hollow of a boulder. She presses the heels of her hands against her eyes until she sees points of light. She drops her hands, stares out. It is no dream.

At the Window

He's there, the evil one, the usurper. The sorceress watches the look of horror come over his face like a shaking of leaves in a wind. Her trick has succeeded: the braid tied to the hook. She sees that he's handsome, a Prince, a young god; the beauty of his face is like needles stabbing her skin. She howls out her hate. Never see her! Never! Her words scorch her throat, burn his eyes. He has all the world, the handsome one, the god-man, he is rich, he is happy, he needs nothing, and yet he has climbed the tower and stolen away her one happiness. Even as black hate bursts from her like smoke, she feels the power of his face, she is stirred. She wants to scratch out his eyes with her claws. The Prince stares at her with eyes that are changing, eyes that are no longer young, then leaps from the tower.

Falling

As he falls, the Prince knows that this is the secret buried in the heart of climbing, climbing's dark twin. Everything he loves is annihilated in this savage mockery of striving, this climbing-in-reverse. As a child he dropped a ball into a well and watched it fall. Now he is that ball. He's rushing away from the dream-chamber, which without him is rising higher and higher—soon it will soar above the clouds and be lost forever. And yet this falling, this soft surrender, fills him with such hardness of not-yielding that he can feel a swell of refusal, an upsurge of protest, and in an ecstasy of overcoming he embraces the last adventure: the rush of wind in his eyes, his hair streaming up over him, the sharp scent of green in his nostrils.

Rapunzel's Father

On the other side of the high wall, which separates his property from that of the sorceress, Rapunzel's father is tending his garden. Since the death of his wife two years ago, he spends more and more time pulling out weeds, straightening the vine poles, watering the soil. The garden grows right up to the high wall, which he has crossed only three times in his life: once when his wife begged him to steal a head of lettuce from his neighbor's garden; once when he returned to steal a second head of lettuce and was caught by the sorceress, who made him promise to give her his child on the day it was born; and once after a year had passed, when he longed to catch a glimpse of his daughter, but found only the sorceress, who shrieked out her rage and told him that if he ever tried to see his daughter again, she'd tear out his eyes and strike his wife blind. Much time has passed since then. Sometimes he thinks of her, the daughter that he gave away, but it is like thinking of his own childhood: it's all so long ago that it doesn't seem part of him. As the Prince falls from the tower, Rapunzel's father bends over a weed that has sprung up at the side of a string-bean vine.

Eyes

And the Prince falls into a thornbush. And the thorns scratch out his eyes.

Time

Time passed. Two words, a breath: time passed. Days rush by like wind in your face, weeks are devoured by months, years are gone in the space of two syllables. Time passed. Time passed, and a great thornbush grew up around the tower. Now the stone was entirely hidden, bristling with thorns as sharp as daggers. The casement window, too, was no longer visible behind twisting branches. Every morning, before the sun rises over the forest, a dark figure appears at the foot of the tower. She seizes a thorn branch, which cuts deep into her hand. As she climbs, lines of blood run along her fingers and arms. The thorns rip her dress, catch her hair, slash at her face and throat. The pain eases her a little. At the top she pushes through the thorn-window into the dark chamber. There she washes herself at the basin, sits at the table, and begins to unbraid Rapunzel's hair. When the hair lies in soft folds on her lap, she brushes it, very slowly. When she is done brushing, she braids the hair carefully, then lays it in winding ropy lines on the bed. All day she sits and gazes at Rapunzel's hair. Sometimes she unbraids it and brushes it again. The sorceress seeks relief, but there is no relief. There is only the fading light behind the window of thorns. When the chamber begins to grow dark she pushes herself through the sharp branches and makes her way down the tower, tearing her body on the long thorns, gripping them with her bloody hands.

The Chamber and the Wilderness

In the days of the tower chamber, Rapunzel would sometimes dream of another world, an open world, without walls that stopped her at every point. Now, in the wilderness that stretches away in every direction, she seeks only shelter: the walls of a hollow rock, an opening in a rise of ground, the low space under a bramble bush. She listens for the sounds of hungry animals. She wraps her two babies in coverings of branches and dry leaves.

Dark

As Rapunzel roams in the wilderness, the Prince wanders in darkness. He has learned which fruits he can eat and which fruits will twist inside him like sharp metal. Sometimes he's so weak with hunger that he chews on pieces of bark, swallows them down. He has learned to listen for the sounds of creatures who might bite his legs, learned to strike out with his sword and feel the warm blood on the blade. He sleeps wherever he can in the forest, seeking out hollow places behind branches that hang to the ground or feeling his way to shallow openings in hillslopes. Once, waking, he feels a tongue licking his face. His skin is hatched with dried blood, his branch-ripped clothes are smeared with smashed berries and leaf-slime. Bits of leaves cling to his hair. Around his waist he wears a girdle of woven vines. Though he's still young, a streak of white cuts like a gash through his tangled beard.

The Second Rapunzel

In the long nights the sorceress is busy. She draws on her deepest powers, snatches visions out of the dark. Sometimes she wakes to find herself on the hard floor. In the mirror her eyes are wild. She neglects her garden, shuts herself up in the shed behind her cottage. One morning at daybreak she climbs the tower with a bundle on her back. At the top she takes a knife from her pocket and cuts a hole in the branches that cover the casement window. Now she can pass her bundle through without catching it on the thorn-points. In the chamber she unwraps the bundle, lays the figure on the bed. Skillfully she attaches the hair. She slips the nightdress over the figure and steps away. A narrow ray of sunlight strikes the faintly flushed cheek, the closed eyes. The forearm is bared to the elbow. The image of wax and blood is so exact that it seems to be the living and breathing girl. A dark joy floods the heart of the sorceress. She sits watching over the sleeping girl. No harm must ever come to her.

Song

Time passes in the wilderness, where the infants have grown into children, but for the Prince there is no time, only a darkness that is always. In the nothing of his days he comes to a place of rock and brambles. Here, there is sun like flakes of fire. Here, there is hot shade that presses up against him like wool. In the dry ground he digs up roots, sucks their bitter juice. At night the air is cold as snow. He sleeps against stone. When something strikes at his leg, he beats it with a rock. The holes of his eyes hurt. One day, resting among spiky bushes that clutch at his arms, he hears a song. He is shivering with fever. He doesn't know whether the song is within him or without. He is back at the tower, the hair coming down like fire. He rises shakily.

The song touches his face. He stumbles forward as though pulled by a hand.

Tears

In the shadow of her rock she looks up and sees him. His arms hang like broken branches. His eyes are dead, his lips a bitter wound. His wild hair, his beard. From the depths of dream he has come to her, the lost one. He looks like a dying tree. She is standing before him, the stranger. She tries to remember the tower, the braided hair. Now her hair is ragged and full of thistles. The children have sucked at the breasts where he has sucked. Tears scratch at her eyes like thorns. They drop onto the stones of his eyes. In the wilderness, water is rushing between rocks, blossoms are bursting from thorns. Slowly the Prince opens his eyes.

Homecoming

Banners fly from the corner towers. Streamers hang from every window. As the Prince enters the main courtyard with his bride-to-be and their two children, voices of welcome fill the air. The Prince sees the faces of dear friends, lovers, companions of the hunt, but he is curiously unmoved. He wonders whether it's because, as they cross the courtyard, he can think only of her. It's as if he fears that at any moment he might lose her again in the dark. But as he moves among the courtiers and ladies, who part before the steps that lead to the Great Hall, he understands that his estrangement will not be temporary. Between him and the faces that welcome him lies the darkness. His wounds are healed, his beard is short and cut to fashion, his cloak is trimmed with ermine, but he is no longer of their world. He turns to look at Rapunzel. He tries to remember the girl in the tower, the hair coming down like a shower of fire, his feet against stone—it's all a story in a book. The woman beside him is marked with a fierce beauty of suffering that makes the court faces seem childlike. As they approach the high steps, he touches her arm. The day has tired him a little. He looks forward to the end of the long celebration, when he and she can be quiet for a time.

In the Tower

In the thorn-tower, where Rapunzel lies sleeping, the sorceress sits brushing the hair in her lap. Rapunzel has been tired lately; it is good for her to sleep. A ray of sunlight slants through the space in the thorn-crossed window. It strikes the back of a wooden chair, runs across the stone floor, climbs the bedside, lies across the coverlet. When she is done brushing the hair until it shines, the sorceress will braid it slowly and carefully, feeling the weight of it in her lap. From time to time she looks up at her darling, who sleeps peacefully, safe from harm. Suddenly the sorceress stiffens with alertness. She lays aside the hair, goes to the window, and looks out between branches of thorns. It was only a crow, landing on a pine branch. She returns to the chair and continues brushing. Later she will get up and smooth the coverlet, plump the pillow. When Rapunzel wakes, the sorceress will prepare an herbal drink. She will feel her daughter's forehead, she will ask if there is any soreness in her throat. But for now she will let her sleep. There's no hurry. They have all the time in the world.

Rapunzel

Walking beside the Prince along the courtyard, toward the steps leading to the Great Hall, Rapunzel is aware of the glitter of many jewels. The costumes are richly colored and catch the sun. On a gallery above the courtyard, men bearing shields look down. Voices cry out in welcome. She tries to recall her childish fear of these faces, but it is like trying to recall the pictures in an old book. Long ago she lived in a tower, in the middle of a great forest. The sorceress, the high window, her hair falling toward the bottom of the tower, all of it is fading away. In the sunlit courtyard she sees flashes of bright hair, high-arched eyebrows, earlobes with rings. She will study them, she will learn what she needs to learn. The Prince no longer doubts her, as he did in the time before the wilderness. Night after night he came to her in the tower. She can feel his eyes on her face. She turns, sees that he is tired. Soon he can rest. She understands that he is done with trials and challenges, with perilous adventures. She understands one more thing: she is stronger than the Prince. It is good. She will laugh again, she will grow out her hair, she will play. But for the moment, as they approach the steps, she will walk beside her Prince among the courtiers and the ladies, inviting their attention, meeting their glances, looking calmly at them as they observe their Princess.

ELSEWHERE

That summer a restlessness came over our town. You could feel it on Main Street, you could feel it at the beach. In the early mornings we'd step from our front doors and head for the paper wrapped in its rubber band at the end of the walk—and in that warm, inviting air we'd stop suddenly, as if in confusion. At work we stared out of windows. At home we sat down, stood up, walked into other rooms. We planned long weekend excursions that never materialized, flung ourselves into complex diets that we forgot the next day, spoke eagerly of changing our habits, our jobs, our lives. Husbands in baseball caps and cargo shorts, pushing power mowers and dreaming of distant mountains, drifted absentmindedly across driveways into neighboring yards, where they looked around in surprise. On the green lawns of summer, you could see the wives in gardening gloves and wide-brimmed hats, kneeling on cushions beside rows of marigolds and azaleas. As they raised their three-pronged weeders, they would sometimes pause for a moment and glance into the next yard. They would look up at the familiar windows at the back of a neighbor's house, at the roof shingles trembling with sunlight, over the top of the roof into the startling blue sky, which seemed to be calling them to come away, come away.

Even the young people of our town seemed infected by unease. Home from school, teenagers in T-shirts and ripped jeans threw themselves down on the family couch with an arm over their eyes. Seconds later they sprang up as if in the grip of a violent passion, then fell back with a shuddering yawn. On burning Saturday afternoons at the public beach, you could see the children crouching down on the hard wet sand at the water's edge. There they began building fanatically detailed castles, with turrets and castellations and arrow slits for crossbows, pausing only to look up as a yellow helicopter flew high above the water. When they looked back down, they had lost interest forever.

In the hot nights we'd sit on our screened back porches, lit by dim lanterns, and listen to the crickets growing louder and louder, as if they were always coming closer, and behind them or through them we could hear a deeper sound, like a distant waterfall: the steady roll of trucks on the thruway, rushing away in opposite directions.

What was it that we wanted? We were doing all right, on the whole, we were happy enough, as things go. Oh, we had our worries, we woke in the dark with thoughts of money and death, but our neighborhoods were safe, no one died of hunger in our town, we counted our blessings and knew we'd been spared the worst. We'd looked forward to summer the way we always did—season of vacations, season of departures from the usual flow of things—but this time there was something left over, as if we'd stretched out our arms wider than the world. Had we expected too much of summer? That blue sky, that yellow sun . . . Never a blue sun! Nowhere a green sky! Sometimes we had the sense that we were waiting for something, a hint, a sign—waiting for a direction in which we could pour our terrible energy.

The first incident occurred toward the middle of June, at about 10:30 at night, in the home of Amy Banks, a sixteen-year-old high-school junior. Her parents, Dr. Richard Banks, a well-known orthodontist with a flourishing practice on East Broad Street, and Melinda Banks, a social worker at the new community center, were upstairs in their bedroom. Amy had been sitting in the family room, watching TV with the sound off and talking to a girlfriend on her cherry-red cell phone. She said good night, snapped the cell shut, and reached for the remote. At that moment she became aware of a motion in the dark corner of the room between the TV and the window. From the window a pair of light curtains hung down past the sill. Amy thought at first that a breeze might have stirred a curtain, even though the room was warm and the window was closed. As she began to get up from the couch, where she'd been sitting back against two pillows with her legs tucked under her, she was again aware of a motion in the corner, which this time, she said, was a "stirring," though not of the curtains. She saw nothing distinct, nothing at all.

Now a fear seized her. At the same time she was uncertain what she'd seen and told herself not to cry out and wake her father, who went to bed early. The stirring continued, without a sound. Just as Amy was about to run from the room, everything returned to normal: the corner was still, the TV cord lay against the baseboard, a woman on the screen sat in her car and silently pounded the heels of both hands against the steering wheel, the light from the kitchen reached across the arm of the reading chair and touched the edge of the lamp table. Amy stood up. She took two deep breaths and walked over to the corner. There she examined the floor, the baseboard, and the back of the TV. She pulled aside both curtains. She raised and lowered the window shade, felt the wall, looked all around. She turned off the TV and went up to bed.

The next night, shortly after ten o'clock, something stirred in the first-floor bedroom of Barbara Scirillo, a high school senior who lived three blocks away from Amy Banks and shared a French class with her. Barbara screamed. Her father, James Scirillo, a physics teacher and a member of the school board, called the police. No trace of an intruder was found. Barbara said she'd been changing into her pajamas and watching the computer screen when she felt something or someone move in the room. She saw nothing, no one. She could provide no further details.

Our local paper, the *Daily Echo,* reported the Scirillo incident on the second page, where Amy Banks's father came across it over breakfast. He put down his coffee cup, shook the paper into shape, and read the piece aloud to his wife and daughter. When Amy then described her own weird adventure, Dr. Banks called the police. The *Echo* gave a full account the next day.

Now we were all on the alert for an intruder, possibly a peeping Tom, though we reminded ourselves that the details were sketchy, the observers impressionable. No doubt the incidents would soon have been forgotten, if it hadn't been for a sudden rash of "sightings," as they came to be called. The victims—or sighters—were mostly junior-high and high-school girls, who reported suspicious movements at night in the corners of living rooms, bedrooms, and darkened hallways. But they weren't the only ones who saw things. A woman in her late thirties reported a stirring in her garage at dusk, several young mothers reported incidents of apparent intrusion, and John Czuzak, a retired policeman, claimed that one night when he entered his kitchen from the TV room he saw something move near the refrigerator, though he couldn't say what it was that moved or even what the motion was like, other than "a kind of ripple."

As the incidents spread across our town, creeping into the bedrooms of corporate lawyers and third-grade teachers and drill-press operators who worked at the machine shop out on Cortland Avenue, people began to propose theories to account for what was happening. Of these the Peeping Tom and the Prankster Theories were the most widely believed. The police warned us to lock our doors and windows at night and report any sign of unusual behavior in our neighborhoods. Some of us wondered whether there might be a physical explanation—maybe the ripples were effects of light produced by passing cars, or the results of air condensing because of a sudden temperature change.

These early guesses quickly gave way to more elaborate conjectures. The incidents, some said, were signs of a collective delusion bred by the boredom of summer—the sightings passed from girl to girl like an infection and then to anyone with a hungry imagination. We were trying to decide whether it pleased us or bothered us to think of the sightings as imaginary when a bolder theory appeared. The article was printed in the Opinions section of the *Daily Echo* and signed "A Friend of Truth." In it the writer argued that the mysterious incidents were nothing less than manifestations of the invisible world—eruptions of the immaterial into our realm of matter. This argument, which many of us found irritating or laughable, was taken up, debated, condemned, and embellished, until in a late version it served as the founding principle of a group that called itself the New Believers. Members proposed that the visible world contains rents or fissures through which the invisible world shows itself. The "manifestations" were said to indicate those places of rupture.

Many of us who resisted these explanations found them more troubling than the incidents they sought to illuminate, for in their extremity, in their eagerness to embrace an unseen world, they seemed to us a sign of the very discontent that burned its way across our summer.

As ideas multiplied and arguments grew more heated, the manifestations themselves grew less frequent. Soon small groups began to form, composed of people intent on observing and even encouraging the incidents. Three or four friends would gather at a set time, at dusk or late at night, in a living room or bedroom. They would turn off the lights, except for a four-watt night-light set in the baseboard. For hours they would talk among themselves as if they were casually gathered there, an easygoing group of friends with nothing much to do on a summer evening, all the while watching closely for signs of stirring in darkened corners. The new burst of sightings that emerged from these exercises caused a brief excitement, but the evidence they offered was always in question, since it was difficult not to feel an element of contrivance and self-deception at the heart of those meetings. By the end of June, the few reports of manifestations no longer attracted serious attention.

It was now that we began to hear of new groups, hidden gatherings. These shadowy associations rejected the belief in manifestations as literal intrusions of another realm, while arguing that they were clues or shadow-events intended to call into question the claims of the visible world. One such group, the Silents, was composed of older teenagers and young adults. The Silents met secretly and followed strict dietary rules that limited them to grains and juices. What brought them to our attention was the rumor that they practiced something called Ultrasex. From our bedroom windows at night we would sometimes see them, young people in flowing gowns, moving through the streets toward secluded places. In basement playrooms, in church graveyards, in small clearings in the north woods, they would hold their meetings, after which they would lie down in pairs and strive for a consummation that had nothing to do with the body. Love, desire, lust itself, according to the Silents, were strictly immaterial events. Touching, hugging, kissing, stroking, rubbing, to say nothing of sexual intercourse, were all forms of failure—descents into the realm of matter. Members of the group were encouraged to lie as close as possible beside a partner, who was often partially naked, and, while rigorously abstaining from the act of touch, give way to sensations of desire of such ferocious intensity that the body seemed to dissolve in flames. It was said that this discipline, far from punishing the flesh, made use of the material body to create sustained heights of spiritual ecstasy, in comparison to which the most violent orgasm was the twitch of an eyelid.

Those of us who deplored such practices understood they could not last, while at the same time we acknowledged that the turn away from the body was only another sign that the old satisfactions could no longer be taken for granted.

It was about this time that we became aware of something else, as we lay awake at night with closed eyes and unquiet minds. At first it was only a faint noise, a scratching sound in the dark. Soon you could almost hear them: breaking into the cement with their picks, digging down with their shovels and spades. From the outset we called them the tunnelers. In houses scattered throughout our town, in ranch-house developments and older neighborhoods, they were said to be at work, the same family men who in other summers had gone bowling or settled down with a beer and a bowl of chips in front of the TV. Sometimes after dinner, sometimes late at night when their wives and children were asleep, they would go down to their cellars and continue digging. And though the tunnelers themselves never spoke of their work, so that we had to rely on rumors and thirdhand reports, we believed in the tunnels, we understood them immediately. In that relentless digging, that digging to nowhere, we saw a desire to burst the bonds of the house, to set forth, from the familiar place, into the unknown. Sometimes a tunneler would raise his pick over his shoulder, swing it against the beckoning dirt, and feel a sudden loosening. A moment later he'd break through to another tunnel, where a neighbor was hard at work. Then the intruder would lean on the handle of his pick, wipe his forehead with the back of a sleeve, and exchange a few awkward words, before retreating and changing direction.

In our beds at night, listening to the call of crickets and the rush of trucks on the thruway, we could hear that other, more elusive sound, which might have been the sound of many shovels striking against earth and stone—and we had the sense that down there, all across town, beneath our bedrooms and kitchens and neatly mown backyards, far down beneath the roots of pine trees and the haunts of garden worms, a web of passageways was being woven, an intricate system of crisscrossing hollows, so that our yards and houses sat upon a thin crust of earth that at any moment might burst open with a roar.

Sometimes at night I would wake up and think: I've got to get away, I've got to go somewhere, right now, soon, first thing tomorrow. Then an excitement would ripple through me, as if I were already packing my bags, already dropping my shoes into the airport basket. In the long hours of the night my excitement would gradually lessen, until by morning I no longer remembered what it was, exactly, that I'd made up my mind to do.

As if in response to the tunnelers, the roof-dwellers appeared. We all knew how it started. One morning David Lindquist, a retired handyman who lived in a two-story carriage house set back on a dead-end road, climbed onto his roof. There he built a simple shelter against the chimney and refused to come down. His wife delivered food through a trapdoor in the attic ceiling. Lindquist had contrived a system of pipes that connected to the plumbing, and he'd brought up a hose to flush down waste. He refused to talk to reporters, but his wife told them that her husband really liked it up there; he'd always been drawn to heights. What struck us wasn't so much Lindquist's eccentricity as his austerity. It was said that he lived on a diet of bread, water, and fruit, sat for long hours gazing out at the surrounding trees, and trained himself to sleep in the angle where two roof slopes met.

A few days later, in another part of town, Thomas Dombek, a college junior home for the summer, moved onto the roof of his parents' house two blocks from the beach. Here and there a few more imitators appeared—it seemed inevitable. But we weren't prepared for the sudden rush to the roof that now took place, in the middle of July. You could see them in every neighborhood, carrying long boards up ladders that leaned against the gutters. Soon we could see shelters springing from rooftops like the TV antennas we remembered from childhood. It was as if the houses of our town were no longer large enough to contain our desires. From our front porches, from folding chairs in our backyards, we watched the odd structures rising on roof crests. The art was to fasten a base over two slopes of roof and continue with walls or a protective rail. All over town you could hear a great ringing of hammers. At lunchtime, workmen in T-shirts sat on sunny roofs, tipping their heads back to drink from bottles of soda that caught the sun. Children looked up, shading their eyes.

Of course not everyone could follow the difficult example of David Lindquist. Most people simply flung themselves into the new fashion for recreational roof-dwelling without a thought of permanent residence. For them, a roof-house was a form of elevated porch. In the hot nights of July you could see them sleeping up there, under the stars.

But now and then a different kind of roof-dweller emerged. Highly disciplined, solitary and fervid, the lonely ones would sit motionless for long hours at a time, wrapped in silence. Sometimes one would rise slowly and address the streets. The roof-dweller would speak of the Way—by which was meant the way out of unhappiness and despair, the way into spiritual peace. People would gather in the street below, listen for a while, and pass on. One of these lay preachers, a tall woman named Verna Coombs, who wore overalls and work boots and a red bandanna, called herself a Transcensionist and quickly attracted followers. The Transcensionists rejected the world below, which was the realm of heaviness and dissatisfaction, and embraced the upper world, the true world beyond appearances.

At times it seemed to us that another place, an unknown place, was trying to emerge from within our town. It burrowed in the earth below our cellars, rose up silently in the corners of living rooms, trembled in the air above our rooftops.

I would come upon it sometimes, that other place. Turning a corner onto a familiar street, with its front porches and Norway maples, its yellow hydrant and brown telephone poles, I would feel a strangeness. The sunlight seemed not to strike the house sides directly but to fall in between. Shadows shifted, objects seemed liberated from the constrictions of light and were on the verge of becoming themselves, the sidewalks shook silently, everything glittered and trembled, while up above, the tight-stretched blue sky was being pulled from both sides until it was about to rip down the middle—then it all stopped, the street settled down, the sidewalks returned to their stillness, and I walked past white-painted downspouts with vertical grooves that stood out clearly, past dandelions thick with petals that, as I glanced at them, became sharp as knife blades.

Was it in the last weeks of July that we began to notice a change in the children? We knew of course that they'd already been affected in small ways by the events breaking out all around them. How could they have escaped untouched? But we had been preoccupied with rumor and speculation, we had grown a little careless, we'd failed to give the children our full attention. It was the Game that brought them back into our awareness. You would see them in their yards, walking slowly, too slowly, and suddenly stepping around something that seemed to be in their way. Sometimes they held out their arms as if they were walking in the dark, though the sun shone down from a cloudless sky and their shadows stood out sharply against the cut grass. Gradually we learned the nature of the Game. The children were summoning up imaginary places and walking around in them for hours at a time. The idea was to stay longer and longer there, to stay there forever. Backyards containing a swing set and a length of hose became dense forests teeming with dwarves and wolves. When the children opened the doors of their rooms, they entered the holds of sunken ships, towers with winding stairways, hollow mountains where white animals drank from black streams.

At dinner the children sat quietly, with dreamy stares. If parents interrupted their trances by hurling questions at them, they answered carefully, politely, with an air of faint distress.

One case that drew some attention was that of little Julie Goudreau. She was seven years old. One afternoon in August she was found sitting on the grass in the middle of her next-door neighbor's backyard. When Mrs. Waters came out to see what was the matter, Julie told her that she was lost and could never find her way home. "But you live right over there, dear," said Mrs. Waters, pointing at the next yard, separated from her own by a driveway and three azalea bushes. Julie turned her head to look in the direction toward which Mrs. Waters had pointed. What struck Catherine Waters was the expression on Julie's face—she stared at her own yard with a little puzzled frown of concentration, as if she were gazing at something she'd never seen before. Then she turned back and looked down at her hand lying in the grass. Mrs. Waters bent over to help her up. At that moment, Julie turned to look at her. It was a look of such rage that Mrs. Waters stepped back. "I hate you," Julie said, quietly and distinctly. She lowered her eyes and sat stubbornly there, refusing to say another word, until her mother came and dragged her home.

Even as we worried about our children, and blamed ourselves for neglecting them under the pressure of our own distractions, we found ourselves drawn to those trancelike stares, those dreamy gazes, and wondered what it would be like to burst open our days with inner voyages.

It may be that I've given a misleading impression. I don't mean things were only that way. Even in the early days of the manifestations, when it seemed that every living room was about to erupt with mysterious life, we drove our cars to work, we sat down to dinner, we pushed our shopping carts along the frozen food aisles. On tree-shaded street corners, joggers with headbands ran in place, waiting for a car to turn. The sound of chain saws and wood chippers filled the suburban air. On a hot, shady porch, in the languor of a midsummer afternoon, a high school girl in jean cutoffs and a bikini top sipped lemonade from a tall straw, while she twirled a loop of reddish brown hair around and around and around her finger.

Meanwhile, as if they'd been watching the children from behind the edges of closed blinds, the old people of our town began to emerge from their hiding places. We saw them late at night, gathered on dark front porches, silently rocking. They seemed to be waiting for something that was about to happen. Sometimes we would catch sight of them moving very slowly across our backyards, taking small steps, their heads bent toward the ground, the rubber tips of their canes and walkers pressing into the grass. The paper reported that one night at two in the morning four "oldsters," ranging in age from eighty-six to ninety-three, made their way down the beach to the water's edge, where they were discovered by a policeman. They were staring out at the water. The tide was coming in, and the low waves had already covered their shoes and ankles by the time the officer found them.

Sometimes we had the feeling that at any moment, around any corner, suddenly the summer would reveal its secret, and a peace, like soothing rain, would descend on us.

By the middle of August we felt the exhaustion of adventures that had never taken us far enough. At the same time we were inflamed by a kind of sharp, overripe alertness to possibilities untried. In the languor and stillness of perfect afternoons, we could already feel the last days of summer, coming toward us with their burden of regret. What had we done, really? What had we ever done? There was a sense that it all should have led to something, a sense that a necessary culmination had somehow failed to come about. And always the days passed, like riddles we would never solve.

It was one of those rich late days of August when the air seemed to quiver with light and heat, so that you felt you were looking at things through a faint haze, though the sky was brilliantly clear. Was it the haze of our accumulated desires? For in the last weeks of summer our longings had grown stronger and more demanding, unappeased by our tunnels and roof-dwellings, our gatherings and investigations, which seemed to us now, when we thought back on them, feeble emblems of whatever it was that eluded us. The day was Saturday— the last one of August. It felt like the last Saturday of the year, the last Saturday of all time. As we moved through the morning and after- noon, filled with vague unrest, we were scarcely present, in our back- yards and on our front porches, at our picnic tables and at the beach, we were straining in other directions, we were elsewhere.

The change began around dusk. We had come home, most of us, from wherever the day had taken us. We'd finished dinner, we were waiting for the rest of the day to come about—waiting, in the peculiar way of that summer, for something worthy of our desires. The sun had slipped out of sight, though the tops of telephone poles and high trees were still touched by light. The sky was pale blue. Here and there, a lamp went on in a window. It was the time of day when it was really two times of day—above, the still-bright sky; below, the begin- nings of night. It was as if the day had paused for a moment, unable to make up its mind. And we, in our various places, were probably not paying close attention, had perhaps fallen into a muse, an inner pause of our own. Someone must have been the first: the hand reach- ing idly out and rippling through the lamp table, drifting through the lamp. It happened in street after street: the shoulder moving through the bathroom door, the hand floating through the armchair, drop- ping through the porch rail. Some reported a faint resistance, like the sensation of passing a hand through cool water, or of pushing through cobwebs. Others felt nothing at all. Some claimed to hear, rising from the houses of our town, a communal gasp or sigh. In the wonder of that moment, we understood that our summer had risen to meet us.

Warily, joyfully, we moved through our houses with arms held wide, passing through objects that no longer resisted us. We entered the streets, where people wandered as if under a spell. Children, crazed with laughter, ran back and forth through the trunks of maples. We walked through hedges and white picket fences, stepped through the sides of porches, passed through the walls of houses into other backyards. Through swing sets and birdbaths we strolled along. We made our way over to Main Street, where streetlights glowed in the pale sky, and crowds tense with awe moved through store windows. Someone pointed up: a sparrow, trying to land on the crossbar of a telephone pole, passed through and began beating its wings fiercely before sweeping back up into the sky.

Who can say how long it lasted? We plunged into that dusk as if we'd always known what lay under the skin of the world. We reveled in dissolution. Under the darkening sky we wandered through our town like children after a first snow.

Just before nightfall, when there was still a little light left in the sky, we became aware of a slight thickening. As we stepped through things, we could feel a satiny tickle. Someone cried out: he had banged his knee against the side of a store. Things hardened part by part. Here and there, a hand was caught in wood or stone.

Later, when we tried to understand it all, when we tried to give it a meaning, some said that maybe, at a certain moment, around the beginning of dusk, everyone in our town had been dreaming of something else. The town, deprived of our attention, had begun to tremble and waver, to grow insubstantial. Others, more skeptical, proposed that none of it ever happened, that a great delirium had struck our town, like an outbreak of the flu. Still others argued that we had been given a revelation but hadn't known what to do with it. Our ignorance had ushered in the reign of hardness.

Whatever may have happened that day, we woke the next morning as if we'd slept for a month. Sunlight streamed into our rooms. We reached out and touched the edges of things. In our kitchens, chairs stood out sharply, as if they'd sprung up from the floor. We felt in our hands the weight of spoons, felt against our fingers the rims of cereal bowls. We pushed against doors, felt on the soles of our feet the thrust of doormats and front steps. Outside, we ran our fingers along bush branches and hedge branches, we squeezed hoses and steering wheels, the rubber grips of lawn mowers. On Main Street we grasped the handles of glass doors, we picked up objects that tugged back, filled shopping bags that pulled against our palms. All day we felt the push of sidewalks, the surge of grass. All day we felt the weight of sunlight settling on our arms. All day we felt, grazing our skin, the blue of the sky, the edges of shade. Sometimes we recalled that other summer, but already it was a story we would tell, in warm living rooms in winter, about the time we wandered through the streets at dusk with our arms held wide, a long time ago, in some other life.

THIRTEEN WIVES

I have thirteen wives. We all live together in a sprawling Queen Anne house with half a dozen gables, two round towers, and a wraparound porch, not far from the center of town. Each of my wives has her own room, as I have mine, but we gather for dinner every evening in the high dining room, at the long table under the old chandelier with its pink glass shades. Later, in the front room, we play rummy or pinochle in small groups, or sit talking in faded armchairs and couches. My wives get along very well with one another, though their relation to me is more complex. People sometimes ask, "Why thirteen wives?" "Oh," I always say, putting on my brightest smile, "you can't have too much of a good thing!" In truth, the answer is less simple than that, though the precise nature of the answer remains elusive even to me. What's clear is that I love my wives, each alone and all together, and can't imagine a life without all of them. Even though I married my wives one after the other, over a period of nine years, I never did so with the thought that I was replacing one wife with a better one, or abolishing my former wives by starting over. Never have I considered myself to be a man with thirteen marriages but rather a man with a single marriage, composed of thirteen wives. Whether this solution to the difficult problem of marriage is one that

will prove useful to others, or whether my approach will add nothing
to the sum of human knowledge, is not for me to say. I say only that,
speaking strictly for myself, there could have been no other way.

Here, then, are my wives.

1

Absolute equals, heart-sharers, partners in love—that's how we
think of each other, my first wife and I. If, on a Sunday morning, I
wake up late to find she's made me a plate of big blueberry pancakes,
just the way I liked them as a boy, with a square of butter melting
its way in, then the next Sunday I'll serve her a two-egg omelet with
green peppers and chopped onions, exactly the kind she remembers
from summers at the cabin on the island when she was a girl. I remind
her of her appointment with the hairdresser for Tuesday at one, she
makes sure I don't miss my dentist's appointment on Thursday at four;
I drive with her to her mother's house in Vermont on the third weekend in July, she comes with me to my father's house on the Cape for
the second week of August; I praise the trim lines of her new yellow sundress, she's pleased by the crisp look of my new light-weave
button-down. These arrangements are perhaps known to every marriage, but ours has developed more intimate refinements. If my first
wife catches her hand in a door, I howl with sudden pain; when I'm
thirsty, she gulps down a glass of iced limeade; if I knock into a table
edge, a purple bruise shows on her leg; if she trips on the edge of the
rug, I fall to the floor. One evening I thought of the answer to a crossword clue we'd both been stuck on the day before; when I entered her
room, I found her sitting up in bed, folded newspaper in hand, filling
in the answer with a yellow No. 2 pencil. Another time, when things
weren't going well with me, I woke in the night and feared she might
be suicidally depressed; when I rushed into the hall, I nearly collided

with her, hurrying toward me with arms held wide and a look of rescue in her eyes. Sometimes, it's true, I grow bored, deeply bored, with
our system of finely measured equivalences. Then I long for an imbal-
ance, a sharp exception, a fierce eruption. Unhappy that I've had such
thoughts, and uncertain what to do, I seek out the one person who's
sure to understand; when I seize her arms and look into her eyes, I see
the same melancholy, the same longing for something unknown; and
as I burst into a dark, uneasy laugh, I hear, all over the room, like the
cries of many animals, the sound of her own troubling laughter.

2

When I am feeling hopeless about my life, when my hands hang
from my sleeves like dead men dangling, when, catching sight of
myself in a plate-glass window, I turn violently away, but not before
I've seen myself turn violently away, then I know it's time for me to
be in the company of my second wife, who knows how to comfort
me. Even as I arrive at the front door, holding my leather laptop case
in one hand and reaching for my key with the other, she's looking at
me anxiously and asking about my day, she's helping me out of my
belted trench coat and hanging up my hat, she's placing my case by
the umbrella stand. Already she is leading me to an armchair—my
favorite one, with the thick armrests—where she places a pillow
behind my head and touches my forehead with her hand, while at the
same time she's lifting my feet onto the hassock, she's removing my
shoes and pressing her cheek against my leg. "Are you all right?" she
asks, looking at me with tender concern. And gazing at me earnestly
she asks, "Have you had a hard day?" Later, when she has undressed
me, and bathed me, and laid me on the bed, she bends over me and
says, "Do you like this?" and "Do you like this?" Still later, waking
beside her, I feel a sudden doubt. Roughly I shake her awake. Star-

ing into her sleepy eyes, I tell her that I could never endure a rival, that I'll leave her instantly if she ever tries a trick like that, she can't take advantage of me, I wasn't born yesterday. During my outburst her large, startled eyes fill with tears. Gradually a relief comes over me, I grow calm, I glance at the clock and see that it's getting late, a yawn shudders through me, and as I close my eyes and begin to drift toward deep, soothing sleep I feel her lying awake beside me, searching for the cause of my distress, rehearsing the events of the past few hours, reproaching herself for not loving me enough, her eyes wide, her heart racing, her cheek resting tensely against my shoulder.

3

At other times, in a more robust mood, the sort of mood in which life's little disappointments no longer seem evidences of failure but welcome challenges to the all-conquering spirit, I seek the company of my third wife, who never spoils me. When I enter her room I find her lying on the bed, reading a book with a frown of concentration. Without looking up, she raises a rigid finger as a sign that she's not to be disturbed; her whole body tightens with attention as she continues reading. After a long while she lays the book on her chest and lifts her eyes to me, with the same frown. At once she reproaches me with having neglected her. As I begin to defend myself, she tells me that the new cleaning lady has broken one of the blue wineglasses; there's no more sliced turkey in the refrigerator, only sliced ham; the door of the linen closet doesn't close properly. I assure her that I'll take care of everything soon, right away, at this very moment if necessary; in response she rolls her eyes in a slow, exaggerated manner. Suddenly she looks at my shirt and asks whether I went to work with my collar like that. Have I checked my hair in the mirror lately? Her head hurts; her allergies are killing her; she's sure she has a sinus infection; there's no air in the room; the window is stuck again. I step over and raise the window easily. She asks whether it gives me pleasure to score a cheap victory at her expense. She's short of cash; her blow-dryer is broken; something's wrong with the switch on the coffeemaker. As I lie down cautiously beside her, she sits up and says it's getting late; besides, she isn't feeling well; she can't breathe; there's no air in the room, even with the window open; what she needs is a dehumidifier; why doesn't she have a dehumidifier; a dehumidifier would make all the difference. I reach out and touch her arm. She stares at my hand and remarks that she hates her blouse—everything sticks in this weather. Slowly, watching her carefully, I begin to undo my shirt. She's not in the mood, she says; besides, I don't care about her; all I care about is myself; she can't even remember the last time I told her I loved her. "I love you," I say at once. She looks at her fingers and asks whether I really believe that I can make our problems go away just by uttering a few words that cost me nothing; but that's just like me. As she removes her blouse she notices her upper arm; look how the flesh jiggles; she's turning into a tub of lard. I assure her that her arm is fine, very fine, even somewhat on the thin side. She's curious to know when it was that I became the world's leading expert on the diet and fitness of American women. As we continue undressing, she complains about the mattress, which is supposed to be a medium but is actually much softer than advertised; it's bad for her back; we ought to return it and get a good one, unless of course I think this is the sort of mattress she deserves; as we make love, she notes the squeaking springs and reports that the cleaning lady arrived fifteen minutes late and neglected to dust the base of the table lamp beside the couch. When we're done she says, "You never take me anywhere." Before I can answer, she asks how I can expect her to sleep through the night with a windowpane that rattles in the slightest breeze. I never pay attention to her; I don't listen; I talk, but I don't listen; she can't breathe in this room; there's nothing to eat in the house; her neck hurts; she doesn't like the way the new cleaning lady looks at her. Her eyes are slowly closing; she glares at me sleepily. After a while I rise with caution, slip into my clothes, and take my leave, feeling refreshed and invigorated after such exercise.

4

All's well between my fourth wife and me; really, nothing could be better; in fact, I have no hesitation in saying that our love is perfect; but isn't this very perfection a cause for concern? When she declares herself supremely happy and swears she has never loved anyone as she loves me, I experience a deep happiness of my own; but doesn't my happiness cause me, to a certain extent, to take things for granted, doesn't it nudge me, however minutely, in the direction of smugness and self-satisfaction, and don't these qualities render me, when all is said and done, less lovable? My fourth wife conceals nothing from me, reveals with utter trust the innermost ripples of her being, but in the act of loving self-revelation isn't there a risk that she will gradually deprive herself of mystery? I can't imagine any woman more desirable than my fourth wife, whom I stare at tirelessly, for her beauty, though flawless, is never cold. But doesn't her beauty contain the danger concealed at the core of all extreme things, the danger of provoking irritation or resentment? In the same way, mightn't it be said of her intelligence, her kindness, even her goodness of heart, that they encourage a search for flaws, that they incite in their admirer a secret craving for ignorance, confusion, and spiritual failure? Our love is perfect; I desire nothing more. Why then should I find my thoughts turning toward imperfection? Why should I sometimes dream of complaining bitterly, shouting at the top of my voice, accusing her of ruining my life? Why should I long to provoke, in the clear eyes of my fourth wife, the first shadow of disappointment and pain?

5

Whenever I want to be with my fifth wife, I find her in the company of a young man. He's handsome in a boyish, somewhat delicate but by no means unmanly way, slender but well muscled, dressed always in a dark sport jacket, a light-blue shirt open at the neck, and jeans. He is polite, self-effacing, and silent. When my fifth wife and I have lunch together in a downtown restaurant, facing each other across a small table, he sits to her left or right; when we talk at night by the fireplace, he sits on the rug with his head leaning against her leg; when I take off her clothes, she hands them to him; when we slip into bed, he's there beside us, lying on his back with his hands clasped behind his neck. At first his presence disturbed me, and filled me with bitterness, but in time I've grown used to him. Once, waking in the night beside her, I saw over her shoulder that he wasn't there; I felt anxious and shook her awake; and only when, smiling faintly, she lifted the covers to display him lying between us in his dark sport jacket, light-blue shirt, and jeans, sleeping soundly with his head between her breasts, did my anxiety subside enough to permit me to fall back to sleep.

6

Always, when I'm with my sixth wife, a moment comes when she rises slowly toward the ceiling, where she remains hovering above me. "Dear," I plead, falling on my knees, "won't you come down from there? I'm worried you'll hurt yourself. And besides, what have I done? I didn't disturb you as you sat at the kitchen table with your sketchbook and your stick of charcoal and drew seventeen versions of a fruit knife lying beside a green pear and a white coffee cup. I didn't clear my throat loudly or walk up and down humming to myself as you leaned back on the couch with your legs tucked under you and twisted a piece of hair slowly around your finger while reading *Anna Karenina* for the eighth time. I didn't step up behind you and kiss you with a wet smack on the back of your neck while you sat fiercely erect at the piano practicing over and over the first movement of Mozart's Piano Sonata in A minor, Köchel 310. And if I've allowed my eyes to stray for a moment to your glittering knees beneath your dark wool skirt, it was only in order to rest from the judgment of your intelligent, severe eyes." "Idiot!" she replies. "Do you really think I can hear you from up here?" And with that she begins to fly back and forth across the ceiling, laughing her tense, seductive laugh, brushing my hair with the tip of her foot.

7

Whatever I like to do, my seventh wife likes to do. When I mow the lawn on a warm Saturday afternoon, admiring the straight strips of fresh-cut grass as bursts of sweet-smelling blades fall at my cuffs, she walks alongside me, clasping the left half of the black rubber grip on the red lawn mower handle. When I read a mystery novel set in a country house in Surrey in the summer of 1935, she reads a second copy of the same book, glancing at me over the tops of the pages and stopping when I stop. On poker night she's the only woman among us; I watch her narrow her eyes as she checks her tightly held cards and slides a white chip sharply forward with her index finger. At breakfast she eats the same cereal I do, using the 2 percent milk I prefer; her orange juice, like mine, has lots of pulp; at the mall, she chooses the same brand of running shoe, with mesh nylon uppers and antimicrobial insoles; our umbrellas match; our sunglasses are identical; when I tell her my childhood memory of running toward a rainbow in a field of high grass, she recounts the same memory. Once, when life was too much for me, when I needed to get away from it all, I drove north for five hours to a drizzly seaside town, where I took the last ferry to an island with a rocky shore before a dense forest, in which stood a single cabin without a telephone. When I opened the door and held up my lantern, a raccoon leaped from the table; bats swept across the ceiling; pinecones lay everywhere; on a wooden chair I saw her purse.

8

A sword in my bed divides me from my eighth wife. If I love her, I must not touch her; to do so would be to violate a vow that she herself has exacted. True to my word, I remain inches from her, sick with desire. My plight would be lessened if I were never to share my bed with her, but my eighth wife insists that she lives solely for these moments. Mindful of my suffering, which is also hers, she sometimes conceals her body from me, slipping between the sheets with her quilted down coat zipped up to her chin. At other times, suffering for my suffering, and desiring to reward my feat of denial with the one pleasure she can permit, she'll adorn herself with blue-green eye shadow, purple-black mascara, crimson lipstick, expensive oils, creams, and lotions, and dabs of perfume behind the ears and on each wrist, and display herself, on her side of the sword, in shimmering and translucent underclothes in a variety of fashionable styles. It's possible of course that my eighth wife wishes only that I'd violate my vow, despite her assurance that to do so would be to destroy her love for me by making her lose respect for my word. How else to explain her presence in my bed, her provocative underclothes, her frequent headaches, her prolonged sighs? Indeed it's tempting to believe that the real test isn't whether I can demonstrate my love for her by remaining true to my word, but whether I love her fiercely enough to smash through an arbitrary prohibition—an event she secretly desires and desperately awaits. But the very temptation of this thought is a warning: in my state of violent desire, dare I trust an idea that encourages me to betray my word and to side with the passion I'm struggling to overcome? It's also true that, despite my suffering, I'm proud of my success in keeping my word; to succumb to temptation would be to experience a loss of self-esteem. Is she perhaps desirable to me only insofar as I'm able to overcome desire? In that case it's I who have encouraged her to exact my vow, it's I alone who am the source of my torment. Sometimes a strange longing comes: to plunge the sharp sword deep, deep into my eighth wife's side. In this desire to be rid of her and thereby end my suffering, I detect a secret flaw. My suffering, however painful, is always qualified by the possibility of failure, the possibility that, despite everything, I'll become like other men and break my word at last; her death, by removing that possibility, would remove the sole thought that relieves my anguish. For all these reasons, I understand with terrible clarity that my plight can never change. In this understanding I sense a final danger: by believing that nothing can change, do I not relax my will, do I not open myself all the more to temptation? And with a last, desperate burst of strength I rouse myself to new rigors of wariness.

9

There are times when I can't bear the company of anyone but my ninth wife, despite the little secret we never discuss. What does it matter to me if, bending to gaze into her brilliant dark eyes, I see her looking a little to the left or right, so that I have to shift my position slightly to create the illusion that we're gazing deep into each other's eyes? Sometimes, as she crosses the room with her graceful strides, she'll happen to knock against me if I'm not quick enough to step out of the way. On these occasions she doesn't stop, doesn't acknowledge me, and the slight smile on her lips remains unchanged. In every way my ninth wife is cheerful and obliging. Why then should I complain if, holding out my hand lovingly to lead her toward the bed, I see her stare past me? Why should I give it a second thought if she steps on my foot as she walks to the bed alone and lies down with her little smile? Once, as I was about to plunge my face into the thickets of her hair, I was stopped by a faint sound that appeared to be coming from her throat. When I bent my ear against her neck, I heard a dim whirring. A small adjustment proved necessary, after which, despite the interruption, I was able to devote myself entirely to the pleasures of the dark.

10

In an atmosphere of drawn curtains, medicinal smells, and perpetual twilight, I visit my tenth wife, who's burning up. Her cheeks are flushed, her eyes are unnaturally bright; on the dark coverlet her pale arm has the whiteness of bone. Illness consumes her. Fever parches her lips, burns along her throat and eyelids; her ears are hot. Her straw-colored hair, brown in the dusk-light and uncombed, streams on the pillow. Her hair was once straight and obedient, but illness has released a hidden wildness: it falls in snarls and tangles, plunges over the pillow-edge, tumbles along the bedspread, where it lies sprawled and spent. I've brought her a few violets and marigolds, picked from our garden, but when she strains to raise herself, lines of tension crease her forehead, as if she's struggling against two hands holding her shoulders down; after a while she gives up and falls back exhausted. I lay the flowers on the bedside table, near the digital clock. A glass of water, decorated with orange and green fish, stands on the table beside a box of tissues. When I hold the glass to her mouth, she drinks eagerly, desperately; suddenly she turns her head away. Water flashes on her face like a wound. I wipe her lips with a tissue; they're cracked like dry leather. With my fingertips I stroke her hot, pale forearm, her bony cheeks. Under her fevered eyelids her large eyes glitter. I want to comfort my tenth wife, I want to lavish her with attentions, but there's little I can do except sit on the chair next to the bed. In this dusky room, in this world removed from the world, I feel myself bursting with health. My vigor strikes me as intolerable, like a shrill, continual noise. What to do? Her illness excludes me—since she cannot be well, I have to become sick. Slowly I bend down and kiss her dry, hot mouth. I want to inhale her fiery germs, I want to drink her fever, feel her disease glowing inside me like hot spiced wine. Deftly I slip under the heavy covers, releasing an odor of stale bedsheets. Am I mistaken, or do I sense a slight soreness in my throat? My forehead feels hot. Is it my imagination, or has my hand grown pale? I will find her, I'll join her at last in her own land. Eagerly I meet her gaze. Her eyes, weary and glittering, stare at me as one might stare at a sudden animal across a stream.

11

Whenever there's work to be done, when things can't be put off a second longer, I turn to my eleventh wife, who knows exactly what to do. It's she who climbs the tall ladder and fastens the loose gutters in place, lifting her hammer into the blue sky as she plucks a gutter nail from between her teeth, while down on the grass I steady the ladder rails with both hands. She's the one who strips the paint from the front porch with the electric sander, bending over the boards in her dust mask and safety glasses, she it is who repairs the cracked ceiling above the basement landing, caulks the second-floor window frames, installs copper flashing in a roof valley, replaces a rotted porch post,

while I carry paint cans, fetch drill bits and putty knives, and bring her
large glasses of ice water that she drinks lustily, with her head flung
back. Standing in the shade at the side of the house, I look up to see
her crawling across sunny roof slopes or leaning far out of upper windows. Tools glint on her body like jewels; her bare arms quiver with
energy. Once she begins a task, it's difficult for her to stop. At night I
can hear the blows of her hammer on the roof; at dawn, through the
partly open blinds of my bedroom window, I can see her ankles and
the rung of a ladder. Sometimes my door opens in the dark and she
comes to me, like a shout in the night. She lifts a screwdriver from
behind her ear; carpet tacks fall from her hair. She's efficient, she's
brisk. Afterward, as I turn my head in the hope of resting against her
shoulder, I see her, through eyes heavy with sleep, striding about the
room, measuring heights with a metal tape, screwing brackets into
the wall, swinging up two-by-fours that rise into a row of shelves.

12

If I speak of my twelfth wife as a negative woman, it's because
she is the sum of all that did not happen between us. In a crowded
room on a summer night at a party overlooking a lake, I did not cross
over and sit down beside her. I did not, seated beside her, begin a
long, ambiguous conversation, during which I bent my face closer
and closer, while she, laughing lightly, tucked one leg under a thigh
and brushed a few crumbs of potato chip from her sleeve. That night
we did not walk hand in hand along the shore while inventing new
names for the constellations and bursting into wild laughter. In July
we did not pick up a rented Opel at the Zurich airport and drive along
winding roads past green hillsides spotted with red-tiled roofs on our
way to a high hotel with a balcony that looked down at the shining
water of Lake Geneva and the dark towers of the Castle of Chillon.

One night in August, in the amusement park, I did not, seated on a blue horse, watch her throw back her head and laugh unheard among carousel melodies as she rose and fell on her red horse with the white bridle and the golden mane. The negations multiply swiftly, forming a rich pattern in reverse; spawned by an initial gesture of refusal, our unacted history outgrows the narrow compass of accomplished lives. We cannot end, for time does not contain us; nor can we suffer change, for the structure of our negative biography rests on the unchangeable foundation of nothingness. We are more than mortal, we two. All lovers envy us.

13

In a sense, I've never seen my thirteenth wife. If, as I help her slip out of her winter coat with the thick fur collar, I look away from her green eyes to watch her pale yellow hair lift up and fall onto the white wool of her sweater, then when I return my gaze to her face I'm lost in admiration of her rich brown eyes and the convolutions of her mahogany-dark hair against her crimson blouse. A moment later, returning from the closet, I'm cast into reverie by her melancholy gray irises with little flecks of amber around the pupils. On a single walk across the carpet, she displays her calves in black nylon tights shimmery as liquid, striped orange-and-white kneesocks turned down once at the top, rose-colored silk stockings imported from Italy, and paint-spattered jeans with the cuffs rolled up, while each turn of her neck reveals a new profile, each movement of her wrist a new hand. The incessant changefulness of my thirteenth wife may of course arise from something deceptive in her nature, as if she's continually casting up new images in an effort to evade responsibility for any one of them, but I incline to a different explanation. Her clothes, her gestures, her faces, all are familiar to me, though sometimes so faintly that the memory is a kind of tremor at the back of the brain. It's the peculiar fate of my thirteenth wife to evoke innumerable pasts that aren't hers; she is composed of my memories of other women. To see her is to experience all the women barely noticed in public parks and crowded bus terminals, the half-seen women sitting at wrought-iron tables under the awnings of outdoor restaurants or waiting in line at ice-cream stands at the edges of small towns on hot summer nights, all the women passing on suburban sidewalks through rippling spots of sun and shade, the briefly stared-at women rising past me on escalators with glossy black handrails in busy department stores, the silent women reaching up for books on the shelves of libraries or sitting alone on benches under skylights in malls, all the vanished girls in high school hallways, the motionless women in wide-brimmed hats standing in gardens in oil paintings in forgotten museums, the black-and-white women in long skirts and high-necked blouses packing suitcases in lonely hotel rooms in old movies, all the shadowy women looking up at departure times in fading train stations or leaning back drowsily on dim trains rushing toward dissolving towns. My thirteenth wife is abundant and invisible; she exists only in the act of disappearing. This perpetual annihilation is her highest virtue, for by ceasing to exist she increases her being; by refusing to be a particular woman, she becomes a multitude. Though I am denied my thirteenth wife, who is always other, denial is her generosity, and I'm grateful to her for more lasting gifts: the gift of memory, the gift of desire, the gift of astonishment.

ARCADIA

Welcome

Are you tired of life's burdens? Welcome to Arcadia, a peaceful woodland retreat founded over one hundred years ago to meet the needs of a very special clientele. Located on more than 2,000 acres of gently rolling spruce and pine forest, Arcadia offers a variety of comfortable and affordable accommodations suited to every taste. Choose among our 48 cozy two-room log cabins, each with stone fireplace and knotty pine paneling, our 36 three-room cottages with private patio, and, for persons with special needs, our 12 guest rooms and suites on the second floor of the Estate. Whatever your age or condition, our expert staff of highly trained Life Counselors and Transition Facilitators will see to your every wish as they work tirelessly with you to help you achieve your personal goal. Although we pride ourselves on our award-winning success rate, which over the past five years has averaged a gratifying 97%, we understand that each individual must advance at his/her own pace. Here at Arcadia we are committed to serving you in a manner most compatible with your particular lifestyle and temperament as together we find the method that will best result in a successful outcome.

Accommodations

Each cabin and cottage is situated on a tract of lush woodland set off by attractive fencing that assures maximum privacy while allowing easy access to all public places, such as trails, streams, and lakes, as well as the deep gorges that are a popular and much-loved feature of our retreat. All cabins and cottages come with fully equipped kitchen, comfy bedroom, modern bath with shower, and screened front porch with cushioned Adirondack chairs and glider. All beds have premium plush mattresses and triple sheeting in luxurious linens. Refrigerators are stocked with bottles of fresh spring water. Although our program policy does not permit computers or cell phones, each cabin and cottage comes equipped with a convenient and easy-to-use touch-tone phone that allows direct twenty-four-hour communication with the Main Office, located to the left of the entrance on the first floor of the Estate. Meals are prepared in our own kitchen and delivered right to your doorstep three times a day by our specially trained Food Delivery Personnel. Our program encourages and protects your privacy and solitude, but members of our staff are available for a talk or a personal visit at any time of the day or night as you make your way toward the decisive moment.

Residents

Our residents hail from all fifty states and five territories, as well as from nations the world over. We welcome guests of all races, all walks of life, all religious and nonreligious orientations. If you are weary and seek rest, if you are heart-sore and cannot find your way, Arcadia is the place for you. Do you feel you have come to the end of the line? Does life seem to hold no promise? Do you wake up each day wishing you had never been born? Look no further. Our doors are open wide. We are here to lend a helping hand. All you who feel that life is without meaning, all you who can't bear it for another second but bear it anyway, you who feel unloved, unseen, unwanted, forgotten: Come to us. We will show you the way.

Testimonial #1

After the terrible accident I wouldn't leave my house for two months. All I could see was my wife and five-year-old son screaming in the flaming car. I slept badly in short snatches during the day and roamed the empty house all night, stopping in different rooms. I left the lights on in every room and never changed the bulbs. They went out one by one. In the end I was living in the dark. The dark felt right. A friend tried to rescue me. I went to grief counseling but they wanted to take my grief away which was all I had. One day in a doctor's office I opened a magazine and saw an ad for Arcadia. This place has changed everything. After only ten days I know myself for the first time and I know what it is that I have to do. They make you see everything clearly here. Nothing will stop me now. Thank you, Arcadia.

Transition Facilitators

Our skilled and friendly staff of Transition Facilitators will provide you with the kind of personalized attention that lies at the heart of our innovative program. A facilitator will be assigned to you on the day of your arrival and you will meet with him/her on a regular day-to-day basis. In addition to these private instructional sessions, your facilitator may ask you to attend one or more motivational group discussions in order to enhance the decision-making process. Our goal is your goal: the overcoming of obstacles. Each of our residents has more than one obstacle to overcome before confronting the final one. Our results-oriented program is specially geared to your needs and we will work with you twenty-four seven to help you achieve a viable solution.

Gorges

The fourteen gorges that cut through our retreat offer an abundance of natural beauty and unique opportunity. Steep, rocky cliffs plunge some three hundred feet toward fast-moving rapids. The cliff-tops are dangerous and only partially protected by old and damaged railings. Narrow, unrailed walkways traverse the gorges and provide breathtaking views of the surrounding countryside and the rapids far below. Rocks continually fall from the cliffsides and may sometimes be heard over the sound of rushing cascades and waterfalls. These gorges are among our most sought-after attractions, drawing residents to the crumbling cliff-tops and unrailed walkways at all times of the day and night.

Testimonial #2

Before I came here I was lonely and depressed and cried every day like a little girl even though I am a grown woman of twenty-eight. I have always been like this because something is wrong with me and nobody knows what it is except I don't look right especially my head. When I was little the other children made fun of me and called me names and later boys used me and were cruel. I have tried religion but that didn't work and I have tried cutting open my wrists but I never knew how to do it right. My life was a dark place and a living hell and there was no way out for me until one day I heard of this place. Here it isn't anything like the way it is out there. They talk to you and tell you things you need to hear. They show you the things that are getting in your way and they show you how to overcome them and follow your inner voices. Now I know what I have to do and I am ready. Before that time comes I just want to say thank you from the bottom of my heart to everyone here at Arcadia especially my facilitator John who has helped me see the way. It has really meant a lot to me.

Failure

One reason for the high success rate of our time-tested program is our understanding of the role of failure in helping you accomplish your long-term objective. Your success is our ultimate aim, but success does not come to everyone in the same way or over the same period of time. Our facilitators understand that failure is sometimes a necessary step on your personal journey. What is failure? you may ask yourself. Failure is a form of *hesitation.* It means you are not yet ready. We will show you that the act of failure contains within it the secret you are looking for. We will teach you to welcome your failure, to make it part of yourself in order to overcome it. Our motto is: The Road of Failure leads to the Palace of Success. Do you find yourself hesitating on the brink? Do you have a tendency to draw back at the last moment? Are you afraid? Do not be discouraged. The act of hesitation is a gathering of energy. Failure is success that has not yet been given a chance to reveal itself completely.

Motivational Witness Program

For those in search of motivational inspiration, our Motivational Witness Program can provide just the boost you need. You may sign up for this popular program as either a witness or a principal. The principal is motivated by the presence of witnesses, who in turn are inspired by the act of witnessing to pursue the same method or select a different one. Further details are available in Informational Packet 3A at the Main Office.

Testimonial #3

Big shout-out to all the good folks in Arcadia for a really great program. I wasn't really all that motivated when I first came out here but now I'm revved up and rarin' to go. One thing I really like is the Motivational Witness Program, where you can get to see how other rezzies make their choices. That's what I like about this place—you find out what's right for you and then you go do it. Trust me on this one. Long story short: I'm psyched.

The Lakes of Arcadia

The lakes of Arcadia are peaceful, still, and deep. Enclosed by gently sloping wooded hills, our lakes are readily accessed by easy-to-walk trails, many of which were formed hundreds of years ago at a time when Native American tribes settled in the area. The pristine beauty of our ancient lakes stimulates meditation and resolution. Although speedboats, Jet Skis, and motorized watercraft of any kind are strictly prohibited on our noise-free lakes, residents are encouraged to make use of the rowboats and canoes that you will find waiting for you at many points along the quiet shores. Small, wooded islands are found in many of the larger lakes, and for some residents the islands with their dark trees and magisterial branches prove more inviting than the lakes themselves, with their silent waters that go down, far down, to depths that no one has ever measured.

The Two Hopes

The first hope is the hope that diverts you from your task. It is the hope that calls you back, the hope that promises a return to a way of life that is the old way but somehow better, wiser, healthier, happier. This is the hope of delusion. The second hope is the hope that is not deceived by hope. It is the hope that abandons hope. This is the true hope, the only hope, the hope that will lead you to lasting peace.

Caverns

Feel free to explore the unparalleled wonders of our underground caverns, celebrated for their beauty and danger. Entrances both marked and unmarked are found throughout Arcadia: in the sides of wooded hills, in forest pits and sinkholes, in lakeside banks and abandoned mines. Sometimes at the side of a trail you will come upon manmade steps, going down. Descend. Our ancient limestone caverns are artificially illuminated for short distances only, before the dark begins. Deep underground, away from the sun and sky, you may wander alone with your thoughts for hours along dark passageways that open onto plunging waterfalls or black, tranquil pools. Often a passageway will have a winding ledge along one side, overlooking a deep fissure or crevasse. Make sure to feel along walls for cracks and crevices, some of which will be wide enough to admit a human form. These openings will lead you to still darker adventures.

Testimonial #4

My life was neither good nor bad, very quiet and ordinary, then I fell in love with a good man who loved me back and my whole life changed. Every morning I woke with a burning happiness, happiness like a flame. I looked forward so much to seeing him, my good man, my beloved, everything I looked at was fresh and glowing in the burning light of my love. And even though the man I loved was married, what did I care, we had each other, he was my one, my only, my sweetheart, he made me feel so alive, my lovely good man. Sometimes he wasn't able to be with me and this was hard, the times in between were not always burning with happiness, sometimes they were burning with loneliness. I wanted him in my life not as a lover only but as a heart-companion, I thought how lovely it would be to do simple everyday things together, shopping and laughing and walking around town holding hands, but he said we had to be careful because he didn't want to hurt his wife. And I understood that, he was a good man, a gentle man, but I said you don't want to hurt her but you're hurting me. When I didn't see him my life felt empty and dark, he was a good man but weak, a weak man, and I hated myself for thinking of him as a weak man but he was hurting me and I couldn't stand it. The only choice I had was to accept things as they were, which meant accepting my life as an empty lonely waiting, there were times I would wake up in the night feeling his body beside me but the bed was cold, he was with her, in their happy home. He was a good man but weak, a weak man who couldn't hurt anyone but he was hurting me, he was murdering me with his goodness and his poisonous weakness. Sometimes I thought back to the time when my life was quiet and ordinary and it felt like a peaceful lovely land I could never see again. Now all my days were long and full of a sort of quiet twisting anguish, the lamp on the lamp table was unbearable, I was like someone with a disease, I was dying and not dying, the thing that had brought me life was taking away my life, then one day I came to Arcadia. It was like returning to the peaceful land. My cabin is quiet and clean. How I love to walk along the winding trails, the woods and streams speak to me, how lovely the gorges that run like rivers through the land, I stand on the cliffs and look down. The peace and solitude embrace me like loving arms, they are only a sign of the greater peace to come, I have found the answer and I am so very grateful.

Amenities

Although our primary aim is to help you move forward with the successful implementation of your goal, we desire to make your stay here at Arcadia as pleasant and comfortable as we can. All rooms come with high-quality hardwood floors and hand-woven area rugs in a variety of distinctive patterns. Select hand-crafted antiques are spread tastefully among cozy contemporary furnishings. Kitchens are fully equipped with all cooking and eating utensils, including a generous selection of German-made precision-forged corrosion-resistant stainless-steel knives with exceptionally sharp edges. Each bedroom is provided with a hand-carved antique Rope Chest containing an assortment of fine-fibered all-natural hemp ropes in different lengths and thicknesses for your convenience. Enjoy the sturdy comfort of your all-weather fade-resistant quilted hammock hung between spruce or pine in the private woodland space behind your cottage or cabin. Not far from each hammock you will find a charming old-fashioned stone well with a depth of over 100 feet. Multicolored hand-painted glass lanterns hang from branches along the private paths and supply soft pools of illumination on the way to darker paths.

Swamps

For those who prefer a more unusual journey, our age-old swamps and marshes offer a dash of adventure. The depths of our swamps are variable and unpredictable. Although the water is generally shallow, the rotted-plant swamp-ground beneath the water may yield suddenly to the pressure of a footstep. Depths of twenty feet and more have been measured. Guides are available to point out the most treacherous places.

Testimonial #5

I want to say something about the gray feeling, not the grand suffering you see in old movies, but the gray feeling, the twilight dimness, always with me, even then. Back in grade school my mother would look at me and say, "What's wrong, Joey?" and I would not know what to answer. "He's shy," people said, but it wasn't that. In high school I had girlfriends, they liked my sad eyes, but I didn't care about them enough, not the way they wanted me to. Later I tried vitamin supplements, antidepressants, a change of diet, but none of it cured the grayness. The grayness was quiet, but also not quiet, a sort of restless emptiness. Some women are attracted to the grayness, they think they can make it go away. I married a good woman. We went to Niagara Falls on our honeymoon, and when we came back we made a down payment on a house. My wife would look at me and say, "What's wrong, Joe?" and I would try to tell her about the gray feeling, but a change would come over her face. It's not you, I wanted to shout. It's the gray feeling, nothing matters more than any other thing, something is missing in me, or maybe some extra piece has been added, the gray piece. One day she went away and never came back. I was alone in the empty house. Now I am married to my true wife, I thought, an empty house. One afternoon I passed a yard sale in the neighborhood. Old living room furniture, lamps with trailing cords. I thought, I am that yard sale. I began to see other signs. I was the faded matchbook lying in the roadside grass. I was the shadow of the stop sign stretching out at evening. I wondered whether the grayness was something I carried inside me, like a tumor, or whether it was something that clung to me, like a burr. One day I came to Arcadia. Here they know the grayness. They have seen it with their own eyes as I have seen it with mine. It is there at the edges of the gorges, it lies in the still centers of the lakes. A peace is flowing toward me. I have only to walk toward it and it will be mine.

Menu

Our menu is a mix of healthy traditional favorites, such as our classic free-range roast chicken served with roasted organic potatoes and steamed fresh vegetables, and a wide variety of unique local dishes. Vegetarian meals, including hearty vegetarian dinners that will please the palate of the most stalwart meat-lover, are available upon request. Our produce is grown on local farms and picked fresh each morning, and is supplemented by fragrant herbs from our own garden. An assortment of fine herbal teas, among them elderberry, wild orange blossom, and lemongrass, is available for your taste delight.

Getting Lost

Our many miles of scenic woodland trails are carefully marked to prevent our residents from getting lost, but we have also kept in mind the needs of those of you who want nothing better than to leave the familiar paths for other, more adventurous journeys. Such residents are encouraged to make use of the numerous byways that branch from the main trails into the thick depths of the forests, where it is not difficult to lose your way. The bypaths end abruptly, inviting pathless wandering through lush undergrowth among ancient conifers covered in moss. Mushrooms and wild berries grow in profusion and should be eaten with caution. Sometimes a sloping hillside reveals a deep opening overgrown with vegetation. For those who seek the pleasures and challenges of getting lost, we highly recommend the thickly wooded hills in the northeast section of forest, with their unexplored caves, their rushing streams and roaring waterfalls, their untamed scenes of natural wildness.

A Facilitator Welcomes You

Hi there. My name is Robert Darnell and I'm proud to be part of Arcadia's team of Transition Facilitators. May I speak frankly? You are unhappy. You see no meaning in life. Your son has died, your husband has left you, your wife has run off with your best friend. You're alone, you're in pain, you hate yourself, nobody loves you, you're fat, you're ugly, you want to die. We understand. It's our job to understand. We understand exactly who you are and exactly what you need. Here in Arcadia we will show you the way. The way is hard for some and easy for others, but it is the only way and you will know it when you see it. You have always known it. Come to us and we will guide you. The path is familiar. The path lies within you. Arcadia lies within you. You have always lived in Arcadia.

Encounters

Although we take every precaution to secure the absolute privacy of our residents, an encounter with another resident may sometimes occur. It might take place on one of the public forest trails, on a lake shore, or deep within a cavern. On such occasions, we advise you to nod silently once, avert your eyes, and continue on your way. Your undisturbed thought process is an essential component of your voyage to discovery and should be watched over with care. If any resident should attempt to strike up a conversation, smile politely but do not answer. Any such violation of the rules should be reported at once to your facilitator. Here at Arcadia, your best interests are our only concern.

Testimonial #6

I remember the first time. I was drinking a cup of coffee at the breakfast table, not thinking about anything in particular, when the thought came to me: Why? I remember my hand stopping in midair, the coffee cup suspended before me. The question began popping up at odd times during the day. I would step into the morning train, sit down at a window seat, open up my laptop, and suddenly think: Why? Or I'd stand watering the back lawn on a hot summer day, looking forward to the evening barbecue, Sherri-Ann, laughter with friends. Then the thought would come: Why? It was as if a little crack had opened up inside me. A dark wind was blowing through. What was wrong with me? Was I having a nervous breakdown? But I felt fine, except for the little voice that kept whispering: Why? When you hear that voice, you can go on, but nothing is the same. The sunlight striking the side of a house is not the same. The glass in the dish rack is not the same. I felt that something was happening to me but I did not know what it was. In the night the voice kept waking me: Why? You could say that my search for an answer is what led me to Arcadia. Within a few days, I was a new man. Here, everything you do has a purpose. When the Why comes, you have the answer: you are making yourself ready, you are preparing yourself. Out there, day follows day, Sunday Monday Tuesday, all without meaning. The numbers on the calendar change but they are always the same number. Here, a leaf falls and it is like the sound of the last page torn from the last calendar. A cup of coffee blares out like a trumpet. Soon it will be time.

Branches

The branches of our venerable trees are sturdy and proud. Many of our lower branches begin not far above the reach of your upstretched hands and thrust out powerfully in every direction, covering the paths and undergrowth with rich shade interwoven with sun. Above the lower branches, row upon row of higher branches form complex patterns of spacing and angulation, often intermingling with the branches of neighboring trees and preventing the observer from seeing branches closer to the top. Among acres of blue spruce and white pine, of Norway spruce and red pine, you will find stands of oak, beech, hickory, mountain ash, alder, and birch. Many of our lower branches are nearly horizontal and invite contemplation. Sit beneath them. Be still. Permit your thoughts to ascend toward those strong, restful places.

Transition Partnering

Although we have found solitary transition to be the most efficacious strategy for the vast majority of our residents, transition partnering is not unknown. Sometimes it happens: a nod to another resident glimpsed on the grounds of the Estate, a glance exchanged with a resident approaching along a woodland path. A possibility arises, at first only dimly, then more clearly and persistently. All partnering arrangements are enabled by your Transition Facilitator, who may advise for or against such a process. The successful completion of your end goal is contingent upon more than one factor, and we will take into consideration any outcome-based procedure that is likely to eventuate in a satisfactory resolution.

Testimonial #7

I guess you could call me one of those small-town girls. You know, family picnics down by the river, church on Sunday, cheering the football team, hot summer nights sitting outside the ice cream parlor on Main giggling with friends and flirting with boys. After high school I began waiting tables in the restaurant across from the movie theater. A few of my friends went off to college, it was like they couldn't wait, most others stayed in town working in the plant and settling down. I was making pretty good money, saving up a little from year to year, going on dates, mostly boys I knew from high school, older now and looking to marry. But I was waiting for Mr. Right. I was renting a room in a house on a quiet street, dinner with Dad and Mom every Wednesday and Sunday, babysitting my twin nieces on the weekends. Time passes slowly in a small town. Mr. Right wasn't happening and everyone I knew seemed to have kids. I began to hear something in my voice I had never heard before, a kind of forced cheerfulness. Summer nights in a town like mine can be tender and cruel—the sound of a distant train, porch lights glowing, couples laughing under the maples. I had a talk with my minister. He told me to be patient, good things would come to me. I was beginning to feel trapped and I didn't know what to do. One day I met an older man. He had kind eyes, he wanted to marry me and give me a house with a backyard and a front porch, but just as things seemed to be working out I found out he was wanted by police on two counts of grand larceny. Sometimes I felt I couldn't breathe. I wanted to scream, I wanted to smash something. I was the waitress with the nice smile, I was the auntie at the riverside picnics, the friendly lady at the church socials. I didn't know what to do. I was tired all the time, I could see lines forming at the sides of my mouth. I felt I was waiting for something, not just a husband anymore, but something different, something better, another town, another life. I thought I should go away somewhere, live in a different place, but where could someone like me go. I wondered whether it was possible to spend a whole lifetime in the same town you were born in, waiting for something that doesn't ever come. I had never taken a vacation. I'd saved up a little nest egg over the years and that is how I came to Arcadia. I can tell you it's made all the difference. Everybody at the Main Office is as friendly as can be. My facilitator is very kind and understanding and talks openly with me about what I am feeling. He showed me there is no shame in it, in feeling that life has passed you by and there is no way out. You want to scream, you want to run away, but you get up and you go to work and nothing changes. He made me see I was still binding myself to the world by hope, the hope that things would get better somehow, even though I knew they would never get better, and once I was cured of the hope-disease I felt a peace come over me and I knew what I had to do.

The Tower

Residents are welcome to visit the old Observation Tower, located on the cliffs of the Northwest Gorge. This imposing structure, constructed over one hundred years ago of granite blocks mined from local quarries, rises to a height of 420 feet and contains a winding stone stairway of 659 steps. At the top is an external observation platform with a waist-high iron railing, badly damaged. The ledge beyond the railing extends a further twelve inches. The Tower has not been repaired for many years and should be entered with caution. On a bright day or moonlit night the old observation platform affords spectacular views of the Arcadian countryside in all its rich diversity. From the cliffside corner you can see down into one of our deepest gorges.

Goal-Oriented Discussion Groups

Although carefully protected privacy is a key component of our program, your facilitator may recommend attendance at one or more of our semiweekly goal-oriented discussion groups led by a Life Counselor in one of the Discussion Rooms located on the ground floor of the Estate. The purpose of group discussion is to increase motivation and focus by means of shared experience. Sometimes a resident who has spent days or weeks alone exploring the trails, lakes, gorges, caverns, and other features of our retreat will find that the group process can generate valuable insights. It may even lead to a moment of personal self-illumination that will prove to be a productive turning point on your developmental path. Participation in all group activities is voluntary. Refreshments will be served.

Testimonial #8

In what I suspect is not the middle of life's journey I came to this bosky dell in search of what shall I say a setting for my soul's plight, a decor for my desolation, hoping by such sleights to outwit destiny and calm the demons of the night, only to find myself enticed by ah! enchantments less *triste*: the seductive sinuosities of pineconed paths, the caress of caverns, an almost amorous beckoning of tranquil shores. And you, my best beloved, light of my life, lovely traitress and laughing fiend out of hell, who even now bends to whisper sweet somethings in my ear, I bid you a fond farewell, my darling demoness, my heart's murderess, as I walk out into the Arcadian night that shines forth like a beacon in the blackness of my ravaged hopes.

Waiting

Sometimes it is best simply to wait. In time it will come to you. Row out into the middle of a silent lake, draw in your oars, and lean back against a cushion. Stand at the edge of a gorge with your hands behind your back and gaze down. Sit beneath the strong branches of a sheltering tree or lie back in your hammock beside the stone well. Pause for a while in the black passage of an underground cavern. Breathe quietly. Listen. The answer is there. It will come to you.

For More Information

For more information, or for additional copies of this brochure, please contact us online at arcadiaretreat.com. We are always here to serve you and to make your residency an unforgettable experience. Whether you come from Maine or Oregon, from small-town Ohio or the bustling streets of Manhattan, from Reykjavik or Mumbai, Arcadia awaits you. Although we exist on the map, in a particular and desirable location, we are really only a step away. Already you have seen us. You have caught glimpses of us in vacant lots, in city parks, in the spaces of blue sky in the stillness of summer afternoons. We are around that corner, across that road. In a very real sense, we are everywhere. Come to us. You will only be coming home.

THE PLEASURES
AND SUFFERINGS OF
YOUNG GAUTAMA

A Father's Worries. One midsummer night, at a time when only
the palace guards are awake, King Suddhodana leaves his bedchamber and makes his way out into the Garden of Seven Noble Pleasures.
As he walks along a path of rose-apple trees, moonlight sifts through
the branches and ripples across his arms. The heavy scent of blossoms stirs his senses like the playing of many wooden flutes, but the
King isn't out for pleasure. Something is wrong with his son. How is
it possible? The Prince has a life that all men envy. He's handsome
as a young god, skilled in disputation and wrestling, rich in the love
of beautiful women. Wise men instruct him. Servants attend him.
Friends adore him. Wild peacocks feed from his palm. If he expresses
a desire for anything—an emerald carved to resemble a hand, an elephant caparisoned with scarlet cloths bearing images of gold swans,
a dancing girl with bare breasts—his wish is instantly gratified. He
is healthy, he is strong, he is young, he is rich. His wife is beautiful.
His marriage is happy. Poets sing his praises. And yet this most fortu-
nate of sons, this model and mirror of young manhood, sole heir to a

mighty kingdom, seeks out solitary places, where he secludes himself for hours or days at a time. Messengers report to the King that on such occasions the Prince walks quietly in one of the Four Hundred Bowers, or sits motionless under a tree on the shore of one of the Two Hundred Lakes and Ponds. Lately the withdrawals have become more frequent. These aren't love trysts, which would please the King, but something less innocent: a turning away, a drawing within. Is there some inner wound in his son, some secret affliction? The periods of despondency end suddenly, and then the young Prince returns to his friends and companions as if nothing has happened. Soon he is laughing in the sun, riding one of his elephants, shouting with joy, roaming among his concubines. It's possible of course that the Prince chooses to isolate himself solely for the purpose of recovering his strength after long nights of enervating pleasure, but the King remains doubtful. There is something disquieting in these removals, something dangerous. He'll get to the bottom of it. Suddenly King Suddhodana stops on the path of rose-apple trees. Before him, in a brilliant patch of moonlight, lies the dark feather of a bird. An irritation comes over him. He will speak to the Chief Gardener in the morning.

A Walk Among Women. In the sun and shade of a pillared portico, Prince Siddhartha Gautama walks among his concubines. Through open doorways the women watch him pass, inviting his attention in ritual poses of enticement and modesty. The concubines are famous for their beauty, their gaiety, their lute playing, and their skill in awakening and prolonging erotic pleasure. Through semitransparent colored silks wrapped around their hips and draped over their shoulders, they conceal and reveal the secrets of their bodies. The tips of their fingers and the soles of their feet are brilliant with crimson dye. On their ankles they wear bracelets decorated with tiny bells. It is said that there are eighty-four thousand concubines, one for each of the eighty-four thousand stars in the night sky. It is said that there are twenty thousand dancing girls. It is said that the Prince can satisfy twelve women in one night. Now he walks slowly along the portico, through shafts of sun that lie across his path like swords of light. Through the open doorways he can see his concubines lying on divans, or sitting on yellow and azure floor-cushions with tassels, bending their necks as handmaidens comb their hair. A girl steps forward to watch the Prince pass. Her silks are the color of yellow champaca blossoms, her hair is as glossy as the body of a black bee. She raises her eyes and lowers them in a sign of invitation. Gautama smiles at her and continues on his way. He can hear the sharp tinkle of anklet bells, the fainter tinkle of the little bells that adorn the cupolas and turrets of the palace roof. At the end of the portico he steps into the sun. The short grass is the shiny green of a peacock's neck. It presses softly into his bare soles. From the women's quarters he hears a ripple of laughter, the strings of a lute. Slowly he continues on his way.

The Three Palaces. The Three Palaces of Prince Gautama are the Palace of Summer, the Palace of Winter, and the Palace of the Season of Wind and Rain. The Palace of Summer has floors of cool marble, interrupted by fountains, bathing pools, and narrow channels of moving water. The Palace of Winter is known for its cedar paneling and its thick carpets woven with images of fire and sun. The Palace of the Season of Wind and Rain has thick walls that shut out the sounds of Nature and enclose many Halls of Pleasure devoted to dancing girls, lutenists, acrobats, conjurers, and skilled actors performing staged plays. The Three Palaces are located in different outlying quarters of the city; they are connected by broad underground passages carefully guarded. Separate passageways lead to the King's palace. Each palace, with its many courtyards and stairways, its hundreds of chambers, its far-flung gardens, parks, and bowers, is surrounded by high ramparts with four gates. Gautama has traveled many times along the underground passageways, but in his twenty-nine years he has never passed beyond the ramparts. Once, as a child, he rode with his father in the royal chariot into the depths of one of the royal parks. In the distance he could see the top of a wall. He pointed and asked his father what lay beyond. His father looked at him sternly, then swept out an arm and said: "Nothing is there. Everything is here." He turned the chariot horse sharply and rode back along the path.

Despondency. Gautama closes the gate in a trellis-wall and walks along a path in the Bower of Quiet Delights. The roof is composed of artfully interwoven twigs and branches, which soften the sunlight that comes quivering down past the leaves of asoka trees. Scarlet-orange blossoms fill the air with a scent that feels like a hand touching his face. The path leads to a dark pool with a stone fountain in the center; water rises from the mouths of twelve marble beasts and falls in a circle of soft splashes. Gautama lies on his side in the grass at the edge of the pool. The sound of the water in the fountain, the three white swans in the dark water, the smell of the asoka flowers, the spots of sunlight in the shade, all these soothe Gautama, who asks himself, for he is in the habit of questioning his own sensations, why he should need soothing. If in fact he does need soothing, then that is all he needs, for he's well aware that he has everything else: a loving wife and son, concubines and dancing girls who thrill his senses, palaces and gardens, friends and companions, musicians, elephants, chariots, rare fruits carried in boats from China and Arabia and placed in a bowl before him. His life is a feast of pleasure. Yet here he is, lying on his side in the Bower of Quiet Delights, like an unhappy lover. But he is not an unhappy lover. What is he, then? A spoiled voluptuary? A restless malcontent, who wants, who needs, who longs for—what, exactly? But perhaps he is making a fundamental error. Perhaps solitude itself should be classified among the pleasures. If that's the case, then he has come here simply in order to experience still another pleasure. Gautama thinks: I have everything a man can desire. It's impossible for me not to be happy. He feels, forming on his lips, a melancholy smile.

The Ramparts. The high walls that surround the Palace of Summer are made of cedar and are the thickness of three royal elephants measured trunk to tail. The walls are covered partway up by thick white-flowered vines that create the appearance of a vast hedge, above which rise the dark upper portions like mountains above the tree line. In each of the four walls stand two gates, one on the inside and one on the outside, connected by a passageway and guarded within by royal warriors armed with bows and two-handed swords. The outer gates are opened only to permit a changing of the guards. The inner gates are never opened. The gates, outer and inner, serve as a precaution against invasion, so that if the walls of the city should ever be breached, soldiers and citizens may be admitted to the safety of the palace grounds. The guards know that this is unlikely, since the walls of the city are impregnable, the armies of the King invincible. The deeper purpose of the gates is to conceal warriors trained to prevent escape, should the Prince ever venture to leave.

In Which Chanda Visits the King. At midday in the Hall of Private Audience, Chanda walks with King Suddhodana along a row of polished pillars adorned with carved and painted lions, elephants, and parrots. He reports that the Prince emerged from the Bower of Quiet Delights on the morning of the second day, in a humor disquieting to those who know him well: his laughter was too bright and quick and failed to rise above his mouth to the level of his eyes. Gautama took part in an archery contest, which he won readily, disappeared for two hours in the women's quarters, and returned with his brilliant laugh and dark gaze. The King asks what is troubling his son.

Chanda reminds the King that Gautama has always had periods of abrupt withdrawal; even as a child he would grow suddenly grave and sit alone in the shade of a pillar. It is partly a question of temperament and partly, if he might venture to offer his unworthy opinion in so weighty a matter, something more. Impatiently the King orders him to continue. Chanda, choosing his words carefully, explains that the life of pleasure arranged by the King for his son, in order to attract him to things of this world, must inevitably lead to periods of satiety. At such times Gautama will draw back from pleasure the way a man who has slaked his thirst will turn aside from a well. The King's philosophers have warned repeatedly against the revulsions inherent in a life devoted to sensation. The cure, in Chanda's view, is to diminish the Prince's dependence on a life of sensual excitement without increasing his attraction to a life of contemplation. What is necessary, he thinks, is a middle way: a life of modest pleasures and occupations—one or two women a night, daily wrestling contests and footraces, pleasant walks and conversations, a single glass of rice beer or wood-apple wine with dinner—that leave no stretches of empty time in which a man might be tempted to concern himself with dangerous questions about the meaning of existence or the proper way of conducting a life. The problem lies in enforcing such restraint. For the Prince, though gracious in all things, is accustomed to having his way. The King places his hand on Chanda's arm. "I rely on you." After all, Chanda is Gautama's dearest friend, as well as a loyal servant of the King. Chanda, uneasy under the burden of such praise, wills himself not to pull his arm away.

An Incident in the Park of Six Bridges. In the warmth of late afternoon, Gautama goes for a walk with Chanda in the Park of Six Bridges. Six streams flow through the park, each crossed by a bridge painted a different color. He would like to speak to Chanda of his spiritual disharmony, of the shadow that he carries inside him, but now, in the warm air, as they begin to cross the Yellow Bridge over the Stream of Happiness, his senses are wide open to the sound of the water moving over white pebbles and red sand, the soft light, the silk shawl moving against his bare shoulder, the sudden flight of a bird into the pale blue sky. His trouble is distant and has the vague shimmer of distant things. Besides, to unburden yourself to a friend is to place your burden on your friend's back, and Chanda's back isn't as strong as his own. He glances at Chanda, who seems preoccupied. It occurs to Gautama that lately he hasn't been sufficiently attentive to his friend, who may only be waiting for the chance to reveal a trouble of his own. But the thought, like the memory of his darkness, passes lightly across his mind. He is at peace with the world. The friends pass over the Yellow Bridge and enter a path under the shade of intermingled branches. Scents of green, like a fine mist, rise to his nostrils. Suddenly, before him, Gautama sees a leaf detach itself from a branch and begin to fall. He stops in astonishment. The leaf drifts slowly down. He cannot believe what he appears to be seeing. It's as if a cloud should drop down from the sky, as if a rock should rise. Dimly he recalls an afternoon in childhood when something green came drifting down from a branch, but his father had said it was a trick performed by the court magician. He hears a noise in the nearby trees. Two Park Protectors, with green shoulder-scarves, rush onto the path. One reaches out and catches the leaf in midfall. The other thrusts out a sack, into which the first man drops the leaf. Both men bow low to the Prince and back away into the trees. It all happens so quickly that Gautama wonders whether he's had one of those visions or dreams provoked by the heat of the day, by the bright drowsiness of a cloudless summer afternoon. He looks at Chanda, who avoids his gaze and begins speaking of the pavilion around the bend in the path, where they can sit awhile with a view of the Six Streams, the Six Bridges, and the distant palace with its turrets and gold cupolas.

Chanda Alone. Alone in his chamber, Chanda sits motionless on a rice mat, in a shaft of sunlight that warms his face and bare chest. The rest of his body is in shade, and Chanda thinks how fitting it is that he should be divided in half this way: the outward sign of his inward division. For if it's true that he is the closest companion of Gautama, the Prince's dearest and truest friend, if it's true that he would do anything for Gautama and would happily die for his sake, it's also true that he spies on his friend and reports secretly to the King. How has it come to this? Chanda's love for Gautama is not in doubt. They have been close companions since earliest childhood, and his love has only deepened with the years. It isn't too much to say that Chanda lives for Gautama, finds the meaning of his life in his friend's happiness. The feeling that moves in Gautama flows out of him and into Chanda, who therefore knows him from the inside out. If Gautama experiences a single moment of discontent, Chanda lies awake all night. How is it, then, that he watches his friend secretly and reports to the King? He answers his own charge by saying that everything he does is for the sake of his friend—that his secret meetings with the King are intended to cure Gautama's unhappiness. He understands the paradox hidden in his argument. He is arguing that his loyalty to his friend runs so deep that he's willing to be disloyal for the sake of loyalty. But although Chanda's nature is fervent and extreme, he is trained to think clearly, and he knows perfectly well that an act of disloyalty is not the same as an act of loyalty. Perhaps it's more accurate to say that, by doing the King's bidding, he is being a faithful subject: he is obeying a higher loyalty. But Chanda doesn't believe in a loyalty higher than that of friendship. It is possible, of course, that he is disloyal by nature, a corrupt man, a treacherous friend, a creature who serves his own interests and cares only for himself. Chanda, despite a modesty that is sometimes excessive, despite a willingness to condemn himself utterly, doesn't believe he is this kind of man. What, then, is the truth? The truth is that a secret divides him from Gautama, a secret that, for his friend's sake, he can never reveal. All members of the court know the secret, which the King revealed to Chanda in a private audience many years ago, after swearing him to silence on pain of death. The secret goes back to the time of Gautama's birth, when a prophecy was uttered by a sage.

The Tears of a Sage. When the Prince was born, a sage came to the royal palace to welcome the newborn son. As he held the child in his arms, the sage began to weep bitter tears. The King, trembling with fear, begged the venerable man to tell him what terrible misfortune was destined to befall his son. The sage answered that the child was destined for greatness. For if the child lived in a palace, he would one day rule the entire world; but if he renounced worldly things and chose the life of an ascetic, he would become an enlightened one. "But why are you weeping?" asked the King, himself alarmed at the possibility that his son might forsake the greatness of the world for a life of poverty and contemplation. "Because," said the sage, "I will never live to see the Awakened One." From that moment, the King vowed to attach his son to the pleasures of the world.

A Cat in Sunlight. One afternoon, a few days after his walk with Chanda in the Park of Six Bridges, Gautama is strolling along a portico in one of the courtyards of the northeast wing of the Summer Palace. Here lie the chambers of the musicians. From the open doorways he can hear the strings of lutes, the thump and tinkle of tambourines, the birdsong of wooden flutes, the calls of conch shells. The day is bright and hot, and he sees the young men taking their ease in their chambers, sitting on mats dyed red and green, or lying back on divans, their bodies naked to the waist, their shoulders glistening. His mood of darkness, his longing to sit apart and brood over the meaning of things, has left him so completely that he can recall it

only in a general way, as one might recall gusts of rain in the middle
of a blue afternoon. He feels a warm affection for the musicians, in
part because they possess the gift of transforming pieces of wood and
shell and animal hide into sounds more beautiful than silk or gold,
but above all because they are solitary beings who from time to time
renounce their solitude and come together to form a miniature kingdom. In the warmth of the shady portico he feels a drowsy well-being,
a welcoming of the sunlight and the shade, the doorways with their
drawn-back curtains, the jewels brightening and darkening on his
fingers, the white swan-cloud in the blue sky, the pebbled paths in
the green grass, the sound of his bare feet slapping softly against the
marble walk. He turns left as the portico follows the shape of the
courtyard. Here the sun strikes in such a way that he sees a pleasing
pattern of shady pillar-sides and sunny pillar-sides, like a wall painting in one of the corridors of his father's palace. At the foot of a pillar,
he sees a white cat asleep in the sun. Its back is beautifully curved,
its head is bent gracefully into its hind paws, and its tail lies across its
hind flank, so that it forms a perfect circle. As Gautama draws near,
the white circle begins to come apart. The cat stretches: its front legs
reach forward, its hind legs reach back and back, its body shudders
with delight. Swiftly it draws in its legs, lays one paw across its face,
and is still. Gautama walks on, but he is no longer at ease. Is he not
that cat? He stretches himself in the sun of his pleasures. He curls up
in the contentment of his days. He lies asleep in the sun. And if he
should wake? The strings of the lutes, the jingling disks of the tambourines, seem to grow louder. They scrape against his nerves like
knives on stone. Impatiently Gautama crosses the courtyard, enters a
cool hallway, and steps out onto a path.

The Two Swans. Through an arched doorway in an earthen wall,
the Prince enters a small wood that leads to the Lake of Solitude.

He sits on the grass at the edge of the lake, in the shade of a high mimosa tree. Swans glide among the white, red, and blue lotuses. Under the swans glide the other swans, the upside-down swans that he has loved since childhood. Two cranes stand in the water near the opposite shore. Gautama waits for the calm to descend. All about him is calm: the mimosa blossoms, the swans under the swans, the two cranes, the smooth water. All will enter him and calm him, as surely as he entered through the arched doorway. He waits under the mimosa tree, his legs crossed, his palms on his knees. The sun moves across the sky, but the calm does not come. It is there, outside him, all around him, but he himself is unquiet. Stubbornly he sits at the edge of the lake. Was it a mistake to have come here? What is he looking for? Nearby, a swan lifts its wings as if to fly, but does not fly. The wings, dipping, stir the water. Under the swan, the other swan is broken. Gautama thinks: I am the swan who does not fly. He thinks: I am the swan under the swan in the dark water. The air is still. The swan over the swan and the swan under the swan glide closer. He can see the two beaks, dark orange in the mimosa's shade, the glassy bee-black eyes. As the double swan comes closer, it grows larger, it becomes more and more of itself, until it rises before him with outstretched wings. He can smell the wet feathers like sweat. The four wings spread wider and wider until they touch the ends of the lake, it is a swan-god, a swan-monster, the feathers are passing into his mouth and eyes, he can't breathe, in a voice that issues from all sides the swan says: "You are wasting your life." Gautama shuts his eyes tight and presses back against the tree. A moment later he opens his eyes. Before him he sees the calm lake, the swan gliding over the swan, among the lotuses, on a summer afternoon.

The Sorrows of Yasodhara. Gautama's wife, Yasodhara, whose beauty is famous throughout the Three Palaces, is not unhappy because her husband roams among the concubines. She understands perfectly that the concubines, like the dancing girls, have been provided by King Suddhodana for the amusement of his son. She herself is skilled in the Eighty-Four Paths of Love, as surely as she is skilled in lute-playing and astronomy, and does not doubt the sexual pleasure she gives to her husband. Sometimes, for his delight, she dyes her lips with red lac, rubs over her body a lotion made of the ground dust of sandalwood, and places jewels along the parting of her hair. At other times, when she steps from the Pool of Everlasting Youth, her hair glowing like black sunlight, her hips shining like rivers, she feels her power drawing the Prince to her. Nor is she unhappy when he seeks out solitary places and speaks to no one. Yasodhara is never lonely, for she is surrounded by her handmaidens and friends, she delights in her young son, and she loves the life of the Three Palaces—the music and dancing, the troupes of visiting actors, the great feasts, the sporting competitions, the walks in the garden with teachers and philosophers who speak to her of right speech, right conduct, and the nature of the heavens. She herself is sometimes overcome by a desire for solitude and silence, for a withdrawal from a life of pleasure into the chamber of her own being, and she therefore understands that Gautama must sometimes forsake the world of the court, and even his own wife, in order to be alone with his thoughts. None of these things causes her unhappiness. No, Yasodhara, the happiest of all women, is unhappy only when she is most happy: when, lying with her beloved husband, staring into his eyes as he strokes her cheek tenderly, she sees in his gaze the shadow. It is the shadow of apartness, the shadow of elsewhere. She feels it in him when they walk together hand in hand in the Garden of Happiness, she feels it in him when, reaching gently for her face, he is not there. He is there, but he is not there. She hears it in his laughter, sees it in the curves of his beautiful shoulders. When he gazes into her eyes and whispers "I love you," she hears, deep within his words, the cry of a man alone in the dark. These are the sorrows of Yasodhara.

Chanda's Plan. As Chanda watches the door close behind his friend, in the earthen wall that surrounds the Lake of Solitude, a picture appears in his mind: a young woman weeping. He doesn't understand this picture, but he feels a familiar excitement, for that is how ideas always come to him: as pictures that he gradually begins to understand. He returns to the Summer Palace, descends to the underground passageways, and summons a charioteer to take him to the royal palace. King Suddhodana is out hunting in the forest; Chanda is forced to wait in one of the pillared recesses of the Hall of Patience. It is here, beneath a painting of a war elephant with swords fastened to its tusks, that the picture in his mind reveals its meaning. Later that day, as he walks beside the King in the Hall of Private Audience, Chanda presents his plan. The Prince's continual retreats, his craving for solitude, his despondency, his dissatisfaction—what are these but signs that the pleasures of the world are growing stale? None of this is new. The King and he have discussed such matters before. What's new is the intensity of the dissatisfaction, the sense that an inner crisis is at hand. The remedy has always been to heighten the old pleasures and to provide new ones. Chanda reminds the King of the young concubines trained by master eunuchs in the Twenty-Four Forbidden Paths of Love, of the recently constructed Theater of Shadow Puppets in the new wing of the palace. And always the result is the same: his friend is drawn back to the world of pleasure for a time, only to turn away more violently when the revulsion comes. Chanda's new plan takes into account the failure of pleasure as a strategy for binding the Prince to the sensual world. What he proposes is to entice Gautama by other means—by nothing less, in fact, than un-pleasure itself, which is to say, by the seductions of unhappiness. It is, he admits, a dangerous proceeding. After all, every sign of unhappiness is rigorously excluded from the life of the Three Palaces. A single tear shed by a concubine is punished by banishment. An attendant who falls to the ground, breaks an arm, and fails to continue smiling is immediately removed from the Prince's retinue. People, horses, peacocks never die: they disappear. Gautama walks in a world without pain, without suffering. Precisely for this reason, Chanda feels certain that a place set aside and devoted to sadness can have only an alluring effect on the dejected Prince, who will be drawn to it as other men are drawn to the hips of a concubine moving artfully among transparent silks. If His Royal Eminence in the wisdom of his Being would be willing to entertain the possibility—but the King interrupts with an impatient wave of his hand and grants permission. He is, he confesses, growing so desperate over the condition of his son that his own unhappiness is increasing. Only last night, while pleasuring a new dancing girl for the third time, he found himself suddenly thinking of his son shut away behind the wall of a private bower. The girl, skilled in the ways of delight, looked at him with a flash of fear—the fear of someone who expects to be punished for failing to give sufficient pleasure. The King calmed her and returned to his bedchamber. Perhaps Chanda's enigmatic remedy will cure more than one man.

A Family Stroll. Gautama, walking along a pebbled path with his wife and son, wonders whether this is a moment the boy will remember: the three of them walking together in the morning, the pink pebbles catching the light, the shadows of father and mother and son thrown out in front of them and flowing together as if the three separate beings were one moving body, the different sounds of their feet on the path, the mother's white silk parasol shading her face but sometimes slipping to reveal a lustrous strip of hair and a crimson acacia flower. Gautama looks at his son with pride, admiring Rahula's dark intelligent eyes, the cheekbones like polished stone, the ruby hanging from his ear. He reproaches himself: he hasn't seen the boy for five days. Here on the path, Gautama feels his fatherhood. He turns to his wife and looks at her tenderly. She draws back and lowers her eyes. Startled, he asks if anything is the matter. "Nothing, my lord," she answers. "Only, you looked at me as though you were saying goodbye."

From the Balustrade. The Prince stands with his hands on the railing of the second-story balustrade of the northwest wing of the Summer Palace, looking out at a broad garden planted with flower beds shaped like six-pointed stars and with ornamental fruit trees resembling swans and small elephants. At the far side of the garden stands a low wall, and on the other side of the wall a procession is making its way slowly in the direction of the Joyful Woods. He sees elephants with festive red stripes painted on their heads, chariots drawn by high-stepping white horses, two-wheeled carts pulled by yoked rams and piled with sections of cedarwood trellis painted yellow and red and blue. Gautama has promised his father not to ride after the daily processions, not even to inquire about them, for their mission is a secret and will be revealed in due time. Although he is mildly exasperated at being treated like a child, he's also deeply pleased: he has always liked secrecy and its excitements, the sense of a revelation about to come. He remembers a day in his childhood when his father handed him a gift, concealed in a small ivory box decorated with a border of carved tigers. For a long time he held the box in his hands, while faces looked down on him and voices urged him to slide back the top. Evidently the trellises are intended for a large enclosure. Some of the workmen's carts, with their two high wheels, carry long, polished pillars that gleam in the sun. Beside the carts walk young laborers with bare chests. There are other paths to the Joyful Woods; Gautama is aware that his interest is being deliberately piqued. He is aware of another thing: his father, Chanda, and Yasodhara have begun to worry seriously about him. They are continually casting sideways looks in his direction, suppressing anxious questions, turning him over in their minds. He can feel, like the touch of a hand, their troubled silences. Their solicitude has begun to interest him. Should they be worried? Now they're trying to draw him out of himself by means of a procession with a secret. They would like to distract him, to seduce his attention. He, for his part, would be delighted for them to succeed. Sometimes he is bored, bored with everything. It's an emptiness he does not know how to fill. At such times, even his inner shadow bores him. The sky bores him, and the earth bores him, and each blade of grass on the earth bores him, and that two-wheeled cart bores him, and his boredom bores him, and his knowledge that his boredom bores him bores him. As he watches a royal guard seated on an elephant adorned with topazes and emeralds, he remembers sliding back the top of the ivory box. But although he can see his fingers on the ivory lid, although he can see the row of carved tigers, and the faces looking down, for some reason he cannot remember what he found inside.

Approaching the Yellow Bridge. A few days later, Gautama is walking on a path in the Park of Six Bridges. He is alone. In the near distance he catches sight of the Yellow Bridge, and as he recalls his recent stroll with Chanda an uneasiness comes over him. He can't accuse himself of deliberately avoiding Chanda, but it's true enough that he hasn't sought out his friend in the old way. The estrangement puzzles him. The deep friendship that flows between them, the fierce closeness, the intimacy deeper than blood, the long nights of adolescence spent pouring out their souls—all this has come to seem oppressive to Gautama, who doesn't want to walk beside a friend who glances at him anxiously, watches hungrily for signs, and observes him as one might observe a child leaning too far over a balustrade railing. Sometimes Chanda blurts out enigmatic half-questions that seem to hint at accusations or confessions. Gautama understands that he himself is partly to blame for this state of affairs, for lately he has felt in himself a kind of inward hiddenness, which is bound to provoke the anxious scrutiny of a friend, to say nothing of that friend's sense of injury. After all, to whom should Gautama turn, in his obscure trouble, if not to Chanda? But Chanda's urgent concern doesn't limit itself to charged looks and riddling utterances. Gautama can feel, beneath those looks, some deeper turbulence. Can Chanda be concealing something from him? On several occasions recently, the Prince has had the peculiar sensation that someone is watching from a hidden place, and he cannot prevent himself from imagining that this unseen watcher might be Chanda. As he steps onto the Yellow Bridge, he looks back suddenly at the path. With self-disdain, with remorse, he returns his gaze to the bridge and looks down at the clear water, through which he can see white pebbles and red sand.

A Tremor of Whiteness. Chanda, walking along a path in the Park of Six Bridges, feels the smoothed earth press into his bare soles. He walks so quietly that he cannot hear the touch of his own feet on the path. Sometimes he stops, his body tense, his senses alert. Sometimes he picks up the pace. He crosses the Azure Bridge and continues along a path bordered on one side by a pond with wild geese and on the other by a grove of blossoming acacia trees. Sometimes, when the path turns, he sees a tremor of whiteness that disappears. Now the path turns again. Chanda follows the curve and stops—stops so completely that it's as if he has come to a closed door. He does not breathe. Directly before him, on the Yellow Bridge, Gautama stands in his brilliant white dhoti and shawl, staring down at the Stream of Happiness. Chanda walks silently backward. He watches as the turn of the path gradually pulls the trees across the Prince, making him disappear.

The Ladder. Gautama crosses the Yellow Bridge and strolls along a shady path under a canopy of branches. If only he were a pebble in a stream! He tries to imagine himself as a pebble in a stream. He is cold and white and round and hard and still. The thought calms him. He wonders whether it is possible to be a discontented pebble in a stream. He imagines a pebble having dark thoughts in a stream. As the path begins to curve to the right, he thinks: My mind is absurd. I am absurd. He rounds the turn and sees ahead of him a high narrow ladder reaching up into the branches of an asoka tree. Near the top of the ladder stands a gaunt man, his face partly hidden by dark green leaves and pale orange blossoms. The man appears to be touching a leaf on a branch above his head. Beside his knees, on each side of the ladder rails, hangs a wooden basket. The man pulls the leaf from the branch, drops it into one basket, and removes from the other basket another leaf. With a needle and thread he carefully begins to attach the second leaf to the place where the first leaf hung. He does not look down as Gautama walks up to the ladder and stands there watching.

Chanda Continues on His Way. In the middle of the Yellow Bridge, Chanda stops for a moment to look down at the clear stream. He wonders what drew Gautama's attention, down there where one sees only smoothly flowing water, white pebbles, and red sand. His friend sees other things, he's sure of it, but they lie within. Chanda crosses the bridge and continues along a sunny-and-shady path that stretches away beneath a canopy of interlaced branches. He walks slowly, listening for the possible sound of his bare soles against the smoothed earth, but he hears only birdsong. Chanda has trained himself to walk so quietly that he can bend over a bird pecking at the ground and pick up that bird in his hands. As he walks, he glances quickly over his shoulder, but no one is there. Is he foolish to imagine that the King is having him followed? The King, after all, is having his own son followed. Before him, where the path turns out of sight,

Chanda hears a clatter of distant cart wheels amidst the birdsong. He follows the turn of the path and stops abruptly. Gautama is standing beside a ladder, staring up. Chanda pauses, looks quickly about, and steps into the trees. The sound of cart wheels grows louder.

The Leaf Artist. Moments later a two-wheeled cart comes clattering into view, drawn by a bare-chested young man whose knee-length white loincloth is decorated with images of green leaves. The cart is filled with leaves so brilliant in their greenness that they appear to be wet. Upon seeing the Prince, the young man falls to his knees and presses his forehead to the path. Gautama bids him rise. The young man explains that he is an assistant to the Leaf Artist—he points to the man at the top of the ladder—who has been ordered by the Park Overseer to make leaves of green silk in his workshop, so that they may replace all leaves in the Park of Six Bridges that are in danger of falling. A report concerning a fallen leaf has caused great agitation. Now the Leaf Artist is passing from tree to tree, inspecting the leaves and replacing weak or damaged ones with sturdy leaves of silk. Gautama asks how many leaves are replaced in the course of a single day. The assistant answers that he doesn't know the precise number of leaves, but he can say that this is the third cartload of silk leaves he has delivered to the park this afternoon. At the top of the ladder the Leaf Artist, awakened from his trance of concentration, glances down. When he sees who is standing at the foot of the ladder, he turns sideways and bows low, very low—so low that for a moment it appears he will fall from the ladder and strike the ground at Gautama's feet. Slowly he uncurls and returns to his task.

Gautama's Knee. Gautama returns from his walk in the Park of Six Bridges, enters his chamber, and sits on a floor mat. The afternoon has not been a success. He feels certain he was being followed, but he doesn't know why anyone should follow him as he takes a stroll in one of his parks. There are many things he does not know. He doesn't know why a leaf falls from a tree. He doesn't know why he is a man and not a pebble in a stream. He doesn't know why he is unhappy. Does he know anything at all? He looks at his left knee. What does he know? He knows nothing. Does he even know that he has a knee? A man should know whether or not he has a knee. He asks himself why he thinks he knows he has a knee. He thinks he knows he has a knee because he perceives a particular shape and color. But what if his eyes are deceiving him? What if he's asleep? Say he closes his eyes and imagines a knee. Is that knee real? Is the outer knee more real than the inner knee? When he opens his eyes, the imagined knee disappears. Is it possible that when his eyes are open, as they are now, he is still not awake? And if he should wake? It's warm in his chamber. His right eyebrow itches slightly.

The Island of Desolation. Accompanied by chariots festooned with crimson and white flowers, by royal elephants draped with necklaces of pearls, by soldiers with javelins and by guards with ceremonial swords, by courtiers, friends, musicians, dancing girls, and jugglers, Gautama stands beside Chanda in the princely chariot as they come within sight of the secret place. The soaring trellis-wall is the height of three elephants. At the arched doorway he turns, embraces Chanda, and stares back at the silks and swords flashing in the sun. He descends. A guard opens the door, closes it behind him. Gautama has entered a realm of dusk. Black trees with black leaves rise up on both sides of a white path. From the covered top of the vast enclosure, globed lanterns hang like small moons. The globe-light shines on the trunks and branches, which appear to be blocks of stone shaped into trees and finished with black lacquer. High above, birds in the branches sing plaintively. Are they carved birds, there in the artful dark? The light of the round lanterns, the gloomy stone trees, the melancholy birdsong stir Gautama and fill him with a drowsy, vague excitement. He follows the path to the edge of a dark lake where black swans glide. Under the swans he can see the other swans, dreaming in the still water. In the middle of the lake he sees an island. As one swan drifts closer, Gautama realizes that it is a boat shaped like a swan. Under the boat-swan another boat-swan trembles slightly. An oarsman in a black robe beckons him aboard. Gautama sinks down among soft cushions as the black oars rise and dip like wings.

Chanda in Sunlight. As Chanda returns in the chariot, where he stands holding the reins in brilliant sunlight, he recalls with particular pleasure the six hundred birds carved by the artisans and fitted with mechanisms that can produce sorrowful birdcalls. If his creation is as successful as those birds, three things will happen: his friend will achieve happiness, the King will be grateful, and life in the Three Palaces can continue undisturbed forever. Chanda feels the sun on his bare chest, the warm breeze on his shoulders. He breathes deep. He can feel his aliveness glowing in him like an inner sun. In his nostrils, sharp smells of green. In his forearms, the pull of the reins. To live, to breathe, to laugh among friends! For no particular reason, Chanda laughs aloud in the sun.

The Black Pavilion. In the dusk of the enclosure the oarsman rows the black swan to the shore of the island. Under the swan-head the other oarsman draws in his oars. The Prince steps from the body of the swan onto white sand. It glimmers under the moon-globes. Before him he sees half a dozen crumbling pillars, which appear to be all that is left of a palace courtyard. He has never seen crumbling pillars before, and as he passes among them he is filled with a gentle, sweet distress. Past the strange pillars he comes to a high cedarwood wall. The doorway is hung with a black silk curtain, behind which he hears the soft, dark notes of a flute. Gautama pushes aside the curtain and enters a clearing among high trees. In the center of the clearing stands a large black pavilion, with an entrance awning supported by poles. From the pavilion comes a flute melody that rises and slowly falls, rises higher and slowly falls. The notes are accompanied by sounds he has never heard before, sounds that remind him of wind in leaves, of water in distant fountains. Quietly he moves forward, as if drawn by whispering voices. He enters the pavilion. Young women dressed in translucent black silk lie languorously on couches with their faces turned to one side. Others sit on floor cushions with their shoulders slumped forward, their cheeks resting on their hands. Still others walk slowly with bowed heads. All the women are taking deep breaths and letting out long sighs. The intermingled sighs create the sound of a mournful breeze. Black jewels adorn their necks and wrists. Black flowers tremble in their hair. He can hear other soft sounds among the sighs: sharp intakes of nose-breath, small high throat-bursts. What are those sounds? Slowly Gautama makes his way into the lantern-lit dark. From somewhere come the rising and falling notes of an insistent flute. One young woman, almost a girl, is lying on her side on a row of floor cushions. She is staring at nothing with her large, unblinking eyes. Her body is half-sunk among the cushions, her cheek lies upon an outstretched arm, one wrist rests languidly on her upswept hip. As he draws closer, he is startled to see her eyes begin to shimmer. Lines of water run down her face. Gautama feels a warmth in his chest. A tender confusion comes over him as he sinks to his knees beside her and takes her limp hand in his hands.

Chanda Receives a Report. For two days and two nights, specially trained Watchers concealed in the nearby woods observe the arched doorway in the trellis-wall and send reports to Chanda that all is well. By the third morning, when a messenger announces that there has still been no sign of the Prince, Chanda can no longer suppress his joy. Gautama has chosen to remain within the enclosure. He has been drawn in by the melancholy light, the Lake of Gloom, the Island of Desolation, the Pavilion of Sorrowing Women. On the fifth day, Chanda visits the King, who rewards him with a silver chest filled with precious jewels. On the seventh day, Chanda detects in himself a faint unease. The plan is working not merely well, but supremely well—far better than he had dreamed possible. Now, Chanda knows that life isn't in the habit of exceeding one's dreams. He calms himself; his friend's craving for melancholy scenes, the disappearance into the dark pleasures of tears and sighs, is precisely what Chanda foresaw. His error lay in underestimating the intensity of Gautama's need. By the end of the ninth day, Chanda can no longer sleep. Has something happened to the Prince? He instructs the Watchers to make inquiries by means of the oarsman, who is in the pay of the King. Anxiously he awaits the report. It is possible that Gautama has fallen so deeply under the enchantment of sorrow that he no longer craves the pleasures of the sun. It's equally possible that he has become sick and lacks the strength to return. But Gautama has never been sick in his life; he scarcely shows signs of tiredness after nights of excess that would leave most men weak with exhaustion. Can it be something else? Are the pavilion women, chosen by himself and one of the King's most loyal advisers, entirely trustworthy? Is the Prince in danger? So deeply does Chanda sink into troubled meditation that he is startled to notice one of the three Night Watchers standing patiently in the chamber doorway.

The Night Watcher's Tale. Chanda motions him in. The story is swiftly told. The Night Watcher has just come from speaking with the oarsman, who had been ordered to pay a visit to the Pavilion of Sorrowing Women. The women reported to the oarsman that the Prince remained with them for two wakings and two sleepings. In the timeless dark, he spoke to them kindly and wiped away their tears. On the third waking, as the mechanical birds began to sing, the women discovered that the Prince was no longer there. He had vanished, like a god. The waters of the lake are broad, the walls high and covered with a trellis-roof. Where is Gautama? As the oarsman rowed from the island, he could hear the women, who once played the part of sorrow, weeping in earnest. Chanda is no longer listening. He is staring at his hand, which has begun to tremble. He has never seen a trembling hand before, and it interests him so much that he is puzzled, when he looks up, to find the Night Watcher still standing over him, awaiting orders.

Chanda Investigates. Chanda steps from the wooden swan, instructs the oarsman to wait, and makes his way over the moon-white sand and through the ruined courtyard to the cedarwood wall with its hanging of black silk. He passes through the curtain into the clearing, and as he approaches the Pavilion of Sorrowing Women he hears the sound of raised voices. Inside, he comes upon an unpleasant scene. Groups of women are quarreling and shouting, throwing their arms about; other women sit sullenly alone. Their silks are rumpled, their faces soiled, their hair disorderly. A hush falls as Chanda enters. He questions the women closely, and the answer is always the same: the Prince vanished, like a god. They speak of his kindness, the gentleness of his eyes, the tenderness of his voice. Chanda can learn nothing from them. He strides from the pavilion and makes his way through the trees to the shore. Swiftly he circles the island. Gautama might have swum across the water to the far shore, but the only way out is through a single doorway, and that doorway is uninterruptedly observed by disciplined Watchers, three by day and three by night. As Chanda returns in the painted swan he considers the possibilities. The girls, instructed to deceive Gautama, are deceiving Chanda; the Prince has made them promise to guard the secret of his escape. It is also possible that they're speaking the truth, and that it is the oarsman himself who is deceiving him. Chanda imagines the grim oarsman rowing Gautama secretly across the lake, opening the door in the trellis-wall, cunningly distracting the hidden Watchers as the Prince creeps away unseen. If the girls and the oarsman are speaking the truth, then perhaps one or two or all three of the Night Watchers have become loyal to the Prince and have somehow conspired in his disappearance. If everyone can be trusted, then the vanishing of Gautama is a perplexing and alarming mystery. For all anyone knows, he may be lying at the bottom of the Lake of Gloom. At the Summer Palace, Chanda assembles one thousand guards, warriors, and attendants in the Courtyard of Eternal Youth. He dispatches four hundred men to the Four Hundred Bowers. He sends two hundred men to the Two Hundred Lakes and Ponds, three hundred men to the palace woods and fields, fifty men to the Fifty Gardens, and fifty men to the Island of Desolation. In his chamber, Chanda waits restlessly. He understands that it is his duty to go at once to the royal palace and report to the King, but he feels that it would be irresponsible for him to be absent for even a moment while the search is under way. He understands with absolute clarity that his commendable sense of responsibility is nothing but a desire to conceal from the King the disturbing news of his son's disappearance. Chanda walks up and down in the courtyard. He returns to his chamber. He paces between his clothes chest and the lute hanging on the opposite wall. He lies down with an arm across his eyes. He sits up, he lies down. At sunset a servant appears at his doorway. He reports that one of the caretakers thinks he might have heard the gate creak in the Bower of Quiet Delights. The servant himself has just returned from searching the

bower thoroughly but has found nothing. Chanda, who has lowered
his eyes for a few moments in order to concentrate on the meaning of
this report, looks up impatiently. Behind the servant, in the doorway,
stands Gautama. "If you're busy," Gautama begins. The servant turns
in surprise. Chanda rises to embrace his friend.

Gautama's Tale. When the servant leaves, Gautama sits cross-
legged on a rice mat and, thanking his friend warmly for the delights
of the Sorrowful Enclosure, tells his tale. He recognized Chanda's
ingenuity everywhere: the stone trees with their black leaves, the
globed lanterns hanging like small moons, the elegant boat-swan,
the women disposed in pleasing arrangements of grief. And his heart
was stirred, not only by his friend's thoughtfulness but by the women
themselves. It seemed to him that they were playing a part, which
pleased him as a lover of theatrical performances, but he soon sensed
that the attitudes of grief had released in them a genuine sorrow that
lay buried in their hearts. He, a man bearing within him his own darkness, spoke to them of life's perplexities, of the shadows born of sunlight. The result was curious: tears that had been artful soon changed
to passionate tears, which flowed along cheeks and dampened the
translucent silk that clung to young breasts so perfectly formed that
they appeared to be the work of a master sculptor. He passed from
girl to girl, until the pavilion was a great hall of woe, a musical com-
position of sobs and moans. The tears he was able to evoke he was
also able to soothe away; by the second night the girls were calm, and
indeed their grief, though heartfelt, did not run deep, for beneath
their flights of sorrow lay the vast country of youthful happiness. His
task completed, he left in the middle of the second night. All the
women were sleeping peacefully, their foreheads smooth and childlike. Mindful of the oarsman, who might be under orders to report
his movements, Gautama made his way to the opposite shore of the

isle. The lake was broad and the water deep, but the son of King Suddhodana was well trained in the art of swimming. He removed his
silks, wrapped them about his head like a turban, and swam to the far
side. A path led to the sturdy trellis-wall. He climbed swiftly, naked
except for the turban of silks. The immense trellis-roof, covered by
interwoven vines, was supported throughout the enclosure by cedarwood pillars disguised as trees. The overhanging edges of the roof
rested so that the horizontal slats lay between the vertical strips at the
top of the trellis-walls. Gautama pushed up an edge of vine-covered
roof, made his way over the top of the wall, and lowered the roof in
place. He climbed down the outside of the wall by placing his toes in
the spaces of the trellis. At the bottom he removed his turban of silks.
He fastened his garments about him and set forth on familiar paths.
Overhead, the moon was so perfectly round and so brilliantly white
that he wondered whether it, too, was an artificial moon suspended
from the heavens by an artisan's assistant. On turning paths, through
well-known woods and parks, he walked until he came to the Bower
of Quiet Delights. For seven days and seven nights he sat beside the
fountain, under a red-blossoming kimsuka tree. For seven days and
seven nights he reflected on his life. On the morning of the eighth day
he rose and went out to seek his friend, to whom he wished to recount
his adventures and announce his decision. But why does Chanda look
troubled? Can he read the heart of his friend?

Father and Son. In the Hall of Private Audience, King Suddhodana listens with alarm and close attention as his son explains that the
time has come. The time has come for him to leave the world of the
Three Palaces and seek his way in the larger world. The way he seeks
is inward. He has had glimpses of it, intuitions, here in the world of
his father, but he is continually distracted by the things that bring
him most pleasure. Moreover, he is causing unhappiness to the very

people for whom he wishes only happiness, namely, his father, his wife, and his friend. For these reasons he seeks permission to go out into the world and find what he cannot find here: himself. The King, as he listens, understands that he must answer with extreme care. He can, of course, simply refuse permission. His son prides himself on obedience. But Gautama is restless; he will obey, but rebelliously. What the King wants isn't a troubled and fretful obedience, but a joyful embrace of a father's wishes. "Are you not happy?" he asks his son. The Prince answers that he is the happiest man alive, but for one thing. "And what is that thing?" "It is this. My happiness is a sun that casts an inner shadow." The King, irritated that his son should speak to him in riddles, restrains his anger. A man stands to inherit a mighty kingdom, and he speaks of shadows. But the King understands that he is losing his son. A shadow passes over his own heart. He replies that it would be irresponsible of him to give his beloved son permission to renounce the kingdom that is his to inherit. But when the father is no longer able to rule, and the kingship passes to the son, then he may do as he likes, for there will be no one above him. The King is startled to feel tears on his face. His tears shake him, and as he weeps he turns his face away from his son.

In Which Gautama Observes a Gate. Gautama sits on the shore of the Lake of Solitude, where the swan once spoke to him as in a dream. Now the swans drift silently on the still water. He cannot disobey his father. He will assume the crown. He will conquer neighboring kingdoms. He will be merciless in battle. His inner restlessness will drive him to victory after victory, until there can be no more victories, since all his enemies will be enslaved or dead. The world will be his. King Siddhartha Gautama! Lord of the Earth and Sky. An impatience comes over him as he watches the swans under the swans in the dark water. Why don't they do something? Why are they just sitting there? Why don't they break away and fly off to unknown lands? This is no place for him. He wants to run, to shout, to ride in his chariot, to hurl a javelin at the sun. He wants—oh, what does he want? He wants to tear out his insides with a sword. He wants to cut off his head and hand it to his father. Here, Father: I cannot obey you. Irritably he rises and makes his way toward the gate in the wall. Outside, he strides along a shady path. Partly because he can't bear the idea of returning to his chamber, where nothing awaits him but his own fretful thoughts, and partly for reasons that elude him, he finds himself stepping from the path into a thicket. Like a boy playing in the woods, he reaches up to a strong branch and pulls himself into the leaves of a mimosa tree. He climbs to the branch above and sits there, a wingless bird. Through the leaves he can see the path, the wall, and the gate in the wall. Slowly the gate begins to open. One of the King's guards steps onto the path. He looks about, turns toward the open gate, and beckons. Chanda emerges. Gautama watches as they walk along the path, speaking in low voices, and pass slowly out of sight.

The Laugh. High in his tree, Gautama laughs. It's a laugh he has never heard before, and though it disturbs him, he discovers that he cannot make himself stop. Gautama knows many kinds of laughter, for happiness reigns in the world of the Three Palaces. There is the giddy laughter of concubines as they splash in the Fountain of Dreams, the playful laughter of friends as they rest after a footrace, the tender laughter of Yasodhara as she listens to him reciting a small adventure of the day. There is the witty laughter of highborn ladies, the fierce laughter of guards as they roll ivory dice in the courtyard. But the laughter that issues from Gautama, as he sits in the branches of the mimosa tree, the laughter that pours from him like flocks of birds, like fire, the laughter that hurts his ribs and scorches his throat and will not stop, though he wishes it to stop, is not like the laughter of the Three Palaces, and Gautama, who is trained to notice how one thing is distinguished from another thing that is like it in all ways but one, tries, even as he laughs, to understand the difference. And as he continues to laugh, harder and harder, he comes to understand that what distinguishes his laughter from the laughter he has known—the laughter of sunlight, the laughter of the summer moon—is that it is a laughter that is not happy.

The Work of a Master. The workshop of the Leaf Artist is located in the northeast wing of the Summer Palace, where the artisans are housed, not far from the musicians' quarters. In the late afternoon, the Prince pays the Master a visit. After their talk, the two men walk in the Garden of Artisans, where the Leaf Artist points out the silk leaves on trees of sandstone and hedges of carved cedarwood, the painted birds in the branches, a pond with artificial swans, and at the base of a sculpted juniper bush blossoming with lifelike flowers, a stone cat asleep on its side. Gautama is full of hope as he walks in the garden, for the Master has promised to set to work immediately. Four days later a messenger hands Gautama a wooden writing board on which a message has been written. He is to meet the Leaf Artist at nightfall in the Pavilion of Deepest Peacefulness, in the woods that border the southern rampart. Gautama dips his swan quill in an inkpot, writes on the board, and hands it back to the messenger. At sunset Gautama passes through parks and gardens, enters a bower, and descends a flight of steps into a mossy tunnel. He climbs a second flight of steps, emerges at the edge of a wood, and makes his way through the darkening trees. In the spaces between black and purple branches he sees the night sky. The sky is so fiercely blue, so shiningly, darkly blue, that it appears to quiver with inner fire. The moon is a white swan in a blue lake. Before him Gautama sees a dim shimmer. A moment later he pushes through a silk hanging and enters the

Pavilion of Deepest Peacefulness. A shadow stands before a divan. Gautama greets the Leaf Artist, who stoops in a streak of moonlight to unbind two bundles at his feet. The great wings are woven from white swan feathers and glimmer like white horses in the light of the moon.

Flight. The Leaf Artist lifts a wing and fastens it with straps of silk rope to Gautama's left arm. He lifts the second wing and fastens it to Gautama's right arm. The wings are heavier than Gautama has anticipated, and as he moves his arms slowly forward and back he thinks that it is like moving his arms in deep water. He follows the Master from the pavilion into the darkness of the forest. On shadowy tree trunks fatter than the legs of elephants he sees patches of moonlit moss. He feels a wing scrape against bark and draws his arms close to his sides. In a sudden streak of moonlight an edge of dark wing glows like white fire. The trees disappear. In the brilliant clearing he sees his long shadow stretching away. The sides of the shadow crack open: dark shadow-wings sweep out. The Master leads him across the clearing, which slopes up at one side to form a steep hill. At the top of the hill the Master examines the wings, tugs at the feathers, tightens the silk straps. He repeats his instructions. Gautama looks down at the clearing, at the woods beyond, at the dark rampart rising high above the world. He swings his swan-arms back and forth. He thinks: I am a Swan of the Night. The Master gravely nods. Gautama begins to run down the hillside toward the clearing, lifting and lowering his wings. Massive trees rise up on both sides. He feels like a child, a fool. The clumsy wings are holding him back, he can feel the ground pressing up against his feet. He remembers an afternoon in childhood when he saw a large bird rise slowly from a lake. Never will his feet leave the grip of the earth. He runs, he runs. Something is wrong. The trees are sinking down. Are the trees sinking down?

He can no longer feel the slap of the path. The great wings lift him higher. He is above the clearing, above the trees. Before him rises the rampart. He is a swan-god, he is Lord of the Night Sky, Prince of Stars. He can feel his blood beating in his wings as he flies upward toward the top of the wall.

Yasodhara's Dream. Yasodhara dreams that she is walking in a sunny courtyard. Across the courtyard she sees her husband, walking alone. She calls out to him. He smiles his boyish, enchanting smile and begins to walk toward her. The sun shining on his face and arms fills her with warmth, as if he were bringing her the light of the sun. Midway between them, on the courtyard grass, she notices a white object. When Gautama draws near it, he bends over and picks it up. He stands with it in his hands as she comes up to him. She sees that it is a white bowl. He is holding the bowl in both hands, staring at it as if he expects it to burst into speech. She stands beside him, waiting for him to look at her. "My lord," she says, but he does not hear her. She tugs at his arm, but he does not feel her. Wearily she sinks to her knees and leans her head against his leg.

The Other Side. Below him Gautama sees the moonlit treetops, the clearing, and the little Master on the hill. Above him soars the rampart. On the moonlit wall he sees the gigantic shadow of his lifting and falling wings. He imagines the wing-shadows rising higher and higher until they reach the top of the wall and suddenly vanish. And then? What lies on the other side? Gautama remembers the boyhood chariot ride with his father: "Nothing is there. Everything is here." He remembers philosophical conundrums posed by his teachers. If you draw a line around Allness, what lies on the other side? If you do not draw a line around Allness, does it never end? Now he is nearing the limit of the known world. And beyond? The swan-wings are heavy, but Gautama is strong. As he approaches the top of the wall, he hears a sound as of rattling or low rumbling. Above him, he notices a narrow aperture that runs along the wall near the top. From the aperture emerges a broad and finely meshed net, stretched between two horizontal poles. Below him, a second net emerges from the wall. The upper net drops and entangles his wings. He thrashes helplessly as he falls into the lower net. Slowly, entrapped in a cocoon of netting, he sinks toward the trees.

Chanda Reflects. As the nets enclose Gautama and gradually lower him to earth, Chanda watches from the high branches where he has concealed himself. He continues peering through the leaves as the Leaf Artist hurries down the hillside, across the clearing, and into the woods to assist the fallen Prince. When Chanda is certain that his friend is unharmed, he returns to the Summer Palace and sends a messenger to the King, who, as Chanda well knows, has followed the entire adventure with close attention. Immediately after Gautama's first visit to the artisans' quarters, the Leaf Artist began to meet regularly with the King. In the presence of Chanda, the King instructed the Master to prepare the swan wings. The next day, he ordered royal guards to penetrate the hollow passages of the rampart and climb the inner stairways in order to operate the two concealed net-mechanisms, installed many years ago for the purpose of foiling foreign invaders. Chanda passes a sleepless night. In the morning he makes his way to the Park of Six Bridges and sits under an acacia tree at the side of a stream. What kind of man has he become? He has always thought of himself as a loyal friend, watching anxiously over Gautama's happiness. Yet lately he can think of himself only as an instrument of his friend's unhappiness, a traitor and spy who serves no one but the King. It's true that the King loves his son dearly and desires nothing but his happiness, so long as that happiness is of the kind that embraces the world and its delights. But Gautama can no longer surrender himself to those delights. Or is it, rather, that the small world of the Three Palaces is no longer large enough for the restless son of a mighty King? Chanda sees again the great wings struggling in the net and turns his inward sight away. The world within the world is too small for a man with a restless heart. He must pass to the other side of the rampart, he must confront the great world in all its splendor. Of course: the other side. There's no time to waste.

Languor. Gautama speaks to no one of his night adventure, which soon comes to seem no more than a summer dream. How likely is it, after all, that he rose like a great bird above the trees to the top of the rampart, one summer night when the moon was a white swan in a blue lake? But ever since his return to everyday life, a strangeness has settled over things. When, standing in the archers' field, he pulls back the bowstring, he feels the bending of the bow and the ripple of tension in his arm, but at the same time he has the sense that he is remembering this moment, which already took place long ago: the sun shining on the wood of the arrow, the iron drum in the distance, the rough bowstring sliding along his forearm, his hair flowing over his shoulders. When, at night, he visits Yasodhara in her chamber and stares deep into her eyes, he feels that he is looking back at her from a future so distant that it is like whatever lies beyond the line drawn around Allness. When he laughs with Chanda, when he walks alone in the Park of Six Bridges or the Bower of Quiet Delights, when he observes his hand slipping beneath the transparent silk that reveals and conceals the thighs of a concubine, he is moved in the manner of a man who, walking along a path, suddenly recalls a moment from his childhood. One afternoon, bending over a pond to examine the water-grass growing beneath the surface, Gautama sees his face gazing up at him from the water. The reflection appears to be resting below the surface of the pond. At once he imagines the face straining to see him clearly but seeing him only through the silken water, which, however clear and undisturbed it may be, remains between the face and what it wishes to see like the pieces of colored silk that hang in the palace windows. There is a quietness in things, a gentle remoteness. At times he can feel the edges of his lips beginning to form a smile, without accomplishing a motion that might be called a smile, as if the act of smiling required of him a concentration, an unremitting energy of attention, that he can no longer summon.

The King Makes Up His Mind. The King is bitterly disappointed in Chanda. Not only has the elaborate and costly plan of attracting the Prince to the Island of Desolation failed entirely, but the failure has led to his son's rebellion and the attempted flight over the rampart. At the same time, the King feels beholden to Chanda, who oversaw the movements of the hidden guards and the testing of the nets in the wall. More than any other person, Chanda, whatever his faults, is responsible for the safe return of his son. The thought of the Prince fills the King with anxiety. His son is withdrawing from the world of rich pleasures into some dubious inner realm that can only unfit him for kingship. And the King is beginning to feel his age: just the other night, rising from dinner, he experienced a slight dizziness that forced him to rest for a moment with both hands on the table, while faces turned to him with sharp looks. The kingdom has never been stronger, but enemies are pressing on the borders and will take advantage of any weakness, any indecisiveness. Is it possible that by shielding his son from knowledge of the world he has encouraged the very tendency toward inwardness he was trying to prevent? The thought is inescapable as he walks with Chanda in the Garden of Seven Noble Pleasures and listens skeptically to the latest plan.

Chanda proposes that Gautama be allowed to ride out beyond the ramparts in order to behold the glory of the realm over which he will one day rule. The route will be carefully chosen in advance. Gautama will ride through leafy alleys and make his way past the mansions of noblemen toward the outskirts of the city. The world, in its vastness and variety, will thrill his soul. He will understand what it means to be the future ruler of a glorious kingdom. The plan strikes the King as dangerous. He can command every motion, every smile and foot-fall, every budding leaf, within the little world of the Three Palaces, but beyond the ramparts the large world streams away. There, things are so little subject to meticulous supervision that entire trees fall down whenever they like. What if the Prince, who has always been protected from the harshness of life, should see something that disturbs him? What if the great, teeming world dizzies him and drives him more fiercely inward? The King rejects the proposal brusquely, passes his hand over his eyes, and uneasily agrees, on condition that ten thousand servants prepare the route by sweeping the roads clean and removing from view all unpleasant sights.

The Eastern Gate. At dawn the Eastern Gate swings open: the two halves of the Inner Gate and the two halves of the Outer Gate. Preceded by a thousand chariots and five thousand horsemen, Gautama rides beside Chanda in a gold chariot drawn by two white horses glittering with emeralds and rubies. Everything stands out sharply: the broad well-swept path, the towering mimosa trees hung with silk banners, the flash of a sword blade against the brown gleam of a horse's flank. Deep among the trees he sees, rising like a vision or a painted image on a wall, a nobleman's mansion with balustrades and turrets. As the progression advances, people begin to appear on both sides of the road, which leads to the outskirts of the city on the river. Gautama sees glistening black hair with red and orange flowers, a

child's knuckles like pebbles in a stream. He can feel his senses bursting open. The world is a torrent. Beauty is a brightness that burns the
eyes. If he reaches out his hand, he'll gather in his palm the sky, the
jeweled horses, the broad path lined with glowing faces. He wants
to swallow the world. He wants to eat the world with his eyes. Each
blade of grass at the side of the road stands out like a sword. Beside
a brilliant yellow robe he notices a dark shape in the grass. He orders
Chanda to halt the chariot. It is some kind of animal—an animal
with hands. Gautama steps down from the chariot. The creature is
an animal-man, seated at the side of the path. There is no hair on the
top of its head, though long white hair-strands fall along the sunken
cheeks. Its eyes are dull and muddy, the skin of its face hangs from
the bone. The creature's fingers, spread on its knees, look like bird
claws. In the half-open mouth, Gautama sees a single brown tooth.
An ugly odor, harsher than stable smells, rises like steam. Gautama
turns to Chanda, who remains standing in the chariot. "What is this
creature?" He sees fear in Chanda's eyes.

What Chanda Knows. Chanda knows that it is still possible to
deceive Gautama, but he also knows that he has come to the end
of lying. His answer will provoke an outburst of ferocious questions,
which he is determined to answer truthfully. The answers will trouble his friend, whose eyes are already darkening. Gautama will turn
back to the palace grounds and shut himself away. He will speak to
no one. How can it have happened? The road was swept clean, the
woods trimmed and painted, the houses carefully searched for the
elderly, the sickly, and the deformed. Wouldn't it be better to say that
the creature is a great insect that makes its home in roadside grass?
Wouldn't it be kinder to describe it as a monster captured from a distant kingdom, where men live on the floors of lakes? Chanda sighs,
looks directly into his friend's eyes, and says: "That is an old man."

Old age is not allowed in the world of the Three Palaces. He will have to explain everything to his friend, who is still a child, in some ways. Gautama is looking hard at him. Chariot wheels shine in the sun.

The Southern Gate. Gautama orders Chanda to turn back from the procession and reenter the Eastern Gate. For seven days and seven nights he sits under the kimsuka tree by the fountain in the Bower of Quiet Delights and broods over the dark shape at the side of the road. The Old Man is within him: he is that man. His son is that man. That man dwells in the blood of his wife, in the blood of all beautiful women. How could he not have known? He has always known. He has known and not known. He has not known but he has known. On the morning of the eighth day he rises and seeks out Chanda. He will ride out again; he is not afraid. Together they ride through the Southern Gate. Gautama remembers how everything stood out sharply when he set forth through the Eastern Gate, and he longs to be wakened from his dark dream by the fierce brightness of the world. In the distance he can see spires and towers shimmering in a blue haze. On both sides of the road stand royal guards, who cheer him on his way. As he greets one guard, who is separated from the next by an arm's length, Gautama notices someone seated on the ground between them. He stops the chariot, dismounts, and stands looking down at a young man as thin as a child. His eyes are clouded. His breath sounds wet. The young man is trembling and groaning in the sun. A greenish liquid flows from his nose and mouth. His leg is yellow with urine. Gautama turns violently to Chanda, who does not lower his eyes. Chanda says: "That is a sick man."

The Western Gate. The journey is broken off. For seven days and seven nights Gautama broods over the decay of the body. On the morning of the eighth day he rides with Chanda through the Western Gate. Scarcely has he set forth when he sees a horse-drawn cart moving slowly at the side of the road, followed by people wailing and hitting their chests with their fists. In the cart a man is lying on his back, his limbs stiff as columns, his face empty as stone. Gautama looks harshly at Chanda. "What is happening?" he asks.

Seeing. Gautama returns through the Western Gate. He speaks to no one. He goes directly to the quarters of the concubines, in order to find forgetfulness. Something is not right. The women smile at him, but their teeth are broken and brown, their breasts sag like sacks of dirt, their arms are crooked sticks. A naked girl lying on her stomach looks over her shoulder at him. A snake crawls out from between her buttocks. Her face is a grinning bone. Gautama flees into the bright afternoon. Overhead, the sun is a ball of blood. He looks at his hand. Cracks appear in the skin. A black liquid hangs from his fingertips.

The Northern Gate. On the eighth day Gautama orders the Northern Gate to be opened. He must see the world as it is. What is the world? He will walk breast-high in blood and excrement, he will kiss the mouths of the dead. Not far from the gate he sees a man walking at the side of the road. The man is carrying a white bowl. He wears a simple robe and walks peacefully. His hair is cut close to his scalp. The whiteness of the bowl, the stillness of the arms, the serenity of the gaze, all draw Gautama's tense attention. Chanda explains that the man is an ascetic, who carries a begging bowl. Once he was a wealthy man, head of a great house with many servants. Now he has nothing, which he calls everything. When Chanda turns to look at his friend, he sees Gautama staring at the white bowl with a look of ferocity.

In the Garden of Seven Noble Pleasures. In the indigo night, King Suddhodana is walking in the Garden of Seven Noble Pleasures. The moonlight rippling over his arms like white silk, the dark odors of the rose-apple trees, soothe him and fill him with peacefulness. He can permit himself to feel a measure of calm, for the reports from Chanda have made him warily hopeful. The Prince has ridden out through all four gates and each time has returned quickly. He appears to prefer the familiar pleasures of the world within the ramparts to the difficult pleasures of the unknown world. He will never be a conqueror of kingdoms. Instead, he will rule from the Three Palaces and embellish the lands that his father has won. It is good. For there is a time of expansion, and a time of consolidation; a time of blood, and a time of wine. The soldiers will obey him, for disobedience is death. And after the reign of King Siddhartha Gautama will come the reign of Gautama's son, who already handles his horse like a man and speaks with the easy authority of one born to rule. Rahula will take command like his grandfather before him, he will ride out and conquer new lands. The young boy fills him with pride. But then, there is no reason to rush things; the King himself is still strong. Only the other day he hunted from dawn to nightfall and later, in the women's quarters, made a young concubine cry out with pleasure.

Leave-taking. Outside the bedchamber, Gautama raises his hand to push aside the heavy curtain in the doorway. He hesitates and does not move. He can hear Yasodhara breathing in the marriage bed, with its high posts topped by carved lotus blossoms and its scarlet bed mat woven with a border of gold mandarin ducks. Through a second doorway is his son's chamber. Gautama imagines himself bending over Rahula, who lies with his face turned to one side and his forearm flung across his chest. He is a healthy boy, skilled in archery and wrestling, an excellent horseman, a leader among his friends. Never does he seek out solitary places, where there is no sound but the dip of a swan's beak in the water. Now Gautama imagines himself bending over Yasodhara. The thin light of an oil lamp shines on her cheek. Asleep, she is like the swan under the swan in the dark water, vivid and shut away. He will step into the chamber and bend over her, he will whisper his farewell. As he stands outside the curtain, imagining himself bending over her and whispering his farewell, he feels that she is far away, though he has only to push aside the curtain and step over to her. Soon the doorway, too, will be far away. Something troubles his thoughts, and now it is growing clearer, now he has it, he sees it: even here, at the threshold of his wife's chamber, where his hand is lifted before the curtain, he is already elsewhere. To push through the curtain is not to say farewell, but to return from a journey that permits no return. An irritation comes over him. Is he still so bound to pleasure? He turns away, toward the night.

Moonlight. Chanda glances back as the great doors of the Northern Gate close behind him. Then he rides ahead with Gautama, each on his horse, along the moonlit path. Chanda is exhilarated and desolate: exhilarated because he is helping his friend escape from the prison-world of the Three Palaces, desolate because he knows that life without Gautama will be meaningless. It is Chanda who has secretly ordered the thirty guards of the Northern Gate to remove themselves to the other three gates, Chanda who has replaced them with six trustworthy attendants; it is Chanda who has prepared the horses and arranged the time of departure. The King will be enraged, he may even have Chanda arrested and flung into prison, but in time he will forgive him and in the end he will thank him. Gautama's departure, the King will come to understand, could not have been prevented.

Far better that his son should escape with a trusted friend who can lead him safely through the dangers of the night to the border of the Great Forest. As they ride along the path, Chanda repeatedly looks at the Prince, who stares straight ahead. His long hair, bound in back, bounces lightly between his shoulders. Chanda suddenly imagines the future knife cutting off the proud locks, the coarse robe replacing the fine silk that ripples in moonlight like trembling water. The son of King Suddhodana will carry a white bowl. His long fingers will shape themselves around the whiteness of the bowl. So vivid is the image of the begging Gautama that Chanda is startled to see the Prince in his long hair and silk robe, riding beside him on a white horse. The trees have begun to thin out a little. At a fork in the road Chanda leads them onto the right-hand path, which turns away from the city on the river. Dark fields on both sides stretch into the night. Although Gautama says nothing and looks only ahead, Chanda can feel, flowing from his friend, a strange lightheartedness. And after all, why not? They are riding out on an adventure, a world-adventure, on a fine night in summer. They're like a couple of boys, playing in moonlight while the grown-ups are sleeping. In the night of the bright moon all things are possible, for moonlight is dream-light, and may the night go on. To be alive! To breathe! And when the adventure, like all adventures, comes to an end, there will be others. Tomorrow, in sunlight, they will walk across the courtyard to the musicians' quarters, they will laugh in the air of summer. But he isn't thinking clearly. Tomorrow his friend will not be with him. His friend will never be with him again. An uneasiness comes over Chanda. The long night has tired him. He can feel the tiredness tugging at him from the inside. He has to stay alert, on this night that must never end. But already he sees the Great Forest rising up before him. How can that have happened? The forest is coming nearer, it's hurrying to meet them. Shouldn't he have been paying closer attention? Now Gautama has stopped. He is dismounting, he is delivering his horse to Chanda. From his arms he begins to remove bracelets of jewels. Chanda wants to slow him down, to stop him forever, to explain that things are happening much too quickly, only moments ago they were riding along, two friends on a summer night. As Chanda receives the jewels, still warm from the Prince's arms, he feels a trembling in his body. With a sense of deep violation, he falls to his knees and begs his friend to let him accompany him on his journey. There are snakes and wolves in the forest. The Prince's feet, accustomed to swept paths, will walk on thorns. What will he eat? How will he sleep? Even as he cries out his need, Chanda is sick with shame and bows his head. He becomes aware of a silence around him and looks up in alarm, but Gautama is still standing there. Chanda hears a light wind in the trees, which seem to be speaking, unless it's the night sky: "The time of sleeping is over." He tries to understand, but he hears only the wind in the leaves. Gautama is pointing at the eastern sky. "Look. Daybreak." Above a line of hills, a thin bar of dawn has appeared. A heavy tiredness comes over Chanda, like a weight of cloth. A yawn shudders through his face and runs along the length of his kneeling body. He bends his neck in weariness. On his shoulder he feels something. Is it the touch of a hand? He wants to shout out in wild joy, he wants to burst into bitter tears. When he opens his eyes he sees Gautama disappearing into the forest. Chanda waits, kneeling before the trees. The sky is growing light. A bird lands on a branch. After a while Chanda rises and, leading both horses, starts back along the path.

THE PLACE

1

It was known as the Place. Even as children we knew there was something wrong with a name like that—you couldn't get a grip on it, the way you could get a grip on JoAnn's Diner, or Indian Lake, or the Palace Cinema out on South Main. It was as if whoever had named it hadn't thought very much about it, or hadn't been able to make up his mind. Later, as we grew older, we thought the very wrongness of the name was what was right about it. It was like an empty room you could put things in. Still later, we no longer thought about the name at all. It was part of what was, like summer and night.

2

It's easy to get there: just head north toward the hill at the end of town. As you get closer, the houses thin out and give way to car dealerships, a retirement community, and an enclosed mall next to an outdoor shopping plaza, before you reach a stretch of fields and woods. On the other side of the woods the hill begins. You can drive a short way up, but you have to leave your car in one of the paved lots and continue on foot. Half a dozen dirt trails start from the lots and wind to the top. It takes most people no more than twenty or thirty minutes to get there, though some like to rest on wooden benches scattered along the sides of the paths. If you don't want to walk, a minibus will take you most of the way up, leaving from the main trailhead every half hour, nine to five during the week, ten to six on weekends. Everything's shut down during the bad weather, first of November through the first of March. Radios and cell phones are strictly forbidden, but no one seems to miss them. You know it's not like a trip to the shore of Indian Lake, two towns over, or to the picnic tables in Burrows Park. You know you haven't come for that.

3

I remember my first visit, at the age of six or seven. I see myself holding my mother's hand as we walk along an upward-sloping path, between fields of knee-high grass stretching away. I could feel the sun, warm on my arms. More and more sky kept appearing, as if we were pushing something aside that had been covering it up. I felt a familiar excitement, the kind I felt when we were on our way to the amusement park, with its wooden horses moving up and down on silver poles and its pink cotton candy shaking on paper cones, or the summer circus in the field by the river. I wondered whether the Place was a park with rides, or maybe a castle with a shop selling swords. "Here we are," my mother said, when we reached the end of the path. I remember standing still and turning my head from side to side, with a kind of desperation, thinking: There's nothing here. The other thing I remember is the change in my mother's face. In those days I always had my mother's complete attention. Even when I was apart from her I knew she was thinking about me, worrying about me, taking pleasure in my existence. But up there, at the Place, something had shifted. It wasn't that she had let go of my hand, because she often let go when she knew I was safe. It was that she somehow wasn't there with me. I thought she must be looking at something, but when I tried to follow her gaze I could tell that she wasn't looking at anything at all. Later, when she drew me to her side and pointed to the little town far below, I gave it a harsh glance and looked away. After a while I began kicking at a stone in the grass.

4

Sometimes a feeling comes. You're walking along a sidewalk, some Saturday afternoon in summer. You're passing through the sun and shade of maples and old oaks, past the familiar yards and porches of your neighborhood. Mrs. Witowski is kneeling on her cushion at the side of the hollyhock bush, jabbing at the soil with her weeder. The Anderson kid is lifting a two-pane cellar window from the back of his Honda; he's going to fit it into the wood-framed space in the concrete strip at the base of the house, where you can see two wing nuts that he will turn to hold the frame in place. The lawn mowers are out; in the warm air there's a smell of cut grass, lilac, and fresh tar. The sun feels good on your arms. All at once the feeling comes. It isn't restlessness, exactly. It's the unmistakable feeling, precise as a knife-cut, that you need to be elsewhere. The street is hemming you in, pressing against you, making it impossible to breathe. This is the feeling that tells you to return to your house, get in your car, and head out to the Place.

5

It's difficult to describe what's there. Unlike Burrows Park or the South Side Rec Field, the Place has no boundary, though it's true enough that the Place is located at the top of the hill. The hill slopes up to a flattish top that might be thought of as a plateau, with dips and rises of its own. Just where the top of the hill begins or ends, who can say? Up there, you have a good view in all directions. At one end you can see the woods and fields at the base of the hill, then the little red-roofed buildings of the retirement community, the country road, and, farther off, the town itself—Main Street with its shops and tiny cars, the roof of the Van Buren Hotel, the residential section, the pond, the park, all so small that it takes you by surprise. Beyond the town you can see other towns, a village with a white church steeple, twisting roads, a ribbon of highway, patches of farmland, a band of low hills. On all sides of the plateau you can see far-off places. The plateau is grassy, with stretches of bare rock, a scattering of wildflowers, small stands of oak and pine, a few blueberry bushes. Here and there you can find benches, the old-fashioned kind with wooden slats, which the town has seen fit to provide for tired travelers. The most striking feature of the Place is the dozen or so crumbling stone walls, about the height of your waist, that run for twenty or thirty feet, in different directions, along the grass of the plateau. The Historical Society says that they're old property walls, erected by farmers in the late seventeenth and early eighteenth centuries, though opinion is divided about whether crops were grown and whether any buildings once stood on the plateau. One historian claims that the walls are not farmers' walls at all, but the remains of a Native American settlement dating back to the mid-sixteenth century. You can walk along the low walls, sit down on them, or ignore them, as you please. Sometimes you see praying mantises, field mice, a red-tailed hawk. The plateau doesn't drop off sharply, but slopes gently down on all sides, so that, as I have said, it's difficult to know where anything begins and ends. The appearance of the Place is what I've attempted to describe, but the attempt itself is questionable. It isn't so much what the Place looks like, after all, as what it does to you.

6

Just as stories collect around old, abandoned mansions, so rumors swirl about the Place. Sometimes the rumors gather so thickly that you have to push your way through them, in order to find the Place at all. Some say the Place was once the site of an ancient monument to the Great Spirit, erected by the ancestral branch of a little-known tribe. Some claim that the Place has life-enhancing powers that cure disease, increase longevity, and reverse memory loss. The Place, some say, contains energy fields that allow you to perceive past events and to communicate with the dead. Although most of us scorn such rumors, which cheapen the Place and threaten to turn it into a psychic parlor, we understand that in some way the rumors are part of what the Place is: the Place summons them, calls them into being, as surely as it gives rise to yellow violets, prickly milkweed pods, and tall, nubbly spikes of mullein.

7

In the spring of junior year in high school I began spending time with Dan Rivers. He had moved to our town in December from somewhere in Colorado, and he was the kind of guy I had always avoided—handsome, sure of himself, easy in his body, easy with girls. Everyone liked Dan Rivers. Maybe because I made a point of being polite and distant, he began to seek me out. One day he walked home from school with me. He started coming to the house, where we played chess and talked books; on the sunny back porch he'd sit on one of the wicker chairs and tell my mother stories about small-town Colorado and listen to her tales of the Lower East Side. In the living room he'd sit in the armchair by the piano and talk to my father about the problem of free will or the correspondence theory of truth. I felt in him a readiness for friendship, a desire to penetrate to the core of another temperament. We spoke about our ambitions, our dreams. One Saturday morning he drove over and said he wanted to see the Place. I hadn't been there since the time with my mother. We drove out past the car dealerships, the cluster of attached retirement homes, past the mall and the shopping plaza, entered the woods, and came to the hill. We parked in a paved lot bordered by wooden posts and began our way up a curving trail. Field grass stretched away on both sides; the sun warmed my arms. I remembered walking with my mother, remembered the leather purse slung over her shoulder, the shadow of her hat on the upper part of her face. At the top of the path Dan Rivers and I turned to look at the view. Far off, in the little town, I could see our high school, the roof of the Equity Trust on Main, a corner of Burrows Park. I turned to Dan Rivers, who was looking at the same view, but I could feel something else in him, something that reminded me of the change in my mother's face. I went off and sat on one of the walls. I could feel the warm stone pressing against the calves of my jeans. After a while I walked to the far end of the plateau, where I looked out at a brown river, a factory smokestack, blue hills. A few other people were strolling around. It was quiet up there; I was a talker, but this was no place for talk. Dan Rivers came over to me, sat down, got up, walked around. An hour later we headed back down to the car. The next day he went back to the Place alone. On Monday he didn't come over to the house. He began driving out to the Place, day after day; he withdrew from his clubs, stopped going to parties, seemed preoccupied. He rarely came over to the house anymore, said he was busy. Once or twice, when we passed each other in the halls, he invited me to drive out there with him. Some other time, I said. When we did get together, now and then, he wanted only to talk about the Place, but at the same time he didn't really want to talk about it. He said that it cleared his mind, helped him get rid of things.

What things, I wanted to know. Mind-junk, he said, and gave that one-shoulder shrug of his. I could feel a new hiddenness in him; he had stepped into himself and closed the door, shut the blinds. When I learned in June that he was moving with his family to Austin, Texas, in July, I felt that we had already said our goodbyes. The day after he left for Texas, I decided to visit the Place alone.

8

Though you might not think so to look at us, our town attracts summer visitors. We're especially sought out by big-city people, who love the idea of getting away from it all, of escaping from the pressures of urban life into what they believe is a peaceful, simple existence. But we're also well liked by residents in surrounding small towns, who are drawn to our outdoor cafés, our shops and restaurants, and our lively nightlife, with its dance clubs and jazz bars. The summer visitors stay at our two inns, with rooms decorated in period styles, at our renovated nineteenth-century hotel, and at a variety of bed-and-breakfasts and family-friendly motels, or they rent our homes by the month. Everyone likes our tree-lined downtown, with its small, locally owned shops and quaint restaurants, its shady wooden benches and its ice-cream parlors, though we also have our share of luxury boutiques and high-end clothing shops. Burrows Park, with its picnic tables, its stream, and its children's playground, is always popular; there are outdoor concerts in July. Not far outside our town lies Indian Lake, where you can swim or rent a canoe or walk the trails; a little farther away you can find a wildlife sanctuary, a golf course, and a restored eighteenth-century village with craft shops and a museum. The summer visitors also come for the Place. They walk to the top of the hill, stroll around, admire the view, and go back down. Few return, especially when they learn that no picnics are allowed up there. The summer people can irritate us, but we also find them interesting: they make us wonder what the Place must feel like, to those who can never be anything except what they already are.

9

I don't know what I expected, the day I went up to the Place alone. I suppose I was hoping to discover whatever it was that had pulled Dan Rivers to it, time after time. It was a hot July morning. I walked around the Place, noticing again that it was no single flatness but a series of small slopes and declines, so that it was possible, even at the top of the hill, to find yourself in a shallow valley. I walked beside the low walls that ran here and there along the rises and dips, stepped through fields of grass showing traces of overgrown paths, passed a man sitting under a tree sketching with charcoal on a large pad that he held on his knees. After a time I sat down against a low stone wall, in warm shade, with the sun behind me. Farther down was another stone wall, broken in places; in the distance I saw blue-green hills. It was peaceful enough up there, though peace wasn't what I had come for. I didn't know what I had come for. In the warmth and shade a drowsiness came over me. I did not fall asleep, for I was seventeen years old and filled with energy, but I sat very still and imagined that anyone watching me would think that I had fallen into a deep sleep. I then saw a woman approaching my wall. She wore a white dress that came down to her ankles and a white sun hat tilted low on her face. Although there was nothing peculiar about her, except for the whiteness of her clothes, I had the sense that I was having one of those half-waking dreams, from which at any moment I might awake. She drew near without seeming to see me, then looked down at me from under her hat and began walking away along the wall, glancing back as if she expected me to follow. I rose without hesitation and began walking after her, though with the sensation that I was still sitting there, with one hand resting on the grass, in the warm shade. She soon came to the end of the wall. There she began going down through an opening in the earth. I followed her down the rough stone steps, which changed direction from time to time, and when the steps ended I found myself in a high, narrow corridor, with doors on both sides. The woman in the white dress was walking swiftly along the corridor, toward a closed door at the far end. She opened the door and disappeared inside, but not before glancing at me over her shoulder. I passed through the open door and entered a vast room or hall, trembling with light. On both sides I saw immensely tall windows through which brightness poured. In the hall stood many long tables at which people were seated; their faces and arms were shining, as if illuminated from within. A stern, gentle man in a white robe led me along the side of one of the tables. As I walked behind him, I could scarcely make anything out because of the brightness. Then I seemed to see, on the opposite side, Dan Rivers quivering in the light. In another place I saw my mother, leaning her cheek on the palm of a hand. The man led me to an empty chair with a high back; it was difficult for me to climb onto the seat. Before me he placed an open book with pages so large that I wondered whether I would be able to reach far enough to turn them. The white room, the blazing windows, the open book, filled me with a sense of peaceful excitement, as if I had found a place I hadn't known I was looking for. As I bent over the white book, which contained words that would explain everything, a stillness came over me, an inner ease, as if I had let go of something, slowly my body began to bend forward, and when my forehead pressed against the page I felt a yielding, a dissolving, I was passing through, at the back of my head a hardness was starting to gather, and I found myself sitting against the stone wall, in the warm shade. Instantly I shut my eyes and attempted to recapture the white dress, the stairway, the brilliant room, but through my closed eyelids I saw only dancing points of sun. I stood up. I felt a new light-ness, as if something heavy had drained away. Call it a dream, call it a drowsy sun-vision on a lazy summer day, but it had come to me from up there, it was mine. I spent the rest of the day walking to the far ends of the Place, in search of a white dress that I knew did not exist, though I also knew that the Place had somehow summoned it. It had me now. It had me. Before I left, I carefully examined the end of my wall, where I knew there would be no stairway. Only a few fallen stones among dusty blades of grass, only a yellow wildflower, and a heavy bee hovering above a blossom of clover.

10

We call them the Halfway Climbers. These are the ones who begin the ascent but stop partway, attracted by the wooden benches placed along the paths, or by the small clearings that invite repose. There they sit down, enjoy the view, perhaps take out a small bottle of energy drink concealed in their clothes. Sometimes they spread out towels in the sun, lie down, and close their eyes; sometimes they read the paper or watch their children wade in a stream. After a while they may move farther up to another bench, another clearing, a bet-ter view. But they do not climb to the top, and the time always comes when they decide they've had enough, and so they return to their cars and drive home. The question we have about the Halfway Climbers is this: Why do they come at all? To be fair, the views along the way are very fine; on a clear day, you can pick out many buildings in our miniature town and look out at the distant villages and hills. But not far above is the Place itself, the very reason to come at all. The Half-way Climbers know that the Place is there, just at the top of the trail. Why do they stop? Can it be that their only desire is to move toward the Place without actually reaching it? It's tempting to think of the

Halfway Climbers as lazy, but this is unlikely to be true, since many of them walk most of the way up and often pass us with vigorous strides. Is it possible that the Place frightens them in some way? Do they fear a change in themselves that they can't bear to face? Perhaps what they want is only to escape from the town for a short time but not to arrive anywhere else, since to arrive might be to weaken their connection to the town—a connection that escape only strengthens. Another explanation is possible. Do they hope for so much from the Place that, filled with doubt, they refuse to climb all the way, in order to avoid disillusionment? They interest us, these Halfway Climbers. Almost to arrive, almost to experience what is tempting and unimaginable—for them, is it really enough?

11

In senior year of high school I fell in love with Diane DeCarlo. I knew it was love because I didn't only want to touch and be touched by her all over our bodies, I wanted to touch and be touched by her all over our minds. Sometimes I thought of her as a sunny house I wanted to move into for the rest of my life. We read our favorite children's books to each other, explored each other's attics, sneaked into each other's houses at night. Mostly we laughed and went driving around together in my father's car. One day I took her up to the Place. I'd been going up a lot since Dan Rivers moved away, and though I never saw the lady in white again I felt good up there, as if I could get rid of something for a while. I wanted Diane to see the Place with me, the way I wanted her to see my room, my body, my childhood bear with the missing arm. It was a sunny day in spring, one of those days that make you want to burst out laughing, because it looks as if it's trying too hard to imitate your idea of a perfect spring day. As we climbed the path, she was taking it all in—the green fields, the wildflowers, a light green grasshopper on a dark green bench. We were holding hands, swinging our arms. When we reached the top she closed her eyes and raised her face to the sun, her cheeks shining in the light as if they were wet. "I love it up here," she said, and gave me one of her tender, playful looks. "What's wrong?" she said. I remembered the time I'd come up to the Place with my mother, but things were now reversed: I saw in Diane's eyes the look that must have been mine as a child, when my mother did not give me her attention. "Nothing," I said. I understood what a fool I'd been, inviting her up here, where she craved intimacy and I wanted—but who knew what I wanted? I knew only that the Place was not for holding hands and staring out together at pretty views. I felt angry at myself, and angry at the Place, and sorry for her. Under the blue sky we walked uneasily side by side, sat down on one of the walls, looked about. We returned to the car in silence. I continued seeing Diane after that, but I never took her back to the Place, and we broke up two weeks before graduation.

12

Some call it the Great Revulsion. That's when you suddenly turn against the Place, for no reason you can understand. The stone walls seem to give you a hostile stare; the sky is a hand pushing against your neck. In the stillness you can almost hear voices calling to you from the town. And so you hurry back to the world below, where you laugh with friends, drive out with your wife and kids to the picnic tables at Burrows Park, plan vacations to the seashore. You can't understand why you ever wasted your precious time at the dead top of a boring hill, while life was swirling down below. Sometimes you forget the Place for a month, for a year. But a time comes when the town begins to irritate you with its familiar roof slopes, its clatter of cups on café tables on Main Street, its shimmering water-jets from lawn sprinklers, its creaking porch gliders. Then you remember the Place, up there, away from it all, and you are shaken: by remorse, by longing, by gratitude.

13

Because the Place is owned by our town, maintained by the Parks and Recreation Department, and paid for by our taxes, it is not surprising that voices are regularly raised in favor of a different use of the land. The Town Board is repeatedly asked to consider business proposals from local groups and outside developers eager to convert the Place to profitable use. One of the more popular plans is for a six-story hotel, with spacious balconies, a farm-to-table menu, and an outdoor café open to the public. Other development projects include a thirty-two-unit town-house-style apartment complex, a private school for girls, a family-owned restaurant with an Irish pub, an assisted-living facility, a recreation center with weight rooms and indoor pools, and a medical building specializing in dementia care. All proposals are presented for voting at town meetings held throughout the year. Those of us who defend the Place against business designs that are clear, well thought out, and of undeniable financial advantage to the town are often hard put to say what it is about the Place that makes us want to maintain it in its unprofitable state.

14

In college I hurled myself into books and friendships as if I had only a few months left to live. I took up fencing, joined the debating club, stayed up till five in the morning arguing about whether happiness is the true goal of human life. I spent the summers at home, working odd jobs and visiting college friends on weekends; I thought of

going up to the Place but somehow never got around to it. The Place
was like an old board game that I thought of fondly but no longer
played. At the same time, it represented a temptation that I needed
to resist: the temptation of falling back into a small-town adolescence
I longed to transcend. After college I returned home for the summer,
during which I prepared my résumé and interviewed for jobs that I
thought of as experiments, while I waited to discover my real work,
whatever that might be. When I was hired as an entry-level paralegal
in a medical malpractice law firm located in a city two hours away,
I began making trips to search for an apartment. On the day before
I left home, I drove over to the hill. I had been saying my goodbyes,
and I suppose this was another. As I walked up the path under the
August sun, I asked myself what I thought I was doing. At the top I
looked around. Except for a slatted metal bench that had replaced
one of the old wooden ones, nothing had changed. It struck me that
each blade of grass was in the precise position it had held when
I had last been here. That was in the summer before college, when I
worked at one of the concession stands at the South Side Rec Field,
went swimming at Indian Lake with friends, and mostly stayed away
from the Place, with its memories of Diane DeCarlo. I'd last gone
up at summer's end and stared hard, as at something already slipping
away. Now I walked about, gazed down at the town, sat against a wall,
where the edges of stones pushed into my back, and quickly stood
up. I could feel myself waiting for something, without knowing what
it was. I glared at the grassy slopes, the distant hills, as if I expected
them to speak aloud. And an impatience came over me. Why had I
come here? I was starting a new life. This was the old life, the time
of childhood birthday parties and family picnics in the park and Dan
Rivers and Diane DeCarlo. I remembered the white dress, the blazing room, but that was only a summer dream. The Place held nothing for me; I was so filled with the future that I was barely in a place
at all. Still I waited, demanding that the Place give me something,
anything—whatever it was I had come for. I felt like bursting into

wild laughter, like crouching down and pounding the ground with my fists. I opened my mouth, as if to shout. Then I glanced at my watch and turned back toward the car.

15

Some people say that the Place is the realm of the spirit, as opposed to the realm of the body. Down below, we feed and clothe our bodies, we work at our jobs, we eat and marry and die. Up above, where our bodies are freed from worldly concerns, our spirits can flourish unimpeded, as we enter a place of contemplation, serenity, and quiet exaltation. This explanation, attractive to those who welcome the Place as a spiritual retreat, as well as to those who ignore the Place but accept that it may be of value to others, is not convincing. One of the pleasures of the Place is the sheer delight our bodies feel, high above the strains and tensions of the town below. The air, fresher and cleaner, is drawn deeply into the lungs, the way a thirsty throat receives cool water; the body is invigorated, filled with an energy that feels nourishing rather than restless. At the same time, it's surely a mistake to think of the town as occupied solely with material things. Down there is where we read, think, go to school, attend piano recitals, make moral choices, experience the ecstasy we call love. If the Place is where we leave the town-world for something else, then we leave all of it, including our most cherished adventures of the spirit. What the Place invites is a withdrawal from all human things—a withdrawal that is like a surrender.

16

On her thirtieth birthday, Lucy Wheeler stood in her sunny-and-shady backyard surrounded by friends and family, who were laughing and telling stories and walking about with glasses of wine and paper plates of shrimp and barbecued chicken, she was looking at the red and yellow balloons her husband had tied to the branches of the old sugar maple, and half-closing her eyes she felt the happiness of her life flowing through her like sunlight through wine. At the same time she had the sensation that she was standing a little apart from herself, watching Lucy Wheeler as she stood there with a flush of happiness on her face, a striking face with its almost dark eyebrows and its rich blond hair pulled loosely back. She had been having these little moments of self-separation lately, these rifts, as she liked to call them, and now, as she stood among her friends and felt her happiness streaming through her, she had a sudden desire to leave herself standing there and walk away, out of the yard, out of her life, a desire so sharp that it made her look around quickly, as if she were afraid that something hard and cold had appeared in her face. The next day, when her husband was at the office and her children were at Jody Gelber's house for the afternoon, Lucy Wheeler drove out to the Place. She had climbed up there once with her husband when she'd moved to our town six years ago, and she had admired the view. Now she stood alone at the top of a rise and felt something fall away from her. She remained standing there for a while and was startled to see on her watch that three hours had passed. She'd forgotten the kids, already her husband was on his way home, she still had to pick up some chicken breasts for dinner. She began driving over to the Place every day, after arranging for friends to care for the children. At night she would wake up at four in the morning, longing for the moment when she could return. At dinner she caught her daughter looking at her. "Is everything all right?" her husband asked one evening, and for a moment she did not remember who he was. One Saturday she drove out to the Place and stayed until the sun was setting behind the distant hills. At home she felt guilty, apologetic, defiant. A week later she stayed beyond sunset, beyond closing time. She wanted to watch the darkening of the sky, the fullness of night. She lay on her back on a low slope below one of the walls. When she heard a car driving up from the trailhead, she understood that someone was coming for her, and she thought of hiding, but what was the point. She heard the footsteps and saw the dark policeman drawing near. She thought: I am so happy. Is there something wrong with me? She thought: Now my life will never be the same.

17

After six years in the city, during which I met my wife, completed a law degree, and went to work in the legal department of City Hall, I moved back to my old town in order to raise a family. I had never thought of myself as the kind of person who would move back to his old town, but there I was, in a house with a porch on a shady street in a good school district. I worked in a local family-practice law firm specializing in mediation, divorce, and child support, and later was able to set up my own practice. We entered a life of backyard cook-outs, neighborhood block parties, day care, ballet lessons, baseball practice, family vacations at a camp on a lake. I was in love with my wife, my family, my work. Smiles burst from me like breaths. One summer afternoon the two of us, Lily and I, drove out to the Place, where we sat on a bench and held hands as we looked down at the town. A week later I returned alone. I hadn't been up there by myself for ten years, and I don't know what it was I expected, now that I was done thinking of myself as a son and a student, but it was as if I wanted to set something right. The memory of my failed visit burned in me. I saw that I had done everything wrong that day—I had made demands on the Place, as though it owed me something. This time I asked for nothing. I merely wanted to get away from the town, for a while. Though the weather was warm, the sky was filling with dark clouds. I walked along the stone walls, under the stormy sky; down below, in the distance, I could see rain falling in slanted lines beside a burst of sun. I became aware of a sensation that was almost physical: a tightness, an inner thickness, was passing out of me. I glanced at my hands, as if I expected to see something flowing from my fingers. I sat down against a wall. I could feel my back against the stone, my legs against the ground. It's difficult to say what I felt next. I'm tempted to call it a contentment, a deep peacefulness, but it was more powerful than that—it was like a dissolution, an unknitting of whatever it was I was. I was the stone in the wall, I was the grass in the field, I was the honeybee hovering above the blossom of clover, I was all, I was nothing at all. When the rain came, I remained sitting there. I could feel the water streaming down my face, beating against my shirt, blurring my edges, slanting through me.

18

There are those who do not like the Place. They point to extreme cases, such as that of Lucy Wheeler, as well as to many lesser instances of confusion, emotional disturbance, and psychic turmoil. The Place, they say, is a force of destruction, which undermines our town by drawing us away from healthy pursuits into a world of sickly dreaming. Many who defend the Place against such charges argue that it produces beneficial, life-enhancing effects, which are not only valuable in themselves but useful in strengthening the health of the town. Others insist that the terms of attack are false: life in our town is not by definition healthy, and events associated with the Place are in no sense sickly. Still others argue that the Place is an essential feature of the town, for without it the town would lack awareness of itself and, in that sense, would no longer be human. For those of us who welcome the Place but don't claim to have penetrated its mystery, the arguments of its enemies are of special value. We ponder them, we

develop subtle refinements and variations of our own, we do everything in our power to strengthen the case against ourselves, in an
effort to lay bare what is hidden from us.

19

   I was standing in a large hall, filled with people who looked like
bizarre versions of themselves. Or more exactly: they looked like teenagers who had dressed up playfully, using a great deal of makeup and
their parents' clothes, in order to present to the world the older selves
they imagined they would one day become. I had never attended a
high-school reunion before. I'd planned not to attend this one, the
fortieth, but at the last moment I yielded to an unexpected impulse of
curiosity. As I stood trying to decide between two drinks that matched
our school colors, I wondered whether I, too, resembled an unconvincing performer of myself, and at that moment I happened to see,
standing some ten feet away, Dan Rivers. He was looking directly at
me. I recognized him at once—the same eyebrows, the same quick
smile, the same ease in his body. Not entirely the same, of course;
but it was as though his features and gestures had settled into a more
complete and unshakeable version of themselves. "I was hoping,"
he said, coming up to me and reaching out both hands. "It's been a
while." "If forty years is a while," I said, taking his hands, larger than I
remembered but still lean and tight. "I kept meaning to get in touch,"
he said, "but, you know"—and there it was, that slow, one-shoulder
shrug. "But now," he said, "we can do some catching up." We fell into
the old easy talk, two seventeen-year-old boys in the bodies of aging
men. Dan Rivers was married, with two kids; he was an architect; he
had designed dams and bridges. At some point I asked whether he'd
ever gone back to visit the Place. I suppose I wondered whether he
remembered. "Oh that," he said, with his boyish laugh. "Of course I

remember it—junior year. That phase I went through. My son used to play fantasy games on his PC six hours a day. It all works itself out." We talked family, travel, the cost of college. When I suggested he come over to the house, he looked at me with genuine distress. "I'd love to—but I've got to get back home. A conference. I was lucky to get away at all. But next time—next time—absolutely." "Absolutely," I said. He gave me a warm, long look. "I'm glad we met up," he said. Someone was tugging at his arm. "Is it Emily?" he cried. "I can't believe it!" "Hi, Emily," I said. "Has it really been forty years?" she said. "It seems like yesterday."

20

Some claim that the invigorating effects of the Place derive from natural causes. The fresh air, free from the fumes emitted by cars, buses, utility vehicles, lawn mowers, gas-powered edgers and trimmers, and the old smokestacks of the electric plant two towns over, contains more oxygen than the air below; the increase of oxygen to the brain facilitates the release of neurotransmitters that promote a sense of happiness and well-being. In addition, each breath of air strengthens the immune system, increases energy, and sharpens the ability to think clearly, while the abundance of natural light stimulates the body's manufacture of vitamin D, which improves bone density and helps maintain hormone balance. Although no one denies the benefits of fresh air and sunlight, those of us who support the Place for other reasons are not fond of the Argument from Nature. Its immediate flaw is that it fails to distinguish the Place from any other elevated rural spot. Its more serious flaw is that it attempts to domesticate the Place, to tame it down, to lower it to the level of the town. The Place becomes an open-air health facility, a rival of the new gym on Auburn Avenue. But the Place, for those of us who try to grasp its meaning, is not an extension of the town. It is what the town is not. It is the shedding of the town, the annihilation of the town. It is the un-town.

21

   Not long ago I went up to the Place and sat on a warm bench, from which I could look down on the little town. In the clear air I was able to see the construction site where the new condos are going up and the nearly completed parking garage on North Main. I thought: Now you've become one of the bench-people, coming up for the view. But in fact I was only resting, after the long climb. My legs are still strong, but my heart has taken to pounding on uphill walks—it's the sort of thing Lily would have urged me to see a doctor about. But all I need is a little rest, before continuing on my way. After a while I got up from my bench and took a walk along the familiar walls, stopping to feel the heat of the upper stones that faced the sun. I asked nothing of the Place. I wanted only to get away from the town, where the edges of houses had begun to glitter like knife blades. And I suppose I'd been thinking of all the recent talk about taking down the stone walls, filling up the dips and hollows, and turning the level land into a high-tech business park, a change that would create scores of jobs and drive property values sky-high. Ever since my wife's passing, my son, a lawyer himself, has been urging me to sell the house and move into assisted living, but I'm used to the way the light falls in every room and have no desire to leave. In the warm sun I slowly climbed a slope. I could feel my heart starting to pound again. When I came to a wall at the top, I saw, in a field on the other side, a woman in a white dress. She was facing the other way. And I was moved, deeply moved, that she had come back to me, after all these years. I was not surprised that she had remained young, as though no time had passed since I was a boy of seventeen. For all I knew, I was still sitting against that wall, with my eyes half closed, waiting for my life to begin. The young woman wore no hat. Her hair, light brown, fell halfway down her back, and she stood with one foot slightly turned in and one hand holding the elbow of her other arm. A moment later I realized that she was a friend's daughter from town, standing there with a white pocketbook over her shoulder. She must have come up as I had. She did not see me watching, and I turned away, so as not to disturb her. The sight of the girl in white soothed and excited me, as if I had been given the gift of witnessing the past and seeing the future. From a nearby wall a shiny black grackle, shimmering with purple, rose suddenly into the air.

2 2

Those who think they know us have sometimes called us the Discontents. At any moment, they say, we will leave our backyards and porches and living room couches, we will rise from our restaurant tables, put down our lawn mowers and garden hoses, abandon our families and friends, and head out to the Place. We will park at one of the lots and climb a winding trail, sometimes resting along the way, until we have reached the top. But scarcely have we come to the fields and stone walls when we are seized by a desire to return to the town below, with its softball games and ATM machines and outdoor barbecues. Restlessly we move back and forth between the two worlds, never satisfied, never at rest. To such arguments we make no reply. We are tempted to say: And you? Are you so pleased with yourselves? Or even: Rest is for the dead. Instead we continue to pass back and forth between the town and the Place, in a rhythm that feels more necessary than restfulness. To have one without the other would seem to us a deprivation, even a punishment. The weight of the town would sooner or later drag us down; the lightness of the Place would release us into empty air. Far better to pass between the two, leaving behind the streets of the town to seek the moment of letting go, leaving the heights to return to the satisfying tug of things. There are those who argue that the town and the Place are nothing but outward and visible signs of an inward and invisible truth: the town and the Place, they insist, lie within. To this I can say only that I do not understand such things. For me, it's a matter of waiting for the time to come. Then I know that I must leave the town and drive out to the hill. You might say that I go up to the Place only in order to come down again, or that I go down to the town only in order to return to the Place. It may be so. That's for others to decide. But if you want to know more about it, it's best to see for yourself. Come. It's easy enough to find us. We're right here. Come for the day. You can have lunch in one of our out-door cafés, where you can watch the tourists passing by. You can take a stroll along Main Street, stopping to look into a shop or two. Then it's time to set out for the hill. You'll pass the car dealerships, and the red-roofed buildings of the retirement community, and the mall and the outdoor shopping plaza, before reaching the woods. On the other side, you can drive partway up the hill and park in one of the lots. Get out and have a look around. Start up a trail. You can rest along the way, if you like. There's no hurry. It isn't far. Come.

HOME RUN

B ottom of the ninth, two out, game tied, runners at the corners, the count full on McCluskey, the fans on their feet, this place is going wild, outfield shaded in to guard against the blooper, pitcher looks in, shakes off the sign, a big lead off first, they're not holding him on, only run that matters is the man dancing off third, shakes off another sign, McCluskey asking for time, steps out of the box, tugs up his batter's glove, knocks dirt from his spikes, it's a cat 'n' mouse game, break up his rhythm, make him wait, now the big guy's back in the box, down in his crouch, the tall lefty toes the rubber, looks in, gives the nod, will he go with the breaking ball, maybe thinking slider, third baseman back a step, catcher sets up inside, pitcher taking his time, very deliberate out there, now he's ready, the set, the kick, he deals, it's a fastball, straight down the pipe, McCluskey swings, a tremendous rip, he crushes it, the crowd is screaming, the center fielder back, back, angling toward right, tons of room out there in no-man's-land, still going back, he's at the track, that ball is going, going, he's at the wall, looking up, that ball is gone, see ya, hasta la vista baby, McCluskey goes yard, over the 390-foot mark in right center, game over, he creamed it, that baby is gone and she ain't comin back anytime soon, sayonara, the crowd yelling, the ball still carry-

ing, the stands going crazy, McCluskey rounding second, the ball still
up there, way up there, high over the right-center-field bleachers,
headed for the upper deck, talk about a tape-measure shot, another
M-bomb from the Big M, been doing it all year, he's rounding third,
ball still going, still going, that ball was smoked, a no doubter, wait a
minute wait a minute oh oh oh it's outta here, that ball is out of the
park, cleared the upper deck, up over the Budweiser sign, Jimmy can
you get me figures on that, he hammered it clean outta here, got all
of it, can you believe it, an out-of-the-parker, hot diggity, slammed it
a country mile, the big guy's crossing the plate, team's all over him,
the crowd roaring, what's that Jimmy, Jimmy are you sure, I'm being
told it's a first, that's right a first, no one's ever socked one out before,
the Clusker really got around on it, looking fastball all the way, got
the sweet part of the bat on it, launched a rocket, oh baby did he
scald it, I mean he drilled it, the big guy is strong but it's that smooth
swing of his, the King of Swing, puts his whole body into it, hits with
his legs, he smashed it, a Cooperstown clout, right on the screws, the
ball still going, unbelievable, up past the Goodyear blimp, see ya later
alligator, up into the wild blue yonder, still going, ain't nothing gonna
stop that baby, they're walking McCluskey back to the dugout, fans
swarming all over the field, they're pointing up at the sky, the ball still
traveling, up real high, that ball is way way outta here, Jimmy what
have you got, going, going, hold on, what's that Jimmy, I'm told the
ball has gone all the way through the troposphere, is that a fact, now
how about that, the big guy hit it a ton, really skyed it, up there now
in the stratosphere, good golly Miss Molly, help me out here Jimmy,
stratosphere starts at six miles and goes up 170,000 feet, man did he
ever jack it outta here, a dinger from McSwinger, a whopper from
the Big Bopper, going, going, the stands emptying out, the ball up in
the mesosphere, the big guy blistered it, he powdered it, the ground
crew picking up bottles and paper cups and peanut shells and hot dog
wrappers, power-washing the seats, you can bet people'll be talking

about this one for a long time to come, he plastered that ball, a pitch right down Broadway, tried to paint the inside corner but missed his spot, you don't want to let the big guy extend those arms, up now in the exosphere, way up there, never seen anything like it, the ball carrying well all day but who would've thought, wait a minute, hold on a second, holy cow it's left the earth's atmosphere, so long it's been good ta know ya, up there now in outer space, I mean that ball is outta here, bye bye birdie, still going, down here at the park the stands are empty, sun gone down, moon's up, nearly full, it's a beautiful night, temperature seventy-three, another day game tomorrow then out to the West Coast for a tough three-game series, the ball still going, looks like she's headed for the moon, talk about a moon shot, man did he ever paste it outta here, higher, deeper, going, going, it's gone past the moon, you can kiss that baby goodbye, good night Irene I'll see you in my dreams, the big guy got good wood on it, right on the money, swinging for the downs, the ball still traveling, sailing past Mars, up through the asteroid belt, you gotta love it, past Jupiter, see ya Saturn, so long Uranus, arrivederci Neptune, up there now in the Milky Way, a round-tripper to the Big Dipper, a galaxy shot, a black-hole blast, how many stars are we talking about Jimmy, Jimmy says two hundred billion, that's two hundred billion stars in the Milky Way, a nickel for every star and you can stop worrying about your 401(k), the ball still traveling, out past the Milky Way and headed on into intergalactic space, hooo did he ever whack it, he shellacked it, a good season but came up short in the playoffs, McCluskey'll be back next year, the ball out past the Andromeda galaxy, going, going, the big guy mashed it, he clob-bobbered it, wham-bam-a-rammed it, he's looking good in spring training, back with that sweet swing, out past the Virgo supercluster with its thousands of galaxies, that ball was spanked, a Big Bang for the record book, a four-bagger with swagger, out past the Hydra-Centaurus supercluster, still going, out past the Aquarius supercluster, thousands and millions of superclusters out there, McCluskey still remembers it, he's coaching down in Triple A, the big man a sensation in his day, the ball still out there, still climbing, sailing out toward the edge of the observable universe, the edge receding faster than the speed of light, the ball still going, still going, he remembers the feel of the wood in his hands, the good sound of it as he swung, smell of pine tar, bottom of the ninth, two on, two out, a summer day.

AMERICAN TALL TALE

Of Green Rain and Porcupine Combs;
of Hot Biscuit Slim and the Amazing Griddle

Let me tell you a story about Paul Bunyan. You've all heard a tale or two about Paul Bunyan. You know the kind of man Paul Bunyan was. He could out-run out-jump out-drink and out-shoot you. He could out-cuss out-brag out-punch and out-piss you. He could swing that ax of his so hard, the wind it made would blow the needles clean off all the pine trees in ten acres of good timberland. Those pine needles, they'd come raining down for days. There never was a logging man could swing an ax like Paul Bunyan. Work! Why, he'd leap out of his bunk before the sun was up, jump into his greased boots, and finish buttoning up his mackinaw before his eyes were done opening. He'd step outside and pluck up a pine tree to brush his beard. Comb his hair with a porcupine. Then over to the cookhouse while his men were snoring away like a plague of mosquitoes and Hot Biscuit Slim standing there waiting at the griddle. You've heard about Paul Bunyan's griddle. That griddle was so big that to grease it you had to have three men skating on it with chunks of bacon fat strapped to their boot soles. Paul Bunyan would swallow those hotcakes whole.

He'd wash them down with a keg of molasses. He'd swallow so many hotcakes that if you laid them end to end they'd stretch clear across Minnesota, and that was before he got serious. After that he'd drink down two kettles of black coffee and a barrel of cider and head out to the woods. You never saw a man like Paul Bunyan for laying down timber. He'd swing that ax so hard the blade would cut through a white pine high as a hill and wide as a barn and just keep going. Time his swing was done he'd have two hundred trees laid out at his feet. He could log off twenty acres of good pine forest before lunch. Meantime the swampers would be cutting trails to the riverbanks, the limbers'd be chopping off branches, the sawyers cutting the pines into hundred-foot logs, and the hitchers hitching the logs to Babe the Blue Ox, who'd snake them over the trails to the riverbank landings. A forest never did stand a chance against Paul Bunyan. You know what they say about North Dakota. Used to be all timber till Paul and his shanty boys came by. They cut their way from Maine to Michigan and from Michigan to Wisconsin and from Wisconsin clear on over to Minnesota. They sawed their way from Minnesota through both Dakotas and on into Montana, swamping and chopping and limbing like men on fire. There never was anything like it. You know all that. You've heard the stories. But there's one story you might not have heard. You might not have heard the one about Paul Bunyan's brother.

In Which I Tell You About Paul Bunyan's Brother

Paul Bunyan never talked about his brother, and no wonder. That do-nothing dreamer drove Paul wild. Just the look of him was enough to set a logging man's teeth on edge. He had Paul's height all right, but that was all he had. He was the skinniest man alive enough to move. He was so skinny the sun couldn't figure out how to lay down his shadow and gave up trying. He was so skinny and scrawny that when he turned sideways all you could see was the end of his nose. He was a slump-shouldered knob-kneed stick-shanked droop-reared string-necked pole-armed shuffling husk of a man, with shambly shovel-feet that went in two different directions. His shoulders were so narrow he had to loop his red suspenders around his scraggy neck to keep his saggy pants from falling off. His knees were so knobby, when he walked it sounded like cookhouse spoons banging in tin bowls. But worse than the broomsticky look of him, this poor excuse for a mother's son was so lie-around lazy he made a dead dog look lively. He'd get up so late in the day it was time to go back to bed again. And what did this drowsy loafer like to do when he dragged himself out of bed slower than a log rolling uphill? Not one thing. He was so lazy it took him two days just to scratch the side of his head. He was so dawdly it took him six days just to finish a yawn. He was so loafy that when he blinked his eyes during a lightning storm, by the time he unblinked them the sun was shining. This spindly splintery slivery slip of a half-dead half-man didn't eat enough in two days to feed a starving spider. If he found an old green pea at the back of a cupboard he'd cut it up into seven pieces and have enough dinner to last a week. If he found a crumb on the table he'd break it in half and wonder which half to have for lunch. And when he wasn't spending his time eating nothing and doing less, you'd find this skin-and-bonesman bent over some book like a hungry man leaning over a haunch of venison. Books! Why, you've never seen such a heap of books as that string-bean snooze-man had. There were books in the cupboards and books spilling out of the sink. There were slippery stacks of books on chair seats and books on the bedcovers and piles of books sticking up so wobbly high you couldn't see out the windows. You couldn't walk in that house without books falling down around you like shot ducks. And when he was done blinking over his books, do you think that slumpy dozer would rouse himself to do a decent day's work? Not likely. Next thing you knew, he'd be taking a walk in the woods with his hands in his pockets just as cool as you please or sitting under a tree staring off at a sunbeam on a tree root or a moonbeam on a pond. If you asked him what in thunderation was he doing sitting under that tree, he'd look at you like maybe he'd seen a human being before but couldn't be sure of it just yet. Then he'd say: Just dreaming. Dreaming! That James Bunyan never drank whiskey, never put a plug of Starr tobacco in his cheek, never spat a sweet stream of tobacco juice over the rail of a porch, never shot a possum or cut open a rabbit or skinned a deer. He didn't know a pike pole from an ax helve. He couldn't tell you how to shoe a draft horse or fix a split spoke in a wagon wheel. And yet this slope-backed dreamer, this walking cornstalk, this drift-about bone-bag and slouchy idler was brother to Paul Bunyan, who could tie a rope around a twisty river and straighten it out with one mighty pull.

How the Great Contest Got Its Start

Now, whatever you may say about Paul Bunyan, with his strut and his swagger and his great blue ox that measured forty-two ax handles and a plug of tobacco between the eyes, there was no denying he had his share of family feeling. Paul Bunyan felt duty-bound to visit that no-work all-play brother of his twice a year. That was once after the spring drive when the men rode the logs downriver to the mill and once near the start of the fall season. James Bunyan lived in a run-down house in the middle of whatever was left of the Northeast Woods, up in Maine. Paul would leave things in the hands of Johnny Inkslinger or Little Meery and go on over to the stable and give Babe the Blue Ox a good tickle behind his ears. Then he'd shoulder his ax and head out east. He'd start out fast with those mighty strides of his, one foot splashing down in the middle of Lake Michigan and the other making waves on the shore of Lake Huron, but the closer he got to Maine the slower he moved, cause the last man on earth he wanted to see was that leave-me-be brother of his. Well now, on this visit that I'm going to tell you about, he arrived on a fine September afternoon with the sun shining and the birds chirp-chirping and not a cloud in the sky. He found that joke of a brother of his flat on his back in bed just opening his eyes to take a look around. So there was James Bunyan lying there looking up at his brother Paul standing over him like the biggest pine tree you ever saw, and there was Paul Bunyan looking down at his brother James lying there like a long piece of rope nobody had any use for, and each one thinking he'd rather be standing up to his neck in a swamp with the rain coming down and the water rising than be there looking each other over like two roosters in a henhouse. Not a one of them could think of anything to say. How's Ma. How's Pa. That's good. Paul was just standing there fidgeting and squidgeting and eyeing the books and the apple cores lying all over the bedcovers and a boot on the chair and a shirtsleeve sticking out from under the bed, and he's burning for his neat bunkhouse with the rows of bunks against the walls and the washbowls with their pitchers all in a row and the boots at the bottoms of the beds. You get up now, Paul says, and I'll find somethin to eat. But in the kitchen all he could find was the other boot in the sink, a raccoon on the table, and nothing to eat but a bunch of dried-out berries and a jug of sour cider. In the front room his brother and him sat down to talk, but there was no more to talk about than there ever was. Paul told him about the spring drive down the river when Febold Feboldson fell off a log and was picked out of the rapids by the hook of a peavey, and he told him about the good timber to be had out in Oregon, and James listened with a look on his face like a man who can't make up his mind whether to close his eyes and take a quick nap or open his mouth and take a slow yawn. The more Paul talked, the more James said nothing, till Paul couldn't stand it no more and said I don't see how a man can live like this and James said It suits me fine and before you know it Paul was shouting Why don't you make somethin of yourself instead of lyin around all day like a dog doin nothin and James was saying I'd rather lie around all day like a dog doing nothing than spend my time killing off good trees that weren't doing anybody a bit of harm and that got Paul so mad he said I can out-run out-jump out-drink and out-shoot you and I can out-chop out-cut out-saw and out-swamp you and James said Maybe you can out-run out-jump out-drink and out-shoot me and maybe you can out-roar out-scream out-howl and out-shout me but there's one thing you can never do not if you live five hundred years and that's out-sleep me. Well now, Paul had never heard words the like of that coming out of his brother's mouth before. And when Paul heard those words coming out of his brother's mouth like a swarm of angry bees he didn't know whether to laugh till he cried at the sight of his bony brother challenging him like a man with muscle on him or cry till he laughed at the thought of himself Paul Bunyan taking up a challenge thrown out by that bloodless no-man brother of his. Then he said I can out-bash out-gash out-mash and out-smash you and there's one other thing I can do more than anyone ever can and that's out-sleep you. So that was how the Great Sleeping Contest got its start.

The Biggest Bed That Ever Was

Well now, first thing Paul Bunyan did when he got back to camp was step into his bunkhouse and give a good look at his bed. That bed of his was so long that when it was morning at one end it was midnight at the other. That bed of his was so wide, Johnny Inkslinger once reached the middle of it riding a fast horse all day. Paul Bunyan took a look at that bed and knew it wasn't a bad bed as beds go, a little cramped maybe, good enough to lie down in for thirty-nine winks before you jumped back to work, but there were bunks all up and down the other wall with men snoring and grunting and talking in their sleep, and sometimes old Babe would stick his head in through a bunkhouse window and lick Paul awake. What he needed was a bed set off by itself somewhere, a bed where a man could settle in for a good long sleep and turn over any which way he pleased and not wake himself up. The more he thought about it, the more he knew what he had to do. So he hitched up Babe to a supply wagon and headed out to Iowa. You know what they say about Iowa. In Iowa the corn grows so tall it takes one man to see halfway up the stalk and another man to see the rest of the way. In Iowa the corn grows so tall you find hawks and eagles building nests up near the top. They say those Iowa cornstalks grow so wide, the farmers have to hire loggers from the Michigan woods to chop everything down and haul it all off to the silos. They say there's so much corn growing in Iowa, if you want to lift up your arm to scratch your nose you have to cross over into Nebraska. Now, what Paul did was this. He hired himself out to harvest half the corn in Iowa. He and big Babe tramped right into the middle of that Iowa corn. Paul swung his ax and stalks began falling so fast and hard the ears popped right out of the husks and landed smack in the wagon. Paul hauled the ears over to the silos and loaded up the stalks in the wagon till the sides creaked with the weight of it. He spit out some tobacco juice and headed out of Iowa by way of Nebraska and then Colorado and made it down to Arizona before the tobacco juice hit the ground. He went on over to the Grand Canyon and looked down into it. You know the story of the Grand Canyon. That was back when Paul Bunyan was traveling west and dragged his peavey behind him. The hook of the peavey is what dug up that canyon. Now, what Paul did there on the rim was this. He tipped his wagon over and watched those cornstalks go crashing down. The cornstalks spread out over the canyon bottom and rose halfway up the cliffs. Paul liked what he saw but he wasn't done yet, not by a long shot.

That layer of cornstalks made a pretty good mattress for a man of his size, but it was scratchy as a pack of alley cats. He stood on the rim of the canyon looking down and thinking hard. Just then a big flock of geese came flying over and Paul got himself an idea. He sucked in his breath till his chest looked like a mainsail in a storm. He raised his face to the sky and blew so hard you could see the sun flicker and almost go out. That big breath of his blew all the feathers off those geese. The feathers came floating down nice and soft and settled over the cornstalks. When another flock flew by, Paul puffed himself up and gave another blow. He kept blowing feathers off so many geese, by the time he was done he had himself a thick cover of feathers laying all over the cornstalks like a big quilt you could slip inside of and keep warm. Only thing missing was a pillow. So Paul, he traveled back to camp and ordered some of his boys to buy up five thousand head of good merino sheep. You know those ranches out in Montana and Utah where they have so many sheep you can take off your shoes and walk river to river on sheepback. Well, while his men were off buying up sheep, Paul set about clearing the stumps from fifty acres of logged-off woods. How he did it was this. He walked along and stomped those stumps into the ground one after the other with one stamp of his boot till they were all set even with the dirt. Soon as the boys came back with the sheep, Paul drove every last one of those merinos onto his cleared-off land. He sharpens two axes and sets the handles in the ground with the ax blades facing each other. Then he sets up two more axes with the blades facing each other only lower down. Then what he does, he runs the sheep between those double axes so you have strips of fleece dropping off on both sides clean as a whistle. That was the first sheep-shearing machine. He loaded up the sheared-off wool in his wagon and headed back down to the Grand Canyon. He lifted out those strips of wool and laid them down along one end of his goose-feather quilt and had himself a pillow so fine and soft that before he was done, three ringtail cats, two mountain lions, and a mule deer lay curled up on it fast asleep.

Up in Maine

While Paul was blowing a storm of feathers down from the sky and running merino sheep through his four-ax shearer, that droopy drag-foot brother of his was spending his time sitting slumped on his backbone in a broke-legged armchair next to a spiderwebby window or leaf-shuffling his sloggy way along a soggy path in the woods with three floppy mufflers wrapped around his stretchy neck and a beat-up book sticking out of his peacoat pocket.

In Which Paul Shoulders His Ax and Sets Off

The Great Sleeping Contest was set to begin a good month into the fall season, first night of October at nine sharp. To keep things fair, Paul went and hired up a crew of sleep-checkers to work three-hour shifts keeping an eye on each dead-to-the-world stone-faced snorer. You could twitch in your sleep and you could turn over in your sleep, you could groan in your sleep and moan in your sleep, but if you opened an eye so much as half a crack you were done sleeping. These sleep-checkers were shrewd-eyed rough-living no-nonsense men known for rock-hard character and knife-sharp sight—a couple of keelboatmen who worked the Ohio River, a buffalo hunter from Oklahoma, three Swede farmers from Minnesota, a Kentucky sharpshooter, two trail guides from the high Rockies, a frontiersman from Missouri, a cattle rancher from Texas, two Utah sheep ranchers, a Cheyenne Indian from Colorado, and two fur trappers from Tennessee. After a cookhouse dinner of thick pea soup and spiced ham baked in cider, Paul Bunyan stood up and addressed his shanty boys. He told them he could out-jump out-run out-fight and out-work any man who ever logged the north woods or walked the face of the earth in spiked boots and he was off to prove he could out-sleep out-nap out-snooze and out-doze any man big enough to brag and fool enough to try. Johnny Inkslinger would take over camp operations while he was away. Any trouble and Little Meery and Shot Gunderson would take care of it with four hard fists and a six-foot pike pole. Then Paul Bunyan said goodbye to his men and specially to Johnny Inkslinger and Little Meery and Hot Biscuit Slim and Big Ole the Blacksmith and Febold Feboldson and Shot Gunderson and Sourdough Sam and Shanty Boy and then he went over to the stable and gave old Babe a big hug around the neck and a big tickle behind his blue ears and set off walking with a swing in his stride and his ax over his shoulder. He stamped through forests and along river valleys, took one step over the Missouri River onto the plains of Nebraska, and dusted off his boots in Colorado. First thing he does in Arizona is pluck up a fifty-foot saguaro cactus to comb his beard. Gets to the Grand Canyon two minutes before nine. One minute before nine he's down on his crackly cornstalk bed. Went and laid himself out on his back and sank into those goose feathers with his feet up against a cliff and his head on his pillowy wallowy wool. He set his ax steel-down in the cornstalks with the hickory handle sticking up beside him, and right at nine sharp he shut his eyes and fell into a mighty sleep.

In Which James Gets Himself Ready

The day the Great Sleeping Contest is set to begin, the sun's going down in Maine and James Bunyan is dragging himself out of bed slower than a one-horned snail in an icehouse. He goes yawning his way into the creaky kitchen and looks around for anything to eat but all he can find is a dead mouse in a cupboard and one stale raisin in a box. He sits down on a three-leg chair at a tilty table with a hungry cat on it and looks at that dried-up raisin like it's a plate of bear stew served with brown beans baked in molasses. He sets to work slow on that wreck of a raisin and when he's done he's so stuffed he just sits there like a dead branch leaning against the side of a barn. He stares at his left hand so long it starts looking like a foot. He stares at his right foot so long it turns into a nose. He figures it's time to rest up after his exertions, so what he does, he goes back to his room and crawls into bed and stretches out on his bone-bumpy back with his hands behind his bootlace of a neck and his stringy legs crossed at his stalky ankles and looks at the ceiling beams jumpy with shadows thrown up by the candle on the bedside table. He sees blue horses riding over hills. The clock hand on the cracked old clock on the wall crawls over to nine slow as a cat on crutches. James closes his eyes and starts snoring.

How the Shanty Boys Spent the Night

Back at the camp the men swamped and felled and limbed from sun-up to noon. They sat on stumps to gulp down sourdough biscuits and black coffee brought over by wagon and went on logging till the sun dropped down. None of it was the same without Paul Bunyan. After the cookhouse dinner they swapped stories round the bunk-house stoves but they all of them knew they were just sitting there waiting. Paul Bunyan was the no-sleepingest man they'd ever seen. He'd throw himself down on his back and before his head hit the pil-low the rest of him would be standing up raring to go. Some said he was bound to come back before midnight, others said he was already back out there chopping in the dark. Little Meery said they ought to get themselves some rest cause he knew in his bones a man like Paul Bunyan wouldn't be back till next morning. Past midnight there was a crashing noise in Paul Bunyan's bunkhouse and the men sat up ready to yell out a cheer and dance him a welcome home but it wasn't anybody there but big Babe, busted out of the stable to knock his head through a bunkhouse window. All next day the men swamped and chopped and sawed but their hearts weren't in it. That night not a story got told round the bunkhouse stoves. The men stayed flat in their bunks with ears open wide as barn doors and eyes shut tight as friz oysters waiting for Paul Bunyan to come on back from his corn-stalk mattress and sheep pillow down there in that faraway canyon under the stars.

The Long Sleep

Johnny Inkslinger could push the men hard when he had to. He told them Paul Bunyan was bound to sleep for a week and they ought to stop dreaming about it and get to work. Why, a man like that could sleep two weeks, maybe three. Weeks passed, the first snow came. It snowed so hard you couldn't see the end of your ax. One day the sun came out, birds sang in the trees. The men drove the logs downriver to the mill and broke camp for the summer. In the fall they hitched the bunkhouses and the cookhouse and the stable to Babe the Blue Ox, who hauled the whole lot of it over hills and across rivers to a fir forest that grew so high the tops of the trees were hinged to let the moon go by. Nights they still talked about Paul Bunyan round the bunkhouse stoves, but it was like telling stories about someone who was long gone and maybe never had been there at all. Remember the winter of the blue snow? Member the time old Paul Bunyan walked across Minnesota and his boot prints were what formed the ten thousand lakes? Member the time Paul Bunyan dug that watering hole for Babe the Blue Ox? That watering hole is Lake Michigan. Then there was the time Paul Bunyan chopped a dog in half by mistake. Put it back together wrong, with two legs up and two legs down. Remember the hodag? The whirling whimpus? In the cold weather the men rose late and stopped work early. Johnny Inkslinger cussed and howled

but it was no use at all. Babe was so sad he stayed put in his stable
and wouldn't come out for anything. The men forgot all about him,
all except Hot Biscuit Slim, who brought barrels of hotcakes out to
the stable every morning. That winter the snow fell for forty-seven
days. Snow was so high you had to cut tunnels to get to the trees. The
trunks were hard as whetstones. When the axheads dragged against
them, the blades got so sharp they could cut a snowflake in half. Some
of the new men said they'd heard about Paul Bunyan, but it was so
cold their words froze in the air and didn't thaw out till spring. In
the warm weather the men drove the logs downriver to the mill, and
when it was over some of the crew went to work in the mill town and
didn't return to camp in the fall. Johnny Inkslinger moved the camp
to higher ground that looked out over miles of fresh spruce forest.
The men cut trails and felled trees and hauled them to the river landings. Snow howled down from black skies. In the warm nights the
men sat outside the bunkhouses, spitting tobacco juice into the fire.
Some said Paul Bunyan had gone to sleep down there in the Grand
Canyon and drowned when the river rose. Some said Paul Bunyan
was a story men used to tell at night around the bunkhouse stove.

In Which James Does Some Dreaming

While Paul Bunyan was sleeping the stony sleep of an ax-swinging
man dead to the world on his mighty bed, that no-account brother of
his was doing what he was always doing up in the woods in Maine:
dreaming his life away. There was nobody ever dreamed so much as
that dodge-life brother did. Dreamed all day on his bone-hard back-
side and dreamed all night on his brawnless back. Now he was nose-up
in his bed dreaming so many dreams you'd think his head would be
crackling like a pinewood fire in a bunkhouse stove. He dreamed he
was a fish swimming in a river. He dreamed he was flying through

the sky like a buzzard or a red-tailed hawk. He dreamed about things you weren't supposed to see, like what it was like walking around up in heaven with angels going by and what it was like far down under the earth where things looked at you in the dark. He dreamed he was red fire. He dreamed he was dead. He dreamed he was so big his brother Paul could stand on the flat of his hand with his little ax on his shoulder. He dreamed he was throwing fistfuls of pinecones into every state and great pine forests sprang up all over the land. Those trees grew so high they brushed up against the Big Dipper. There wasn't anything but trees every which way you looked. Towns and cities got swallowed up. Birds spoke words you could understand. People lived on riverbanks and grew what they needed. Bears and coyotes lay down with wild turkeys and deer. Loggers turned their axes into harmonicas. It was summer all the time. They say James Bunyan dreamed so hard it plumb wore him out and he had to go on sleeping just to keep himself alive enough to dream some more.

In Which the Great Contest Is Decided

You know the kind of man Paul Bunyan was. Once he set his mind on something, there was no stopping him. He slept down there in that canyon when it was so cold you could see ten-foot icicles hanging from his chin. He slept in that canyon when it was so hot, red rocks melted away in the sun. He slept with coyotes and bobcats curled up in his beard and two bald eagles nesting in his hair. He slept when howling winds sent boulders crashing down cliffsides right onto his bed and he slept when raindrops the size of McIntosh apples whipped against his face and soaked through his mackinaw. One day a strange thing happened. Paul Bunyan opened his eyes. Just like that. Up above him, a crowd of people standing on a rim trail pointed down and started shouting. Somebody called out, Ten years and twelve hours! Paul stood up so fast, goose feathers flew all around him like a storm of snow. First thing he did, he plucked a spruce tree off the top of the North Rim and combed his beard. That beard was so long it grew down to his feet and wrapped around his wool socks and kept going. It kept going till it reached a cliff and grew halfway up like ivy. Next thing he did, he stepped up out of the canyon all covered in feathers like a giant goose. He brushed off his mackinaw with a ponderosa pine and put his ax on his shoulder. A powerful hunger was in him, but he needed to do one thing before he ate and that was see that brag-mouth brother of his. He headed east and got to Maine so fast he was knee-deep in ocean before he realized he had to turn back. The house in the woods wasn't the same. Bushes rose up over all the windows, wildflowers grew on the roof. The porch was mashed in by a dead pine covered in moss. Inside, long branches stuck in through the smashed-up windows. Squirrels and possums scampered over the mossy furniture. The door to the bedroom stood open and in the dark of the room he saw a stranger sitting in a chair at the side of the bed. In the bed his brother was stretched out on his back with his broom-straw arms crossed over his twig of a chest. His stringy beard was so long it came slithering down over his legs and curled around his chicken-hawk feet. From there it dropped to the floor and twisted itself around a bed foot. A bony dog lay up on the bed next to him whimpering for all he was worth. Moss and wild mushrooms grew in that beard. His brother's long nose was thin and sharp as an ax blade. The whimpering dog, the dark room, the stranger in the chair, the graveyard silence, it was all making Paul mighty uneasy. He looked at his brother's caved-in cheeks and forgot the Great Sleeping Contest. He forgot everything in that dead-quiet room. All he wanted to do was get out of there quick as a fox on fire and go back to his loggers, but he couldn't hardly make himself move. He bent down to look close at his brother. Those nothing shoulders stuck up through his shirt like chicken bones. Paul wondered what it would feel like to touch him. He wanted to give him something. He took his ax off his shoulder and put it down on the bed next to his brother. He laid it out real slow. Just then James opened one eye and looked at him. The stranger in the chair said, Ten years twelve hours and sixteen minutes. Paul jumped back and gave out a roar. He roared so loud the bony dog who was licking James's face went flying off the bed and rolled into a corner. Paul Bunyan roared so loud the branches blew away from the windows and let in the sun. James scrunched up his eye in the sunlight and laid a spidery arm across his face. He said, Can't a man get a little shut-eye around here? Then he rolled over and went back to sleep.

After

Paul knew he was beat, and beat by his own rickety bone-pile of a no-good brother. But before he had time to feel powerful bad, a mighty hunger rose up in him. He hadn't had a bite to eat in ten years twelve hours sixteen minutes and then some. He was so hungry he could've eaten his own boots fried in butter. He was so hungry he could've bitten off half of Maine and washed it down with the St. Lawrence River. In his mind he saw Hot Biscuit Slim standing over his griddle with the batter spattering and the hotcakes flipping over in the air. Paul picked up his ax and left that cabin in a hurry. He was in such a hurry he jumped onto a hurricane going his way but got off fast when he saw it was blowing too slow. He got one foot wet in Lake Huron and the other foot wet in Lake Michigan. Time he reached camp the men were looking up from the middle of the woods wondering what all the ruckus was about. When they saw Paul Bunyan standing there like the tallest tree in the forest some let out a cheer, some looked surprised, and some scratched their heads in wonder. Paul went straight to the stable and hugged his blue ox so hard they say Babe turned green and then red before he went back to his right-ful color. Then over to the cookhouse so fast his hug had to catch up with him later. They say Hot Biscuit Slim out-cooked himself that day. He set up a big chute at the side of the griddle and sent those hotcakes down one after the other so's they'd fall smack on Paul's platter and stack up all by themselves. Ten men kept filling the batter kettle and twenty men kept throwing split logs and brush under the griddle to keep the fire roaring. Paul ate so many hotcakes that morn-ing that rivermen and sawmill men came from far away as Idaho just to watch that ax-man eat. He ate so many hotcakes there wasn't any flour left from Maine to Oregon and they had to haul it down in bar-rels on flatboats from Canada. Paul kept throwing hotcakes into his mouth and washing'm down with a kettle of molasses till he figured it was time to pick up his ax and do a little work. He went out into the woods and swung his ax so hard, when the trees hit the ground they split into piles of trim pine boards. He worked so quick he felled an acre of white pine before you even heard the sound of his ax. As he swung he roared out: I can out-run out-jump out-drink and out-shoot you and I can out-bash out-gash out-mash and out-smash you and my own little brother up in Maine can out-sleep out-nap out-snooze and out-doze you even if you're a grizzly bear holed up in a cave in winter. All that night the men in the bunkhouses could hear trees fall-ing and no sign of Paul Bunyan. They say he swung that ax fourteen days and fourteen nights before he stopped to wipe a drop of sweat from his cheek. Some say he chopped his way over the Rockies clear past the coast of Oregon and stood knee-deep in the Pacific chop-ping waves in half. He chopped so hard he never did have time to see that no-muscle brother of his again. They say James Bunyan was so almighty tired after battling it out with his brother he spent all his time trying to catch up on his sleep. Some say he's sleeping still. I wouldn't know about that. These are stories you hear.

A VOICE IN THE NIGHT

1

The boy Samuel wakes in the dark. Something's not right. Most commentators agree that the incident takes place inside the temple, rather than in a tent outside the temple doors, under the stars. Less certain is whether Samuel's bed is in the sanctuary itself, where the Ark of the Covenant stands before a seven-branched oil lamp that is kept burning through the night, or in an adjoining chamber. Let's say that he is lying in an inner chamber, close to the sanctuary, perhaps adjacent to it. A curtained doorway leads to the chamber of Eli, the high priest of the temple of Shiloh. We like such details, but they do not matter. What matters is that Samuel wakes suddenly in the night. He is twelve years old, according to Flavius Josephus, or he may be a year or two younger. Something has startled him awake. He hears it again, clearly this time: "Samuel!" Eli is calling his name. What's wrong? Eli never calls his name in the middle of the night. Did Samuel forget to close the temple doors at sunset, did he allow one of the seven flames of the lamp to go out? But he remembers it well: pushing shut the heavy doors of cedar, visiting the sanctuary and replenishing the seven gold branches with consecrated olive oil so that the flames

will burn brightly all night long. "Samuel!" He flings aside his goat's-
hair blanket and hurries, almost runs, through the dark. He pushes
through the curtain and enters Eli's chamber. The old man is lying
on his back. Because he is the high priest of the temple of Shiloh,
his mattress on the wooden platform is stuffed with wool, not straw.
Eli's head rests on a pillow of goat's hair and his long-fingered hands
lie crossed on his chest, beneath his white beard. His eyes are closed.
"You called me," Samuel says, or perhaps his words are "Here am I,
for thou didst call me." Eli opens his eyes. He seems a little confused,
like a man roused from sleep. "I didn't call you," he answers. Or perhaps, with a touch of gruffness, since he doesn't like being awakened
in the night: "I called not; lie down again." Samuel turns obediently
away. He walks back to his chamber, where he lies down but doesn't
close his eyes. In his years of attending Eli he's come to understand a
great deal about the temple and its rules, and he tries to understand
this night as well. Is it possible that Eli called his name without knowing it? The priest is old, sometimes he makes noises with his lips in his
sleep, or mutters strange words. But never once has he called Samuel
in the night. Has Samuel had a dream, in which a voice called out his
name? Only recently he dreamed that he was walking alone through
the parted waters of the Red Sea. Shimmering cliffs of water towered
up on both sides, and as the watery walls began to plunge down on
him, he woke with a cry. From outside the walls of the temple he hears
the high-pitched wail of a young sheep. Slowly Samuel closes his eyes.

2

It's a summer night in Stratford, Connecticut, 1950. The boy, seven
years old, lies awake in his bed on the second floor, under the two
screened windows that look down on his backyard. Through the windows he can hear the sound of summer: the *chk chk chk* of crickets

from the vacant lot on the other side of the backyard hedge. For don-keys it's hee-haw, for roosters it's cock-a-doodle-doo, but for crickets you have to make up your own sound. Sometimes a car passes on the street alongside the yard, throwing two rectangles of light across the dark ceiling. The boy thinks the rectangles are the shapes of the open windows under the partially raised blinds, but he isn't sure. He's listening: hard. That afternoon in his Sunday-school class at the Jewish Community Center, Mrs. Kraus read the story of the boy Samuel. In the middle of the night a voice called out his name: "Samuel! Samuel!" He was an attendant of the high priest and lived in the temple of Shiloh, without his parents. When he heard his name, Samuel thought the high priest was calling him. Three times in the night he heard his name, three times he went to the bedside of Eli. But it was the voice of the Lord calling him. The boy in Stratford is listening for his name in the night. The story of Samuel has made him nervous, tense as a cat. The slightest sound stiffens his whole body. He never thinks about the old man with a beard on the front of his *Child's Illustrated Old Testament*, but now he's wondering. What would his voice be like? His father says God is a story that people made up to explain things they don't understand. When his father speaks about God to company at dinner, his eyes grow angry and gleeful behind his glasses. But the voice in the night is scary as witches. The voice in the night knows you're there, even though you're hidden in the dark. If the voice calls your name, you have to answer. The boy imagines the voice calling his name. It comes from the ceiling, it comes from the walls. It's like a terrible touch, all over his body. He doesn't want to hear the voice, but if he hears it he'll have to answer. You can't get out of it. He pulls the covers up to his chin and thinks of the walls of water crashing down on the Egyptians, on their chariots and horses. Through the window screens the crickets seem to be growing louder.

3

The Author is sixty-eight years old, in good health, most of his teeth, half his hair, not dead yet, though lately he hasn't been sleeping well. He's always been a light sleeper, the slightest sound jostles him awake, but this is different: he falls asleep with a book on his chest, then wakes up for no damn reason and strains his neck to look at the green glow of his digital clock, where it's always some soul-crushing time like 2:16 or 3:04 in the miserable morning. Hell time, abyss time, the hour of no return. He wonders whether he should turn on his bedside lamp, try to read a little, relax, but he knows the act of switching on the light will wake him up even more, and besides, there's the problem of what to read when you wake up at two or three in the godforsaken morning. If he reads something that interests him he'll excite his mind and ruin his chance for sleep, but if he reads something that bores him he'll become impatient, restless, and incapable of sleep. Better to lie there and curse his fate, like a man with a broken leg lying in a ditch. He listens to the sounds of the dark: *hsssh* of a passing car, *mmmm* of a neighbor's air conditioner, *skriiik* of a floorboard in the attic—a resident ghost. Things drift through your mind at doom-time in the morning, and as he listens he thinks of the boy in the house in Stratford, the bed by the two windows, the voice in the night. He thinks of the boy a lot these days, sometimes with irritation, sometimes with a fierce love that feels like sorrow. The boy tense, whipped up, listening for a voice in the night. He feels like shouting at the boy, driving some sense into that head of his. Oil your baseball glove! Jump on your bike! Do chin-ups on the swing set! Make yourself strong! But why yell at the boy? What'd he ever do to you? Better to imagine the voice calling right here, right now: Hello, old atheist, have I got news for you. Sorry, pal. Don't waste your time. You should've made your pitch when I was seven. Had the boy really expected to hear his name in the night? So long ago: *Bobby Benson and the B-Bar-B Riders* on the radio, his father at dinner attacking McCarthy. War in Korea, the push to Pusan. Those old stories got to you: Joseph in the pit, the parting of the Red Sea, David soothing the soul of Saul with his harp. In Catholic working-class Stratford, he was the only boy who didn't make the sign of the cross when they passed Holy Name Church on the way to school. Girls with smudges of ash on their foreheads. His God-scorning father driving him to Sunday school but taking him home when the others went to Hebrew class. No bar mitzvah for him. His father mocking his own rabbi for making boys jabber words they didn't understand. "Pure gibberish." A new word: gibberish. He liked it: gibberish. Still: Sunday school, "Rock of Ages," the story of Samuel, why is this night different from all other nights. The boy lying there listening, wanting his name to be called. Had he wanted his name to be called? Through the window the Author hears the sound of a distant car, the cry of the crickets. Sixty years later, upstate New York, and still the cry of the crickets in the summer in Stratford. Time to sleep, old man.

1

Samuel wakes again. This time he's sure: Eli has called his name. The voice stands out sharply, like a name written on a wall. "Samuel!" He throws off the goat's-hair blanket and steps onto the straw mat on the floor by his bed. He has lived with Eli in the temple of Shiloh for as long as he can remember. Once a year his mother and father visit him, when they come up from Ramah to offer the annual sacrifice. When he was born, his mother gave him to the Lord. She had asked the Lord for a son, and that's why his name is Asked-of-the-Lord. That's why he wears a linen ephod, that's why his hair flows down below his shoulders: no razor shall ever come upon his head. Samuel:

Asked of the Lord. He enters Eli's chamber, where he expects to find Eli sitting up in bed, waiting impatiently for him. Instead, Eli is lying on his back with his eyes closed, like a man asleep. Should he wake Eli? Did Eli call Samuel's name and then fall back to sleep? Samuel hesitates to wake a man who's old and filled with worries. Though Eli is the high priest of the temple, his sons are wicked. They are priests who do not obey. When flesh is offered for sacrifice, they take the best part for themselves. They practice iniquities with women who come to the doors of the temple. "Here am I!" Samuel says, in a voice a little louder than he intended. Eli stirs and opens his eyes. "For thou didst call me," Samuel says, more softly. The old priest raises his head with difficulty. "I called not, my son. Lie down again." Samuel doesn't protest, but lowers his eyes and turns away with the uneasy sense of having disturbed an old man's sleep. As he enters his own chamber, he tries to understand. Why has Eli called his name twice in the night? He called out in a loud, clear voice, a voice that could not be mistaken for some other sound. But Eli, who speaks only truth, has denied it. Samuel lies down on his bed and pulls the blanket up to his shoulders. Eli is very old. Does he call out Samuel's name and then, when Samuel appears beside him, forget that he has called? Old men are forgetful. The other day, when Eli spoke to Samuel of his own childhood, he could not remember a name he was searching for and grew troubled. Samuel has seen an old man at the temple whose body trembles like well-water in a goatskin bucket. His eyes are unlit lamps. Eli is old, his eyesight is growing dim, but his body doesn't tremble and his voice is still strong. On the shoulder of his purple and scarlet ephod are two onyx stones, each engraved with the names of six tribes of Israel. When he stands in sunlight, the stones shine like fire. Slowly Samuel drifts into sleep.

2

It's the next night, and the boy in Stratford again lies awake, listening. He doesn't really believe he'll hear his name, but he wants to be awake in case it happens. He doesn't like to miss things. If he knows something important is coming, like a trip to the merry-go-round and the Whip at Pleasure Beach, he'll wait for it minute by minute, day after day, as if by taking his attention away from it for even a second he might cause it not to happen. But this is different. He doesn't know it's going to happen. It probably won't happen, how could it happen, but there's a chance, who knows. What he really needs to figure out is how to answer, if his name is called. In the story, Samuel was told to answer "Speak, Lord; for thy servant heareth." He tries to imagine it: "Speak, Lord; for thy servant heareth." It sounds like a boy in a play. Better to say "Yes?" which is what he'd say if his father called his name. But the Lord is not his father. The Lord is more powerful than his powerful father. He's more like the policeman in front of the school on Barnum Avenue, with his dangerous stick hanging from his belt. Better to say "Yes, sir," as he'd say if the policeman called his name. If he hears his name, that's what he'll say: "Yes, sir." Don't shout it: say it. Yes, sir. A voice in the dark, calling his name. The thought stirs him up again. He's too old to be scared of the dark, but the fear still comes on him sometimes. He likes to play a scare-game with his sister, the way they did when he was five and she was two. She lies in her dark room pretending to be asleep and he whispers: "Booooo haunt moan. Booooo haunt moan." Then they both burst into wild, scared laughter. But a voice in the night is not funny. He's through with witches, ghosts, monsters, isn't he, they're not real, so why is he scaring himself with the story of Samuel? It's only a story. His father has explained it to him: the Bible is stories. Like *Tootle* or *The Story of Dr. Dolittle*. Trains don't leave the tracks to chase butterflies, the pushmi-pullyu with a head at each end isn't an animal you'll ever find in the zoo, and the Lord doesn't call your name in the night. Stories are about things that don't happen. They could happen, but they don't. But they could. What if his name was called? He would want to be there. He'd want to know what comes next. What did the Lord say to Samuel? He can't remember. The most important part, and he can't remember. That's one thing about him: he can't remember the important things. He can remember the prince climbing the hair to the top of the tower but he can't remember the capital of Connecticut. Is it Bridgeport? The library in Bridgeport has long stone steps and high pillars. It's what he first thought of when he heard that Samuel was serving the Lord in the temple of Shiloh. A temple is different from a church. Jews go to temple and Christians go to church. But Catholics go to Catholic church. And everybody goes to the library. He's getting tired. At the backyard hedge, Billy turned to him and said: "Do you believe in Jesus?" His eyes were hard. There're two answers to that question. One is "No." The other's what his father said to him: "Jesus was a great teacher." But he was a coward and looked down. A door opens and he hears footsteps in the hall. Do his parents know he's lying awake, listening for his name? He hears the door to the bathroom open and close. Sometimes his father is up in the night. If he opens his door and waits for his father? Tell me about Samuel. Tell me. Tell me about the voice in the night. If you heard that voice, nothing would ever be the same. He pushes the thought away. Tomorrow they're going to drive out past the Sikorsky plant to Short Beach, where he can wade out to the sandbar.

3

1:54 in the morning. The gods are out to get him. Sleep for an hour, wake for no reason, stare like a madman, waiting for sleep.

Dragging himself through the day like a stepped-on snail. Won't take a pill, they leave him groggy. Sloggy and boggy. That all you've got? Draggy and saggy. Baggy and shaggy. Like a hag, haggy. Now he's alert, full of useless energy. In the old days he'd recite fistfuls of sonnets. My mistress' eyes are nothing like the sun. Three things there be that prosper up apace. Now all he can do is lie there thinking about things, far-off things, high school, grade school, the boy in the room in Stratford, listening for the voice in the night. Did it really happen that way, or is he embellishing? Habit of the trade. But no, he lay there waiting for his name. The two windows, the two bookcases his father had made from orange crates, the bed against the other wall for his sister to sleep in when one of the grandmothers came to stay. One grandma from West 110th Street, one from Washington Heights. Father's mother, mother's mother, first one, then the other, never together. Waiting for the train at the Bridgeport station, with the long dark benches and the row of hand-cranked picture machines. The something-scopes. Turning the handles, making the pictures move. The grandmother with crooked fingers who brought packs of playing cards and dyed her hair orange and wore lots of rattly bracelets, the grandmother with the accent who made cold red soup with sour cream. Mutoscopes. Two women born in the nineteenth century, who can grasp it, one in New York, one in Minsk, before skyscrapers, before horseless carriages, before the extinction of the dinosaurs. His own mother growing up with Russian-Jewish parents on the Lower East Side. Her father escaping the czar, embracing America, naming his first son Abraham, middle name Lincoln. Moving them to a new apartment every few months, skipping out on the rent. She said he sat reading Dostoyevsky in Russian while his sons waited on customers in the store. The Stratford boy's own early childhood in Brooklyn, all there in the photo albums: pretty mother with flower in her hair on a bench in Prospect Park, pretty mother in wide-brimmed hat standing with little son in sailor suit on the Coney

Island boardwalk. The two of them riding the trolley. Trolley tracks in
the street, wires in the sky, the grooved wheel at the top of the trolley pole: a forgotten world. His invisible father holding up the light
meter, adjusting the f-number, staring down into the ground-glass
screen of the twin-lens reflex. Then Stratford, working-class neighborhood, where else can a professor afford to live. Milk delivered in
glass bottles to the back porch each morning. Italians and Eastern
Europeans, Zielski and Stoccatore and Saksa and Mancini. Riccio's
drugstore. Ciccarelli's lot. Ralph Politano. Tommy Pavluvcik. Mario
Recupido. What is a Jew? A Jew is someone who doesn't cross himself
in front of Holy Name Church. A Jew is someone who stays indoors
practicing the piano on bright summer mornings while everyone else
is outside playing baseball. His mother playing Chopin nocturnes
and waltzes, DEE dah-dah-dah, DEE dah-dah-dah, teaching him
scales, reading on the couch with her legs tucked under her. The
mahogany bookcase by the stairs, the two bookcases by the fireplace.
His father driving them home one night. "Did you see that? Not a
book in the house!" What is a Jew? A Jew is someone who has books
in the house. His father demolishing an argument for the existence
of God, his lips twisted in scorn. Jewish Community Center but no
bar mitzvah. A tree every Christmas, a menorah once or twice. No
baby Jesuses, no Marys or mangers. A package of matzo once a year:
like big saltines. The strange word: unleavened. Dyeing Easter eggs,
walking under the roof of cornstalks and branches at Sukkoth, biting
into hollow crumbly chocolate bunnies, lighting the yahrzeit candle
for the grandmother from Minsk. What is a Jew? A Jew is someone
who thinks of Easter as a holiday celebrating rabbits. His mother a
first-grade teacher, his father a teacher at the university. The grandmother with crooked fingers, once a piano teacher. The whole family
teaching up a storm. A tutor who tooted the flute. Tried to tutor two
tooters to toot. What is a Jew? A Jew is someone who comes from
people who teach. Erleen, from the project in Bridgeport, watch-

ing gently over him each day when he came home from school. The rhyme in the street: Eenie meenie miney mo, catch a nigger by the toe. His father serious, quiet-voiced, his mouth tight: "People use that word, but not in this house. It is disgusting." Negro: a word of respect. Respect people. His all-Jewish Cub Scout troop. "You don't look for trouble," the scoutmaster said. "But you don't let anyone call you a kike." Not in this house. A new word: kike. He tried to imagine it: kike. Hey, kike! Hit him, kill him. Did he really lie awake night after night, listening for his name? The child Samuel. All about obedience. Saul's flaw: disobedience. Samuel thrusting his sword into the belly of the King of the Amalekites. That's what happens when your name is called in the night. The righteous life, the life of moral ferocity. His father and Samuel, two of a kind. Samuel: "Thou art wicked." His father: "You are ignorant." A special sect: the Jewish atheist. The thirteenth tribe. And you? Who are you? I am the one whose name was not called in the night.

1

The voice calls again. This time Samuel doesn't hesitate. He swings his legs out of bed and rushes through the dark to Eli's side. "Here am I," he cries, impatient now, "for thou didst call me." Eli is lying on his back, his eyes closed, his hands crossed on his chest. All at once he's leaning up on an elbow, searching Samuel's face. Samuel feels aggrieved, anxious, expectant. What is happening? Something is happening. He doesn't know what. The long hand of the priest rests on Samuel's arm. Samuel suddenly understands two things: Eli did not call his name, and Eli knows who did. Does Samuel know? He almost knows. He knows and doesn't dare to know. But Eli is speaking, Eli is telling him who it is that has called his name. It is the Lord. "Go, lie down; and it shall be, if he call thee, that thou shalt say, Speak, Lord;

for thy servant heareth." The searching look, the hand on his arm: Samuel understands that he must ask no more questions. He returns to his bed and lies down on his back with his eyes open. He wants to hear with both ears. One hand is pressed against his chest. His heart is like a fist beating against the inside of the bone. What if his name isn't called again? Eli said, "If he call thee." Three times, and he failed to answer. Should he have known? He knew, he almost knew, he was about to know. Now he knows. What he doesn't know is whether he will hear the voice again. If his name is not called, he will never forgive himself. And if his name is called? Then what? What should he say? Oh, don't you remember? Speak, Lord; for thy servant heareth. Speak, Lord; for thy servant heareth. He remembers the first time he saw Eli, the high priest of the temple. A powerful man, with shining gems on the shoulders of his ephod. His legs were like tall columns of stone. His hands the size of oil jars. Now Eli's beard is white, he mutters in his sleep. Difficult sons, wicked sons he cannot restrain. Calm yourself. Stop trembling. Listen.

2

The third night, and the boy in his bed in Stratford still hasn't heard his name. He's not really listening, is he? He thought he heard it once, a distant call, fooling him for a second, that cat cry or whatever it was. He no longer expects to hear anything, so why's he still waiting? By now there's a spirit of stubbornness in it: he's waited this long, might as well wait some more. But that isn't it. What it *is* is, he doesn't believe the voice in the night will come, but his unbelief upsets him as much as belief would, if he believed. If the voice doesn't come, it means he hasn't been chosen. He likes being chosen. He was chosen to represent his class in the school spelling bee. It's easy to spell, he doesn't know how to spell words wrong, but it still feels good to be chosen. He's not so good on the playground, can't kick the ball as hard as most of them, lucky if he gets to first. He wants the voice to call him in the night, even though it won't happen. He doesn't believe those old stories, doesn't believe the prince climbing the hair or the thorns growing up and covering the castle, so why should he believe the story of the voice in the night? His father doesn't believe those stories. His father doesn't believe in God. But when the boy asked, his father didn't get the angry look, he got the serious quiet look. He said you have to think about it yourself and make up your mind when you're older. The boy wonders how old is older. When is when? If he hears the voice now, he'll know. But he already knows. He knows he won't hear the voice. Why should he be chosen? He's no Samuel. He's a good speller. He plays the piano with two hands, he can write a poem about George Washington and draw a picture of a kingfisher or a red-winged blackbird. But Samuel opens the doors to the temple when the sun comes up, Samuel fills the lamp with oil so that it burns all night. Down below he hears a car going by. It's passing his yard and the vacant lot, the two bars of light sliding across the ceiling, now it's passing the bakery down by the stream, he loves the bakery, smell of hot rye, the gingerbread men and the muffins with raisins, now it's climbing the hill, sound of tires like the waterfall in the park earlier this summer, over the hill toward Bridgeport. He feels old, very old, older than Eli, he wishes he were young again, a child. He wishes he'd never heard that stupid story. Shhh. Sleep now.

3

Another night, another waking. Not a good sign. Death by insom-nia at sixty-eight. All Samuel's fault, keeping everybody up when they ought to be snoring away. The boy in Stratford battling it out at the age of seven. By high school, no tolerance for the once-a-week churchgoers. Priest or atheist: choose one. The move to Fairfield, the beach, Protestant churches galore. Presbyterian, First Congregational, Episcopal. Roper. Warren. Kane. No Jews allowed in the beach club. Who'd want to join a beach club? Reading the five arguments for the existence of God and their rebuttals. The ontological argument. The teleological argument. Walking along the beach at night, the deserted lifeguard stands, the lights of Long Island. Challenge to a friend: Why do you go to church? Why only on Sunday? He knew what he knew: always or never. If the voice calls your name, your other life is over. No going back. Short of that, sorry, please pass the ketchup. By the age of fifteen, done with religion, like the baseball books of his childhood. No regrets. Girls in tight skirts reaching up into lockers, girls in tight blouses hugging books to their chests as they hip-swing down the halls. Let me touch! Let me see! The house for sale on his friend's street out near the junior high. "They'll never sell to a Jew." "Why not?" "You know how those people are." "How are they?" "They take over the neighborhood." "You're talking to one." "Oh, you're not *that* kind of Jew." At age eleven, the talk with his father: "We don't do anything in Sunday school. Just play games and fool around. I don't want to go anymore." His father taking his pipe out of his mouth, looking at him gravely: "You don't have to go." He'd expected resistance, a look of reproach. Might as well blame it all on Jehovah. Could have called his name in the night. The boy in Stratford, listening. Something extreme in his temperament, even then. Shy and extreme. Stubborn. You don't call my name, I won't call yours. Even Steven. Dr. Dolittle and Pecos Bill instead of Samuel and King Saul. Don't have to go. The neighborhood goes to church, the family stays home and reads. In high school, asking his father whether he liked teaching. His father's pause, his grave look, his utter attention: "If I were a millionaire, I would pay for the privilege of teaching." The son knows he's heard something important. He is moved, he is proud of his father, he's envious. He thinks: I want to say that someday. They call it a calling. Samuel's call in the night. His father's calling. Lying awake remembering these things. Walking in his bathing suit, towel around his neck, to the beach in Fairfield with his parents' friends from the city. Janey with her long black hair and tight white one-piece, waving her arm at the street of ranch houses: "Suburbia." Her voice mocking, disdainful. New York judging Connecticut. Jews moving out of New York: abandoning the tribe. Always the connection to the city. The four years in Brooklyn, corner of Clinton and Joralemon, the grandmother on West 110th Street and the grandmother in Washington Heights, mother growing up on the Lower East Side, father on the Upper West Side. Childhood trips to the city, the stone bridges of the Merritt Parkway. The Museum of Natural History with dinosaur skeletons like gigantic fishbones, lunch at the Automat: the sandwiches behind the little glass windows. Horn & Hardart. Early admission to Oberlin, but he chooses Columbia. Walking along the eighth floor of John Jay Hall, the thrilling sound of violins and cellos behind closed doors: the good Jewish boys practicing their instruments. Weingarten, or was it Marinoff: "What kind of Jew are you?" A Jew from suburbia. A nothing Jew, a secular Jew, an unjewish Jew. A Jew without a bar mitzvah, a Jew without a bump in his nose. Later he develops the idea of the Negative Jew. A Negative Jew is a Jew about whom another Jew says, "You don't *look* Jewish." A Negative Jew is a Jew who says to another Jew, "Judaism is a superstition that I reject," and to an anti-Semite, "I have Jewish blood." A Negative Jew is a Jew who says "I don't believe in Judaism" while being herded into a cattle car. Hitler, the great clarifier. His father's German-Jewish colleague, Dr. What's-Her-Name, one of the first women admitted to a German university, her passion for Kant, for all things German. Stayed put till 1939. Blamed it all on the Polish Jews. "They gave us a bad name." The boy in Stratford, lying awake at night. Hard to remember how it was. A game, was it? Scare yourself with witches, scare yourself with Jehovah. A shudder of delight. All those old stories, wonderful and terrible: the voice in the night, the parting of the Red Sea, Hansel in the cage, the children following the piper into the mountain. *Hamlet* and *Oedipus Rex* as pale reflections of the nightmare tales of childhood. Everything connected: David playing the harp for Saul, the boy in Stratford practicing the piano, the cellos and violins behind the closed doors. The boy listening for his name, the man waiting for the rush of inspiration. Where do you get your ideas? A voice in the night. When did you decide to become a writer? Three thousand years ago, in the temple of Shiloh.

1

And the Lord came, and stood, and called as at other times, Samuel, Samuel. Commentators disagree about the meaning of the word "stood." Some say that the Lord assumes a bodily presence before Samuel. Others argue that the Lord never takes on a bodily form and that therefore the voice has drawn closer to Samuel, so that the effect is of a person drawing closer in the dark. In one version of this argument, the boy hears the voice and imagines a form standing beside him. All this, the Author thinks, can be left to the interpreters. What matters to us is that the voice of the Lord calls Samuel's name. After all, Eli had said: "If he call thee." For it was not inevitable that the voice, which had called three times and not received an answer, would call again. Now the boy Samuel has heard the voice a fourth time and knows who is calling him. He doesn't yet know why the Lord is calling him, but he knows how to answer, for Eli has told him exactly what to say: "Speak, Lord; for thy servant heareth." Samuel resists, the words refuse to come, then he says it aloud: "Speak; for thy servant heareth." He hears his words clearly in the dark: "Speak; for thy servant heareth." There is no doubt: he has said "Speak" and not "Speak, Lord," as he was instructed to do. Was he so frightened of uttering the sacred name? He feels a rush of self-reproach, before commanding himself to be still and listen. He lies motionless, alert all over his body, fiercely calm. He has served in the temple of Shiloh ever since early childhood, but nothing has prepared him for this moment. He does not try to imagine what the Lord will tell him, but he readies himself to remember every word, in the order of speaking. Eli is awake, waiting in the next chamber. Eli will ask him what the Lord has said. Though the voice of the Lord is strong, Samuel knows it cannot be heard by Eli, and not because Eli is too far away to hear. The voice is for him alone. He knows this without arrogance. And he will remember. He has a good memory, he's proud of his memory, though he watches over his pride so that it doesn't become vanity. Words read to him or heard by him remain unchanged inside him. It has always been that way. Now the Lord speaks, and Samuel listens. There is nothing in the world but these words. The words are harsh. The house of Eli will be judged for its iniquity. The sons of Eli are wicked and Eli has not restrained them. Therefore the Lord will perform against Eli all things which he has spoken concerning his house. The sons of Eli will die on the same day. The House of Eli will come to an end. When the Lord departs, it is like the silence after thunder. Samuel lies awake in the dark. It seems to him that the dark has become darker, a dark so dark that it is like the darkness upon the face of the deep, before the Lord moved upon the face of the waters. The words have shaken him like a wind. He can feel Eli lying awake in his chamber, waiting for Samuel to tell him what the Lord has said. But Samuel cannot bring himself to leave his bed and go to Eli's chamber. If Eli asks him, and Eli will certainly ask him, he will speak the truth, but he does not want to speak the truth unbidden. Samuel lies in the dark a long time, listening for the Lord, listening for Eli, but all is silent. Has the darkness become less dark? Can darkness be less dark and still be dark? The darkness is growing lighter. Soon it will be time to open the temple doors. Eli will ask what the Lord has said, and Samuel will repeat the terrible words. Samuel understands that nothing will ever be the same. But now, as the darkness is fading, without yet losing its quality of darkness, he wants to lie in his bed as if he could be a child forever, he wants to lie there as if his name had not been called in the night.

2

It's the fourth night, and by now the boy in Stratford knows he'll never hear his name. Still, he's awake, and in case he's wrong he's still listening, no harm in that, though at the same time he makes fun of himself for lying there, waiting, and for what? His name? It's only a story in a book. You might as well lie awake waiting for a genie to rise up out of a lamp. And even if it isn't only a story, why would the Lord call his name? Samuel was an attendant of the high priest of the temple, Samuel was already favored by the Lord. The boy in Stratford goes to the Jewish Community Center on Sunday for two hours and skips Hebrew lessons. He doesn't make the sign of the cross in front of Holy Name Church, but he looks forward to Christmas as if it's the greatest day of winter. No crosses or angels on his tree, no lit-up statues of Mary blinking on the front lawn, but still, stockings, colored tree-lights, glittery tinsel, presents piled high. Christmas: a holiday celebrating the end of the year. Rosh Hashanah: a holiday he can't pronounce, celebrating something he can't remember. The Lord, if he's even up there, shouldn't call his name. And that's fine with him. He doesn't want his name to be called. If your name is called, everything changes. It would be like going to Sunday school all week long. He likes the way things are: catching fly balls and grounders in the backyard, walking in the hot sand at Short Beach, firecrackers on the Fourth of July, sitting in front of the fireplace in winter reading a book while his father grades papers at one end of the couch and his mother reads at the other end, birthday parties, reading *The 500 Hats of Bartholomew Cubbins* to his sister, playing double solitaire with Grandma Lena, watching the black-and-white pictures rise into the white paper in the developing tray in his father's darkroom, riding slowly in the boat through the Old Mill at Pleasure Beach. He doesn't want to leave his family, doesn't want to leave his room with the two windows looking down at the backyard, the big record-player in the living room where he and his sister listen to *Peter and the Wolf*. His mother looking at him one day, touching him, her eyes shining: "Oh, my firstborn." His father answering all his questions with that serious look, as if nothing is more important than those questions. What happens when you die? What is God? What is the most important thing in the world? He doesn't want to leave it all for the temple of Shiloh. School starts in a few weeks, he's still got lots of summer left, picnics by the river, drives into Bridgeport, the smell of hot roasted nuts in Morrow's Nut House, the elevator operators in their maroon jackets and white gloves in Read's department store, the wooden ships with rigging in the window of Blinn's. He's done with Samuel, done with the voice in the night, but now, as he feels sleep coming on, he gives a final listen, just in case, straining his ears, holding his breath, listening for the voice that came to Samuel in that old story that's only a story but one he knows he'll never forget, no matter how hard he tries.

3

Again. Enough already. But hey, look on the bright side: four in the morning, three hours of sleep instead of one. The long walk after dinner, over an hour, hoping to outwit insomnia. Walk for one hour, wake up at four. Walk for two hours, wake up at five. Walk for three hours, wake up at six. Walk for four hours, drop dead of a heart attack. His flab-armed father's muscular calves. Walked all over Manhattan in his

City College days, late 1920s, Harlem to the Battery. A safe city. The boy in Stratford walking up Canaan Road to the White Walk Market, walking to school along Franklin Avenue and Collins Street and the street that led past Holy Name. Calves skinny as forearms. His father walking a mile to the bus stop each morning to catch the bus to Bridgeport, no car till the boy is in second grade: city people don't drive. No television till fifth grade: TV is for people who don't read. Last in the neighborhood. Back from Manhattan with a ten-inch box, an Air King, set up on a table next to the piano. The feverish pleasure of black-and-white cartoons. Czerny exercises and Farmer Al Falfa. Mozart and Mighty Mouse. His mother playing Schumann and laughing with him at *The Merry Mailman*. His grave father bent over the Scrooge McDuck comic, praising the diving board in the money bin. Reading *Tootle* to him, telling him how good the first sentence is. "Far, far to the west of everywhere is the village of Lower Trainswitch." Far, far to the west of everywhere. His father said, "There are three great opening sentences in all of literature. The first is 'In the beginning God created the heaven and the earth.' The second is 'Call me Ishmael.' The third is 'Far, far to the west of everywhere is the village of Lower Trainswitch.' " A father who's serious and funny: you have to watch his face carefully. The book about the whale: he knows where it is on the shelf, he's held it in his hands, thinking, When I'm older. The whale, God: when he's older. Books, always books. Ten years old: his father lashing out at Eisenhower. "He doesn't open a book!" The trip to Spain after Columbia, one-way ticket, two pieces of luggage: one for clothes, one for books. The boy in Stratford lying awake at night because of a story in a book. What's a story? A demon in the night. He wants to protect the boy, warn him before it's too late. Don't listen to stories! They'll keep you awake at night, suck out your blood, leave teeth marks in your skin. Let him sleep! Let him live! His New York Jew parents in working-class Stratford, with their books and their piano. The professor who doesn't do work with his hands. Joey's father a machinist at the helicopter plant, Mike's father a carpenter who builds his own house in the vacant lot on the other side of the hedge. Joey turning to him with a fighting look: "Can your father make a wheel?" The old sun-browned Italian men working in their gardens. The grapevines growing all over Jimmy Stoccatore's high fence, the bunches of purple grapes, heavy in the hand. Old man Ciccarelli chasing kids out of his lot. Eenie meenie miney mo, catch a tiger by the toe. Not in this house. The Jewish Boy Scout troop, where he learned to tie a sheepshank but never could identify poison sumac. His refusal to be Jesus in the Sunday-school play. Mrs. Kraus's shocked surprise. "But why?" "Because Jesus betrayed the Jews." Her confusion, fear. "I never taught you that!" His father: "Jesus was a great teacher." Sixty years later, awake at night, at the mercy of memory. Rapunzel! Rapunzel! Let down your hair! And the Lord came, and stood, and called as at other times, Samuel, Samuel. The boy in Stratford, listening. Thank you, Old Man of the Sky, for not calling his name. Better for all concerned. He can't really have believed it, can he? Working himself up into a temporary blaze of half-belief, a possibility: a ghost in the dark. Better for him to stay out of the temple of Shiloh, better to go play in the green backyards of Stratford, grow up in a world of family excursions and shelves of books until the writing fever seized him and claimed him for life. A calling. Not Samuel's call, but another. Not that way, but this way. Samuel ministering unto the Lord, his teacher-father ministering unto the generations. And the son? What about him? Far, far to the west of everywhere, ministering unto the Muse. Thanks, Old Sea-Parter, for leaving me be. Tired now. Soon we'll all sleep.